THE
BUSH

THE
BUSH

A Guide to the
Vegetated Landscapes of Australia

IAN G. READ

UNSW
PRESS

ACKNOWLEDGEMENTS

The compilation of this book would not have been possible without the assistance of others. Firstly, I wish to thank those authors in the field of study of vegetation and plant life who, unbeknown to them, made the idea of this book possible. It must be pointed out that personal observation can only add just so much to a book such as this. My debt to them is considerable. Secondly, I wish to acknowledge the staff of the Shoalhaven District Library, Nowra, as well as the staff of the La Trobe Library, Melbourne, and the university libraries of Wollongong, Western Australia and Murdoch. Thirdly, many thanks to everyone who used the first edition of *The Bush* to increase their knowledge and understanding of Australia's unique vegetation and landscapes — this current edition is dedicated to you.

Finally there are the individuals. Thanks to Marion Seeber who set me straight and helped to start the whole project; to Patsy Graham who did a marvellous job typing the final manuscript; to Colin Graham who was forever enthusiastic; to Bill Templeman of Reed Books for taking the first publishing risk; to my current publisher, Doug Howie of UNSW Press, for taking the next one; and a special thanks to Coralyn Treasure who typed numerous drafts, proofread, accompanied the author on numerous journeys and never gave up when it all seemed too much. Without her this book would never have seen the light of day.

Ian G. Read, Nowra, 1994

This edition published in 1994 by
UNIVERSITY OF NEW SOUTH WALES PRESS LTD
Sydney 2052 Australia
Telephone (02) 398 8900
Fax (02) 398 3408

First published 1987 by Reed Books Pty Ltd

© Ian G. Read 1994

Maps by Elizabeth Boyd
Printed by Merino Lithographics Pty Ltd

Available in North America through:
ISBS Inc
Portland Oregon 97213-3644
Tel: (503) 287 3093
Fax: (503) 280 8832

National Library of Australia
Cataloguing-in-Publication entry:

Read, Ian G.
  The bush : a guide to the vegetated
            landscapes of Australia.

Bibliography.
Includes index.
ISBN 0 86840 254 0.

1. Plant communities – Australia.
2. Botany – Australia. I. Title.

581.994

CONTENTS

LIST OF FIGURES

LIST OF SYMBOLS

NSW	New South Wales	**m**	metres
Vic	Victoria	**km**	kilometres
Qld	Queensland	**°C**	degrees Celsius
SA	South Australia	**sp**	species (singular)
WA	Western Australia	**spp**	species (plural)
Tas	Tasmania	**ssp**	subspecies
NT	Northern Territory	**fig**	figure
ACT	Australian Capital Territory	**nr**	near
mm	millimetres	**Stn**	station
cm	centimetres	**syn**	synonymous

PREFACE

'The child has an inner life that must be nurtured along with the body. The senses need to be tuned so that they can comprehend beauty in later life otherwise the individual will grow up with a sterile soul unable to appreciate the richness of the world. I am more interested in seeing a child develop with a capacity of clear imagination and an ability to look at the world with wonder.'

(Sister Joan Salter, the *Age*, 9 April 1981)

'It's only wilderness when you're days away from and out of sight of civilisation.'
　'I feel one needs to be at least two days from civilisation to experience a wilderness sensation.'
　'. . . one needs to be in a wilderness environment for a number of days before it begins to take . . .'

(Quotes of respondents to a 'Wilderness Survey' contained in Mosley, 1978)

'The air was balmy, but there was something in the mournful aspect of the scene that weighed upon the spirits, and made one feel inexpressibly lonely in the midst of that boundless wilderness of forest. Time soon takes the edge off novelty, and long ago I learned to feel perfectly at ease and cheerful, whilst lying in the midst of a much deeper solitude, with no companions but my horse grazing near me and the fire at my feet. There is no country in the world so safe for the traveller as Western Australia.'

(E.W. Lander, 1841, source unknown)

Perceived character of natural areas:
- less than 4 per cent see natural areas as bad, ugly, noisy, dirty, repulsive, evil, wasteful, boring, dead, uninviting, dull, useless or depressing;
- between 4 and 25 per cent see natural areas as bleak, dangerous or fragile;
- between 25 and 50 per cent see natural areas as happy, friendly, sacred, huge, roadless or pure;
- more than 50 per cent see natural areas as good, remote, alive, exciting, unique, wild, challenging, inspiring, valuable, restful, unspoiled, free, beautiful or natural.

(Based on research for a doctoral thesis by Keith McKenry, contained in Mosley, 1978)

'Is it that this life of ours is simply an episode of consciousness between two oblivions, or is there some further transcendental experience of which we can know nothing until it comes?
　'I myself have the strong belief that we have to be open to the future . . . each of us can have the belief acting in some unimaginable supernatural drama . . . then we wait with serenity and joy for future revelations of whatever is in store after death.
　'Unless we get this perspective in time and space of our position in the human story, I don't think we'll ever be wise.'

(John Eccles, the *Age*, 28 March 1981)

The Pitjantjatjara

A Pitjantjatjara group, the Anangu Pitjantjatjaraku, has occupied a huge tract of land for millennia. Their land extends from beyond Docker River and Ayers Rock in the north to beyond Warburton in the west, the Great Victoria Desert in the south, to beyond Granite Downs in the east. During their occupancy a complex social and ritualistic structure has evolved based on their relationship to the land.

The Pitjantjatjara believe that the land is a visibly crystallised dimension of what was a previously fluid world; this fluid containing the life which is the progenitor of *all* living things.

During the times of the Dreaming the superbeings or heroes of mythology lived on the earth. They performed monumental and memorable deeds. These deeds have been handed down, their details carefully preserved in the form of dance, design and storytelling for the entertainment and instruction of successive generations. The deeds are accounts answering the fundamental questions regarding the mysteries of life.

Between the Dreaming and the present the fluid earth crystallised, the heroes retiring to their subterranean habitats where, in the fabric of the land, the heroes' souls reside. Thus each stream, hill, rocky outcrop and waterhole along with the trees and stars is a visible reminder of the deeds of the superbeings, their souls now the life force existing within the earth.

The life force of *kuriti* is seemingly equivalent to the essence an object possesses in terms of Western philosophy. The essence implies that an object is more than the sum of its parts. For instance that quality of a rock which gives it its 'rockness' is more than the sum of its constituent minerals. It implies the forces that both created the rock and hold the rock together. It also implies the concept of rock as understood by its observer. This relationship of observer and rock when viewed in a broader context is not one to one, it is just one, i.e. both the observer and the rock create a whole. Such is the relationship between the Aborigine and the land.

For at least 40 000 years the Aborigines have had this relationship with the land. The land exists within them as much as they exist within the landscape. To carry the analogy further, though the rock itself may change that quality of 'rockness' still exists.

We are all, in one manner or another, both products and victims of our immediate environment, culture and habit and we operate, almost automatically, within that fabric. For many of us that is the extent of our consciousness. By failing to see that we are more than the sum of our parts and by divorcing our environment from ourselves we are open to feelings of isolation and ennui. To overcome these anxieties we seek security in those habits and environments which initially led us to that condition.

Often unrealised there is created a cycle of experience, a vicious circle. All this time the landscape remains a backdrop to our existence yet the landscape itself (and our place in it) contains the forces of life. It takes a sideways step to leave the circle, to enter an unknown place, the wilderness, be it the wilderness of the mind or of nature.

All the knowledge in the world does not tell us how human consciousness arose. Evolution alone does not explain man's awareness of himself. As science became a more severe orthodoxy than the religions ever were there is instant suspicion and hostility against those who go beyond mere facts. This is often reported as being emotional when conflict arises regarding development and conservation. It is science, or more correctly scientific method that has produced Western society. It was based on reasoning and rationalisation. This in turn is derived from cause and effect. By its very nature cause and effect implies time; first the cause and then the effect. Whatever the benefits of viewing society and consequently life in such a way, cause and effect does not account for that quality or essence which exists between the consciousness of the observer and the object being observed.

Chapter One

INTRODUCTION

Australia is a vast land of never-ending horizons, broken back ranges, eerily silent forests and golden, blue shores. It is also a land of vast suburban sprawls, monotonous cropping country, eroded hillsides and long lines of traffic leading to the beach. It is a land that has been populated for millennia and a land that has attracted new populations to its more equable southern and eastern coastal fringes. It is both an old Australia and a new Australia.

To the European man Australia was firstly a mere conception, a conjecture on the earliest world maps, the Great South Land. With exploration and discovery the land grew in the minds of the explorers, the map makers and the ruling classes of Europe. To Asian man Australia was a reality, particularly its northern shores which were frequently visited by peoples of the islands to the north. To the Aborigines Australia was home and has been for at least 40 000 years.

Europeans, being the latest of mankind's races to make contact with Australia are, due to their history and traditions, the least capable of understanding the land. Having only settled here for seven or eight generations many European types have yet to establish a connection with the land beyond that of viewing the land as a resource. The last two hundred years has seen the land undergo significant changes, the changes of occupation. No longer is the land in a state of balance but a state of change based on economic development.

As this development gained momentum during the twentieth century the new arrivals became less dependent on the land for their existence. There was a shift of values regarding the land, values which (until recently) alienated the land further from the occupiers. European man did not see the land as a nurturer but as a resource to be exploited. Irrespective of the rights and wrongs of exploitation the result was that it created in the mind the notion that the land is a separate entity from man himself, a concept which develops into notions of separateness, not only from the land but of those physical and spiritual elements that nurture man, the built environments that shelter him and the relationships between himself and others. Each facet of life is seen as a separate entity; the land as a productive resource or a wasteland, a person as black or white, exploiter or conservationist.

Separateness implies detachment and uninvolvement, each further reinforced by media images and stereotypes, often to such an extent that one eventually becomes a voyeur moving through the motions of living and living in a world of desire. Thought processes become rationalised and analytical, couched, by habit, in the terms of the prevailing ideology with the end result that the pieces do not add up to a 'whole'. The unifying, underlying essence that constitutes this 'whole' is missing from one's sensory experiences and presumably one's inner life as well. The result is that, after two hundred years of occupation, European man, now Western man, is a creature of habit, finding temporary relief (or boredom) in the day-to-day routines of life, knowingly or unknowingly avoiding the effects his actions have on the land that still indirectly supports him. The more entrenched the habit the more difficult it is to allow awe and mystery to enter the mind and to be able to wonder 'what if . . .?'

Outside the window, at this very moment, is a vast land with a multitude of landscapes. These landscapes are complex phenomena. They present a visual display of natural and cultural features that is the result of both past activities and present-day perceptions; yesterday's wasteland is today's wilderness.

Intrinsically the landscape is a combination of form and light as seen by the observer, the visual component of that ubiquitous medium, the environment. An appreciation of the landscape is important, not only for knowing where one happens to be but also for the physical and spiritual support that the landscape can provide. The variations of hues and tones, activities and serenities that emanate from, and can happen in, the landscape influences one's perception of that landscape and one's perception of oneself.

Landscape appreciation is demanding for it requires interpretation of what is being seen and often a reconsideration of learnt and habitual values. To many the sight of run-down and delapidated buildings is alien and depressing. Such feelings are not inherent but are learnt and reinforced by popular cultural values. Reactions to such sights need not be negative. Those delapidated buildings can exude a presence if one knows their history or they may be simply quite beautiful if one can see beyond their preordained use and shape. Some weathered building materials, on close inspection, portray varied colours and textures, patterns that enhance rather than detract from those buildings under inspection. The decay of a building is as valid a part of the concept of 'building' as was its construction and utilisation. What the building 'says' is that decay is as much part of its life as was its conception. The point being made is that it is not the object that requires changing but rather the perception of that object. The same can be said for landscapes.

The history of European occupation of the lands of Australia is not a good one. Through fear, ignorance, greed or power much of the land has suffered. It is thought that the earliest settlers wanted to create a landscape similar to where they came from so they imported plants and animals and a way of life in order to tame what they thought was a harsh environment. The discovery of gold brought more people who came to exploit the land without returning anything to it; needless to say many remained on the goldfields though most returned to the coastal cities or to whence they came. Then followed a period of pastoral expansion whereby over ten per cent of the land was cleared of trees and another sixty per cent was grazed, browsed and trampled by sheep and cattle. Even today vast tracts of country are being cleared of vegetation. Much of the brigalow country of Queensland is disappearing, plans have been put forward to clear parts of the Western Division of New South Wales for crops while the conservative elements in Western Australia had plans to clear the Yilgarn and Dundas wildernesses so that the sons of farmers could work their own properties. All this was (and is?) to occur in the face of unreliable rainfall, rising salt in the soil (which makes the land useless in less than three generations), and a loss of countless habitats. Though fear of the land may have been reduced over the last two hundred years ignorance, greed or power are still potent masters, and each still operates to alienate the European from his or her new landscapes.

The landscape does not evoke fear or alienation, the mind does. The landscape can trigger those feelings but it is the perception of that landscape through ignorance or a lack of understanding that induces a negative reaction. Changing one's perception requires more than changing one's mind but it may be that understanding and interpreting what is being seen is all that is required. Interpretation need not be involved because all it requires is a knowledge of its components. (It's how these components fit together that is complicated.) To be able to put a name to something greatly assists in interpreting what is being seen while to actually discover that named 'something' is a rewarding experience in itself. Hence this book.

Originally this book was to be a description of those components of the landscape that anyone, in any area of Australia, can see outside his or her window. It soon became obvious that it would take at least ten volumes to do that. In order to write just one volume a theme or aspect of the landscape had to be chosen. The most obvious part of the landscape in most

places is its covering of living matter, that is its vegetation. Although the vegetation of Australia has been written about in scientific journals and books and although Australian plant life has been described in more popular articles and publications there seemed to be lacking a reference or guide book to how the land is clothed, readable by non-scientific types. This book's basic aim is to provide a descriptive framework so that the landscape's clothing, i.e. the *Australian bush*, can be recognised in the field. (It's much more fun than just looking out the window.)

The vegetated landscape, or the Australian bush, on first appearance presents a bewildering display of living matter, a higgledy-piggledy mass of trunks, leaves, branches, shrubs and grasses seemingly without form. The more observant may notice that the higgledy-piggledy mass varies from one place to another, that in some places there are trees as tall as large buildings while in other places there are no trees at all.

Because of all this confusion the 'bush' is often thought of as boring (fear, ignorance?); saltbush plains are uninteresting and dreary, mallee scrubs are tedious and forests block the view. To anyone travelling through the countryside the destination becomes more important than the journey. This need not be the case.

By the application of a systematic approach to viewing vegetation the bewildering display of plant life can take on a new meaning thus altering one's perception of what is being seen. To give what is seen a name further reinforces that meaning. Suddenly the jumble of plant life reveals structures and beauties probably hitherto unseen. Variations in those structures allow one to differentiate between one place and another thus making one aware that there may be reasons for these differences. An understanding and an ability to name these different vegetation structures makes one feel more at home in the bush and to see the bush as non-threatening, something that need not be feared nor destroyed. Go and take a look before some mad bugger nukes it out of existence.

Chapter Two

PLANTS AND THEIR HABITATS

Introduction
Natural Factors Influencing Vegetation
Climate, Soil, Geology, Topography, Another influence.
Other Factors Influencing Vegetation
Climatic Zones

Introduction

In the wild, plants cover most of the land surface of Australia. They range from forests nearly 100 m tall to sparse desert shrublands and alpine feldmarks that appear to be dominated more by rocks than by plants. An obvious thing is that the covering of the land surface by plants varies from place to place and, not so obviously, from time to time. This coverage is dependent on many factors and combinations of factors, all of which are interrelated. The result is a complex diversity of plant life seemingly in harmony with the prevailing conditions. The combination of these relationships, of the various individual plants and animals which exist within the fabric of these relationships, and of the dynamics of change that occur to these relationships is referred to as the ecosystem.

To understand how the ecosystem works it is best to consider how an individual plant operates within this system. The driving force behind the ecosystem is the energy received from the sun, commonly referred to as solar energy. Through a combination of solar energy, carbon dioxide derived from the atmosphere and photosynthesis, the energy of the sun is stored in the plant's cells. While a plant is photosynthesising it gives off two valuable by-products; oxygen which is needed by animals for their existence, and water vapour which is returned to the atmosphere by a process called transpiration. For a plant to be able to do this it requires a number of things from the environment in which it is located. These environmental factors go a long way in determining the types of plants that may be found in any one place for the environmental factors vary from place to place.

One of these factors is soil. Plants require soil for support and for the essential nutrients required for their maintenance and growth. For plants to obtain nutrients from the soil they need water in order to be able to transport these nutrients from the soil to their cells. In the vast majority of cases this water comes to the plant from the soil itself. To reach the soil it had to arrive from the atmosphere via precipitation (rain, snow, etc.) and/or by flooding.

Solar energy, soil and precipitation, just three of the elements that combine to influence a plant and its ability to maintain itself. This is just the tip of the iceberg. Before going into any more details it would be best to complete one's understanding of ecosystems. Already it can be seen that a plant requires certain inputs from its environment but for a system to be complete there has to be a complementary return or outputs from the plant itself. This return is a release of 'energy'. Some of the energy stored in the plant's cells is eaten by animals. This is how they receive their energy. Other portions of stored energy remain with the plant until it dies. On death the plant decomposes by the action of bacteria and fungi. Not only do animals receive energy from the decomposing plant but also the soil receives nutrients which helps to maintain its fertility. As a result this fertilised soil is available to a new generation of plants. The processes of growth and decomposition vary. In very humid or wet environments growth is quick and decomposition is rapid; in very arid or dry environments these processes are relatively slow.

This then is a simple guide to how the ecosystem operates. Like most things it is not that simple. Rather than introducing more factors into the system, consideration should be given as to what happens to ecosystems over time. In the short term the ecosystem will maintain itself for it can make adjustments to changes in precipitation, reduced solar energy in winter, even fire, etc. In the long term, over thousands of years, some or all of these factors will change. Climates change, resulting in changes to soil, precipitation and temperatures which result in changes to moisture availability to plants, soil fertility and so on. Presumably plants adapt to or evolve with these changes with the result that there are changes to the prevailing plant life. If all the plants of a given area are considered, then obviously there has been, and will be, changes to that plant life which prevail now. In order for an understanding of ecosystems to be complete, account must be taken of both the short-term and long-term changes that occur within the ecosystem. With that in mind the reason for plant life and vegetation varying from place to place and for there being such a diversity of plant species is a little easier to grasp.

Figure 2.1

Average Annual Rainfall

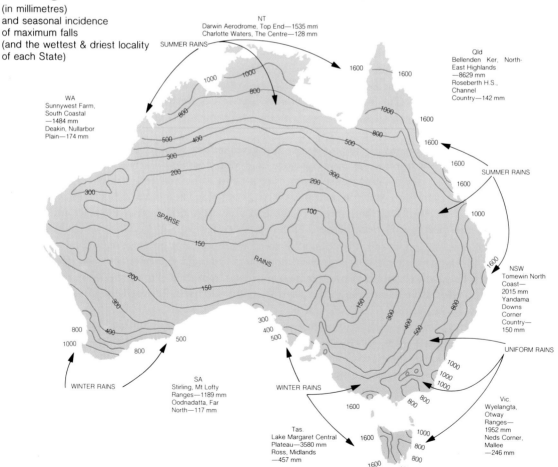

(in millimetres)
and seasonal incidence
of maximum falls
(and the wettest & driest locality
of each State)

NT
Darwin Aerodrome, Top End—1535 mm
Charlotte Waters, The Centre—128 mm

SUMMER RAINS

Qld
Bellenden Ker, North-
East Highlands
—8629 mm
Roseberth H.S.,
Channel
Country—142 mm

WA
Sunnywest Farm,
South Coastal
—1484 mm
Deakin, Nullarbor
Plain—174 mm

SUMMER RAINS

SPARSE

RAINS

NSW
Tomewin North
Coast—
2015 mm
Yandama
Downs
Corner
Country—
150 mm

UNIFORM RAINS

WINTER RAINS

SA
Stirling, Mt Lofty
Ranges—1189 mm
Oodnadatta, Far
North—117 mm

WINTER RAINS

Vic.
Wyelangta,
Otway
Ranges—
1952 mm
Neds Corner,
Mallee
—246 mm

Tas.
Lake Margaret Central
Plateau—3580 mm
Ross, Midlands
—457 mm

Fire is an important ecological factor in the Australian bush (a low intensity burn at Booti Booti, North Coast, NSW)

Natural Factors Influencing Vegetation

To date consideration has been given to how one plant handles some of its environmental inputs; solar energy, soil types and precipitation. Consideration must now be given to all the obvious factors that influence not only individual plants but the community of individual plants which go together to form a distinctive vegetation type, herein called a *formation*. Each formation of vegetation in Australia is subjected directly or indirectly to each of these factors whether the formation is in its natural state, has been partially or considerably altered, or is a new formation consisting of introduced and exotic species. Each formation is a complex ecosystem which is not necessarily restricted to the boundaries of the formation, for some formations are merely a part of a larger or alternative formation; also seed dispersal by wind or animal movements extends the observable limits of some ecosystems beyond the limits imposed on recognisable formation boundaries. In addition some unnatural factors will alter, interfere with or destroy natural ecosystems both within and without the formation boundaries. These factors will be discussed later.

The natural factors are conveniently classified as follows; climatic influences, soil influences, geological influences and topographical influences. Other unseen factors include the history and evolution of formations over time and any past alteration by indigenous peoples, i.e. the Aborigines. (The Aborigines have been included here for they are considered to have lived in harmony with the Australian environment for over 40 000 years; that is some 1350 generations. By comparison European settlers have been here 200 years in a few places but barely 130 years throughout much of the country; that is about 4 to 5 generations — no-one has yet said that European man is living in harmony with the Australian environment although a few are trying.)

CLIMATE

Climatic influences are many and varied. Variations occur daily, season to season, year to year and millennium to millennium; the relative effect of each influence also varies from place to place. Vegetation formations have adapted to, and can cope with, all natural influences, not only climatic ones.

As mentioned previously precipitation is an important factor influencing vegetation. Although precipitation can take on many forms it is the total amount received, its incidence and variability as well as intensity which decides how much moisture will be available for the plant community. This amount is also influenced by the *evaporation* rate of a particular area; its effect is altered by temperature, wind speed and the amount of cloud cover experienced by the vegetation. Together precipitation and evaporation combine to form *effective precipitation*, i.e. how much moisture is available to the plant community. (See figure 2.1: Average Annual Rainfall and Seasonal Incidence of Maximum Falls.)

For the plant and its community to be able to function the amount and intensity of *light* received has a great influence on the process of photo-

15

synthesis. Light amount and intensity is dependent on the latitude of the community (different latitudes have varying lengths of daylight in summer and winter as well as variations in duration and intensity of incoming solar energy); the altitude of the community (higher altitudes receive more ultraviolet light); aspect, i.e. whether the vegetation grows on south-facing slopes away from the sun or north-facing slopes which receive the midday sun 'full-on' (this will obviously influence the effective precipitation); degree of cloudiness and the location of the individual plant within a formation (the tops of trees receive more light than sheltered specimens beneath the canopy).

Temperature plays a part by influencing the growth rate of plants. This is a result of the period or duration that plant communities experience absolute maximum and minimum temperatures. Some plants die in freezing conditions while others may wilt, even die, if high summer maximum temperatures are maintained for extended periods. Temperature also plays a major role in the rate of evaporation, consequently influencing the effective precipitation.

Finally, *wind* also influences vegetation. It increases the rate of evaporation hence reduces effective precipitation, is involved in seed dispersal and may destroy formations through cyclonic activity. A combination of climatic influences means that much of Australia's vegetation is prone to, and has adapted to, *fires*. Further information regarding fires can be found by consulting the index.

SOIL

The influence that soil has on the type and formation of vegetation is very important. Soils provide not only support for plants but also moisture and nutrients, the availability of which depends to a large extent on the soil type. Soil is made up of many things; a complex of mineral particles, rock fragments, organic matter, water, air and living organisms. The resulting combination of each of these factors depends on a number of variables, namely the original rock type on which the soil was derived, the climatic influences involved in the breakdown of the rock, the climatic influences which still affect the soil and decomposition of plant and animal matter on and within it, the location where these processes are taking place or have taken place and the period of time in which its formation occurred. The various combinations of these factors and how they interact result in there being a number of different soil types.

In Australia there are nearly fifty different types of soil (Stace, 1968). Each type has a different set of characteristics based on differing structures, textures, moisture retaining abilities, colours and degrees of acidity or alkalinity. Each characteristic and combination of characteristics has a considerable bearing on the type of vegetation, and as a consequence, the formation of that vegetation. Before considering these characteristics in a little more detail it should be noted that small plants with shallow root systems are influenced by the upper layers of the soil while larger plants with extensive root systems will be influenced by all layers in the soil. The characteristics of soil vary with depth.

Soils have the following characteristics. The *colour* of soil indicates the presence or absence of iron oxides, whether the soil is well drained or not, the degree of organic matter within the soil and the degree of leaching that occurs in the upper layers. The presence of yellows, browns or reds indicates iron oxides and/or that the soil is well drained; poorly drained soils are grey to black. Organic matter darkens the soil's upper levels while leaching (the removal of particles from upper to lower levels) produces pale upper levels.

Structure and *texture* are indicative of how the soil is held together which in turn indicates whether the soil is well drained and aerated or not. Soils with a large percentage of clayey particles are generally poorly drained, a consequence of which is that they are reluctant to release soil moisture and nutrients. Sandy soils, on the other hand, are well drained and aerated, often to such an extent that they retain little moisture and nutrients. The degree of acidity or alkalinity of a soil, usually expressed as a soil's pH, has a great bearing on the availability of nutrients to plants. Acid soils are generally sandy while alkaline soils are generally clayey. As a rough rule of thumb one can expect sandy soils to support heathy and shrubby plants while clayey soils will support grassy and herbal plants. Needless to say there is a wide variation in the degree of sand or clay within the different soil types and each type is capable of supporting some type of formation of vegetation.

When considered with different climatic influences individual types of soil are capable of supporting different types of vegetation. For details of each of Australia's soil types, with approximate locations, landscape colours, climatic zones, typical landforms and some typical vegetation formations that may be found on them see Appendices 1, 2 and 3.

GEOLOGY

The direct effect of geological influences on vegetation and its formations is small except where expanses of rock impede water infiltration and promote rapid runoff thus denying moisture to all those plants not lying in positions where water may collect. The major influence of geology is the influence it has on the soils which were derived from it. As a rough guide rocks exhibiting large particles generally produce sandy soils while those with minute or microscopic particles generally form clayey soils.

TOPOGRAPHY

The term topography describes the lie of the land. Its effect on vegetation and its formations are important because variations in topography result in variations in plant habitats. These effects can be summarised as follows. *Aspect* describes the direction a slope faces in relation to the sun. Northerly facing slopes in Australia are hotter and drier than southerly facing slopes because they receive more solar energy. This has an influence on the effective precipitation available to plants and on the humidity of the plant's habitat. The *position* or *location* of plants results in variations to habitats. Mountain peaks and hilltops are prone to exposure by hot or cold winds; valley bottoms are generally more sheltered although they are subjected to colder temperatures on still, winter nights. Nearness to the sea also results in variations to habitats. Along the coast temperatures are tempered by sea breezes and precipitation is usually greater than further inland. Exposed coastal positions are prone to strong winds and maybe salt spray. Salt spray results in an effect commonly known as wind-pruning.* Further inland the moderating influence of the sea is reduced thus a wider range of temperatures can be expected.

Altitude influences plant habitats by generally reducing average temperatures and increasing precipitation amounts when compared to adjacent lowlands. Some changes of vegetation with altitude are shown in figure 2.2.

Major topographical features such as hill and mountain ranges influence weather conditions on the upwind and downwind sides. On the upwind side any moisture-laden winds are likely to precipitate as they rise over the topographical barrier. Should these winds be prevailing then it is reasonable to expect a higher average rainfall on that

* The salt spray coats seaward facing leaves and branches killing young shoots; this results in the wind-pruned effect.

The Changes of Vegetation with Altitude

Figure 2.2

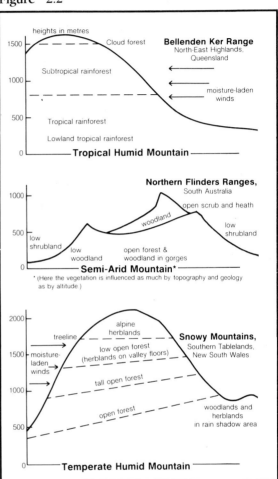

side of the barrier. Conversely the other side will be comparatively drier due to the drying effect of the descending winds. This dry side is called a rain shadow. Descending drier winds also increase temperatures thus further reducing the effective precipitation. Major wintertime rain-shadow areas occur on the eastern side of the Great Dividing Range in southern New South Wales and eastern Victoria, the eastern side of the Mt Lofty and southern Flinders Ranges in South Australia and the eastern third of Tasmania. All along the western side of the Great Dividing Range from northern Queensland to southern New South Wales is another rain-shadow area, especially during the summer.

17

The end result of dieback, a complex phenomenon that converts woodlands and forests to grasslands. It is generally found where land clearance and ringbarking has left few trees for regeneration. (nr Kentucky, Northern Tablelands, NSW)

Variations in topography result in different plant habitats and formations of vegetation. Where the topography changes markedly over short distances there will be many different types of habitats; where topographical changes are less marked habitats are more uniform and extensive. Variations in these circumstances are more subtle and are more likely to indicate differences in soil types. Nonetheless it can be seen that topography, soils, climate and geology all interact to produce a considerable diversity of plant habitats.

ANOTHER INFLUENCE

The Aborigines, before displacement by European settlers, used to fire the vegetation in some places in order to retard shrub development, improve grazing lands for kangaroos, etc. and to make hunting and movement across the landscape easier. When the European explorers first visited the better watered country they saw and described the vegetation as grassy woodlands suitable for the grazing of sheep and cattle. Since settlement much of these grazing lands have developed into shrubby woodlands because the patterns of burning, which have operated from a few hundred to many thousands of years has been altered. The vegetation at the time of first contact with Aborigines, some of which has remained unchanged, is the result of many thousands of years of occupancy.

Other Factors Influencing Vegetation

The effect of European settlement in Australia has been remarkable. When viewed in terms of what changes have occurred to the vegetation the result is that some formations have remained unaltered, others have been marginally altered, some have

Intensive agriculture and grazing requires extensive clearing of the vegetation when economics is the main decision-making input. (nr Morowa, Northern Wheatbelt, WA)

been radically altered while a few have been totally destroyed. These changes to the natural vegetation are best expressed in terms of the prevailing land use since settlement. The major types of land use in Australia are urban, industrial and mining activities which virtually destroy formations; cropping and pastoral activities which greatly alter or destroy formations; rangeland activities which partially or greatly alter formations and forestry activities which either destroy or radically alter the structure of formations. No-one argues that these activities should be stopped or even reduced although there are grounds, and a growing support, for the carrying out of these activities sympathetically within the fabric of natural ecosystems wherever possible. Future developments should be considered in the light of past mistakes and a conscientious effort be made to promote and retain any remaining stands of natural vegetation especially within those areas already denuded by the activities listed above. Developments based on dubious motives and vague promises of wealth have to be weighed against the cost of further reducing natural ecosystems, plant habitats and vegetation formations because a lack of diversity in these natural conditions not only influences the life contained within but also the viability of agricultural practices and the long-term wealth and well-being of one and all.

Mining activities destroy vegetation in localised areas, often through poisoning by concentrated mineral wastes. (Peelwood, Southern Tablelands, NSW)

A summary of the effects of European settlement is presented in figure 2.3. Figure 2.4: Australia's Vegetation — Degree of Disturbance, provides a rough guide to the degree of disturbance by the various activities listed above. A few terms need to be explained; rangeland activities are described as the extensive grazing of beef cattle and sheep; pastoral activities are described as the intensive grazing of sheep, beef cattle and dairying; agriculture and cropping are used synonomously.

Climatic Zones

To facilitate the understanding of the effects that climatic influences have on the formations of vegetation and to subdivide the continent into broad, homogenous geographical regions in order to assist the location of individual formations the following criteria, called climatic zones, will be used. These criteria are based on the area occupied by each zone, its broad climatic regime, its general appearance and dominant life forms or land uses. In southern Australia and Tasmania variations related to altitude are also differentiated.

Australia can be subdivided into two major climatic regions: *temperate* regions which are located south of the Tropic of Capricorn and *tropical* regions which lie to the north. Although this line of demarcation is precise the natural boundary is not.

Nonetheless temperate regions are indicated by seasonal weather patterns with mild to hot summers and cold to mild winters. Tropical regions are characterised by warm to hot conditions all year round with a period of summer rainfall and a winter drought. (Along the north Queensland coast this winter drought is less pronounced.)

Further subdivisions can be made, namely humid, subhumid, semi-arid and arid. In all cases the boundary between each is not distinct. These zones should be considered as a transition between wet areas (humid) and dry areas (arid). Due to changes of seasons and periods of extended droughts or unusually wet periods some characteristics described below can apply to adjacent climatic zones depending on the prevailing conditions. For instance during droughts some subhumid zones may take on the characteristics of the semi-arid zones.

How Vegetation and its Formations have Changed since European Settlement

Figure 2.3

Major Land Use	Effects and Changes to Vegetation
Urban, Industrial and Mining Activities	natural vegetation virtually removed
	exotic vegetation planted
	pollutants added to the environment
	soils altered or changed
	flooding by reservoirs
	altered stream characteristics
	scarification by mining
	creation of waste dumps, refuse and radioactive materials
Forestry Activities	natural vegetation altered and structures changed
	partial or complete destruction by woodchipping operations
	exotic vegetation planted or introduced
	altered fire regimes
	penetration by roads increases risk by fire and weed invasion
	some pollutants added to the environment
	increase in dieback disease
Cropping and Pastoral Activities	natural vegetation removed in most areas
	exotic vegetation planted and weeds introduced
	exotic animals introduced
	pollutants added to the environment
	altered fire regimes in remaining stands of vegetation
	soils altered or changed
	ground cover altered with increased erosion
	increase in dieback disease
Rangeland Activities	natural vegetation partially removed
	exotic animals introduced
	ground cover altered in some areas with increased erosion
	altered fire regimes
	some pollutants added to the environment
	vegetation cleared by mining surveys e.g. seismic lines
Unused Areas including Wilderness Areas	minor incursions of exotic plants
	incursions by exotic animal species
	some areas radioactive after nuclear tests
	vegetation cleared by mining surveys e.g. seismic lines

It should be pointed out that some of these effects are not limited to the areas in which they originally occurred. For instance pollutants applied to cropping lands may be transferred by wind and water to other areas far beyond those places where they were originally applied.

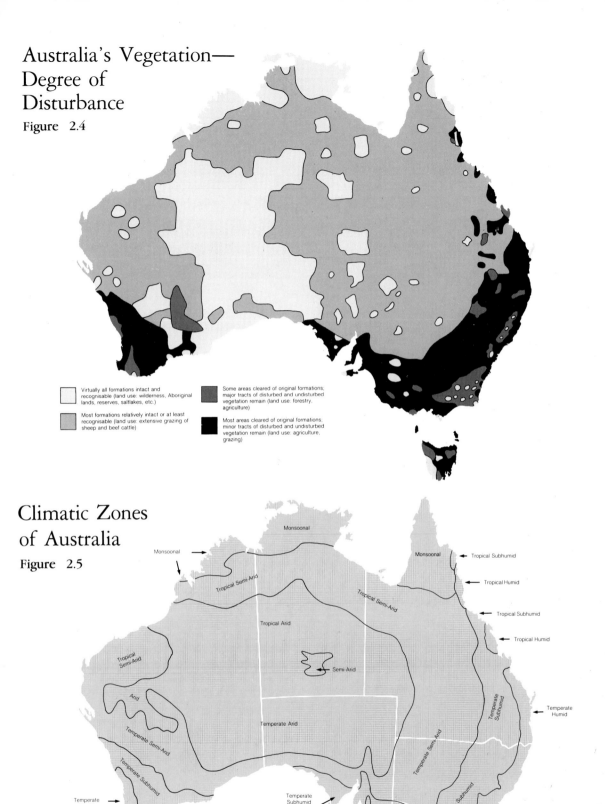

Australia's Vegetation—Degree of Disturbance

Figure 2.4

Virtually all formations intact and recognisable (land use: wilderness, Aboriginal lands, reserves, saltlakes, etc.)

Most formations relatively intact or at least recognisable (land use: extensive grazing of sheep and beef cattle)

Some areas cleared of original formations; major tracts of disturbed and undisturbed vegetation remain (land use: forestry, agriculture)

Most areas cleared of original formations; minor tracts of disturbed and undisturbed vegetation remain (land use: agriculture, grazing)

Climatic Zones of Australia

Figure 2.5

Monsoonal

Monsoonal

Monsoonal

Tropical Subhumid

Tropical Humid

Tropical Semi-Arid

Tropical Semi-Arid

Tropical Subhumid

Tropical Humid

Tropical Arid

Tropical Semi-Arid

Semi-Arid

Arid

Temperate Subhumid

Temperate Humid

Temperate Semi-Arid

Temperate Arid

Temperate Semi-Arid

Subhumid

Temperate Subhumid

Temperate Humid

Temperate Subhumid

Temperate

Temperate Humid

Temperate Humid

Temperate Humid

Temperate Subhumid

21

The location of each of these zones described below is shown in figure 2.5.

Humid zones are characterised by having annual precipitation amounts in excess of 500 mm in reliable winter rainfall areas and higher amounts in other areas. In cultivated or pastoral country the general appearance of the landscape is green (except, of course, during periods of drought). Droughts are generally rare although some humid areas experience dry summers, thus there is a drying out of the landscape. Dry summers are experienced along the southern and western coasts in the temperate humid regions. Humid regions account for approximately 6 per cent of the land area and include 75 per cent of the country's population. Most of the country's forest lands are found within this zone. The zone can be subdivided into temperate and tropical types.

Subhumid zones are characterised by an annual precipitation between 350 and 500 mm, falling to 250 mm in areas of reliable winter rainfall. Generally they present a yellowy-brown appearance in cultivated or pastoral country but appear green during the wet season or after wet periods. Some areas experience a summer drought while widespread droughts are fairly common. Subhumid regions occupy 13.5 per cent of the country and house 21.5 per cent of the population. Within this zone is found most of Australia's cropping lands, pastoral lands and woodlands. This zone is mainly temperate although there are a few minor tropical regions.

Arid landscape: precipitation here is very low and the vegetation likewise; the slight greening of the landscape is due to summer showers. (nr Lake Harry, Saltlakes, SA)

Semi-arid landscape: the norm here is one of low rainfall hence the vegetation is relatively sparse; the prevailing colours represent those of the plants, rocks and soil. (nr Mootwingee, Far West, NSW)

Semi-arid zones are characterised by precipitation amounts ranging from 200 to 350 mm with the lesser figure applying to areas receiving reliable winter rains and the greater figure to areas in the tropics which experience high evaporation rates and a long 'winter' drought. The appearance of the landscape is a yellow-red-brown colour except after wet periods. Approximately 37 per cent of the country is semi-arid and it houses 3 per cent of the population. This zone is mainly used for extensive grazing and much of its landscapes are covered with shrublands. The zone is divided into temperate semi-arid and tropical semi-arid.

Arid zones are found in areas which receive less than 250 mm of rainfall per annum. Rainfall is rare and may occur at any time, often in the form of intense scattered showers. Generally the country presents a yellow-red-brown face except after recent rains. Much of the land is covered with shrublands and most of it is unoccupied. Other areas are used for extensive grazing. It occupies 35.5 per cent of the land area and is home to 0.1 per cent of the population. In this text it has been occasionally subdivided into tropical and temperate zones but this distinction is rarely necessary. Drought conditions are the norm.

Monsoonal zones are characterised by a wet season and a dry season. Precipitation is greater than 350 mm during the wet while the dry sees a wintertime drought. Appearances change within the zone; during the wet everything is green, by the end of the dry it is a definite yellow-brown colour. The monsoonal zone occupies 8 per cent of the land and houses 0.5 per cent of the population. Many monsoonal regions are used for extensive grazing. All monsoonal regions are within the tropics.

Montane ridge landscape: this valley is probably the deepest in Australia, rising from submontane altitudes to alpine tops; consequently a variety of habitats is exhibited over a small distance; such slopes experience a high orographic rainfall. (Olsens Lookout, Snowy Mountains, NSW)

Submontane landscape: a cool, misty May morning at around 400 m altitude in southern Australia means low temperatures and a restricted growing season. (Mt Franklin, Central Victorian Hills, Vic.)

In southern Australia there are obvious changes of climatic zones with altitude. These changes also occur in the north-eastern tropical mountains. There are four zones to be considered.

Submontane or **tableland zones** generally lie above 600 m in the southern mainland regions and 300 m in Tasmania. The regions are typically humid except in rain-shadow areas where they are subhumid. They are subjected to rare or occasional falls of snow. Most areas are either forested or given over to intensive grazing.

Montane zones occur above 1000 m in the southern mainland regions and 600 m in Tasmania. Most are humid and are covered in forests. They generally experience short but regular winter snowfalls.

Subalpine zones occur above 1400 m in New South Wales, 1200 m in Victoria and 900 m in Tasmania with some lower altitude valleys exhibiting subalpine characteristics. Virtually all areas are humid and covered with low open forests, woodlands or herblands. Most places are covered with

Montane valley landscape: montane valleys are subjected to severe cold during autumn and winter which reduces the growing season and imposes limits on plant growth. (nr Yaouk, Snowy Mountains, NSW)

snow for at least one month of the year.

Alpine zones occur above 1800 m in New South Wales, 1700 m in Victoria and 1200 m in Tasmania. These areas are characterised by treeless country and may be covered with snow for up to 8 months of the year (some snowpatches are known to last all year in sheltered vales on the highest of peaks). The alpine zone may reach to lower altitudes in some upland valleys.

Subalpine landscape: the hillslope on the left is subalpine in character as evidenced by the low trees; the valley bottom and the range below are alpine; this area represents the limits of tree growth on the mainland. (Charlottes Pass, Snowy Mountains, NSW)

Alpine landscape: this glacially formed tarn occupies a high, treeless valley some 1900 m above sea-level; the growing season is very short as the area is under snow for much of the year. (Lake Albina, Snowy Mountains, NSW)

Part Two

THE STRUCTURAL FORMATIONS OF AUSTRALIA'S VEGETATION

Chapter Three

THE CLASSIFICATION OF VEGETATION

Introduction

Vegetation can be classified in a number of ways. No one way is perfect because classifications inherently carry with them certain parameters or restrictions which are arbitrarily decided upon. Although the parameters may be made to best suit the classification it is impossible to apply a fixed structure to something that is quite variable and expect it to neatly fit into pre-conceived pigeonholes. When one classifies something then one draws together common elements or components and adjusts the restrictions or parameters around them in order to create groupings. Hopefully the things being looked at will fit into these groupings. In any classification it is the individual grouping which is named so that anything which meets the criteria of that group will be known by that name. In other words classifications are groupings which act as tools used to create some order out of chaos and vegetation without classifications is very chaotic.

The Classification of Vegetation

Figure 3.1

Type of Vegetation	Projec-tive Foliage Cover	Broad Description of Vegetation Formation	Fully grown height of the highest level of vegetation		
TREES single-stemmed woody plants over 5 metres tall when fully grown			**Over 30 metres**	**10 to 30 metres**	**5 to 10 metres**
	70–100%	Closed forest	Tall closed forest	Closed forest	Low closed forest
	30–70%	Open forest	Tall open forest	Open forest	Low open forest
	10–30%	Woodland	Tall woodland	Woodland	Low woodland
	less than 10%	Open woodland	Tall open woodland	Open woodland	Low open woodland
SHRUBS usually multi-stemmed woody plants less than 8 metres high			**2 to 8 metres**		**less than 2 metres**
	70–100%	Closed shrubs	Closed scrub		Closed heath
	30–70%	Open shrubs	Open scrub		Open heath
	10–30%	Shrublands	Tall shrubland		Low shrubland
	less than 10%	Open shrublands	Tall open shrubland		Low open shrubland
HERBS plants with non-woody stems			**Description Based on Dominant Type of Herb**		
	70–100%	Closed herblands	closed herbfields, closed grasslands, closed sedgelands, closed tussock grasslands, closed fernlands		
	30–70%	Herblands	herblands, grasslands, tussock grasslands, sedgelands, fernlands		
	10–30%	Open herblands	open herblands, open grasslands, open sedgelands, open tussock grasslands, open hummock grasslands		
	varies	Non-vascular plant formations	mossy types, algal types and other types		
VARIOUS TYPES	varies	Formations of extreme, varied and altered habitats	**Description Based on Habitat Types**		
			ephemeral formations; mangrove, salt marsh, wetland, coastal dune, coastal cliff formations; alpine, desert complexes, altered formations		

(Left margin labels: **WOODY PLANTS** spanning TREES and SHRUBS; **NON-WOODY PLANTS** spanning HERBS)

How Vegetation is Classified in this Book

STRUCTURAL FEATURES

The classification used in this book is based on works devised by Specht (Leeper, 1970 and Groves, 1981). His classification is based on three factors; the type of vegetation, its height and its projective foliage cover (a term which will be explained shortly). The combination of these factors creates groupings or *formations* of vegetation based on the vegetation's *structure*.

Type of vegetation This is the form the vegetation takes. In this classification it refers to the *dominant* vegetation, i.e. that part of a formation which is dominated by the tallest and most common plant type. For example, in forests trees are the dominant type of vegetation; in grasslands grass is the dominant vegetation. Dominant vegetation (or all vegetation for that matter) is considered to be one of three types; trees, shrubs and herbs.

• *Trees* are single-stemmed woody plants that are generally over 5 m tall when fully grown; note that some trees may have a stem which separates into two just above the ground.

• *Shrubs* are multi-stemmed woody plants or single-stemmed woody plants with branches close to ground level; generally they are less than 8 m tall when fully grown.

• *Herbs* are non-woody plants such as grasses, rushes, etc. They also include unusual types of plants such as mosses, algae, seaweeds, etc., herein referred to as non-vascular plants.

Height The height of vegetation is an arbitrary feature. In this classification tree formations are called *tall* if the dominants are over 30 m high, *low* if between 5 and 10 m high and *very low* if less than 5 m. In some shrub formations shrubs are called *tall* if over 2 m or *low* if less than 2 m. Herb formations are generally less than 2 m high and no distinction is made between tall herbs and low herbs in this text.

Projective foliage cover This is a term which describes that area of ground, expressed as a percentage, which is 'covered' by the foliage of the *dominant* plants. As foliage cover varies from species

The Structure of Plant Formations

Figure 3.2

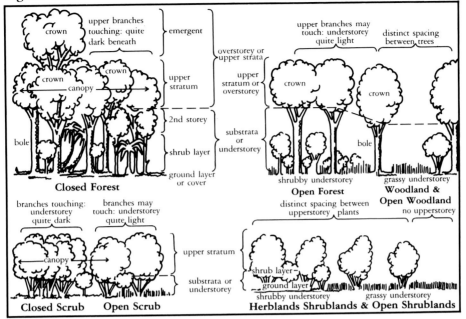

to species depending on leaf size, etc., it could also be thought of as expressing that area of ground vertically 'covered' by the crowns or canopy of the dominant plants. In other words it is an expression of density of growth of the dominant plants. The value of the projective foliage cover and its relationship to plant height and type of vegetation is displayed in figure 3.1. The resulting terms, e.g. tall open forest, low shrubland provide a broad description of a formation's structure.

(N.B. In some formations there are trees or shrubs that grow above the general level of the dominant plants. These plants are usually scattered and do not form a continuous or even broken canopy. Called *emergents* they should be disregarded when determining the heights and projective foliage cover of the dominant plants. Emergents are commonly found in the closed forest or rainforest formations.)

It should be emphasised that the height and projective foliage cover is applied to mature plant formations. In some instances, especially wetlands, plant formations may have not yet reached maturity and consequently they may not exhibit the heights or projective foliage covers as described in this text.

OTHER FEATURES

The broad description of a formation's structure can be further narrowed down by the consideration of other features, so describing, quite specifically, virtually every type of formation within a given

area, namely Australia. Consequently just about every type of formation can be recognised in the landscape and given a name.

These other features are based on the dominant flora (expressed by the plant's genus), the type of understorey and on geographical location. Not all these other features are necessary to describe a particular formation although when naming a formation consideration is usually given to the dominant's genus and/or the type of understorey.

Genus of the dominant plants Because there are so may species it is better to consider the genus to which a specific plant belongs. For instance there are about some 450 types of eucalypts in Australia and over 600 wattles. Each of these species of eucalypts and wattles belong to the *Eucalyptus* and *Acacia* genera (plural of genus) respectively. Consequently an open forest which is dominated by eucalypts can be called a *Eucalyptus* Open Forest. Similarly a tall shrubland dominated by mulga can be called an *Acacia* Tall Shrubland.

Even though there are numerous genera of plant types in Australia only a small proportion actually dominate formations. Each dominant genera for tree and shrub formations has been described in Part 3. Do not be alarmed by the number described for most of these are found in rainforests or closed forests according to our terminology and closed forests have been described not by the dominant genus or genera but by the nature of the understorey. Those genera described in Part 3 should help one to recognise their characteristic features; some typical species have also been described although it is suggested that a more detailed reference be referred to if positive species identification is required. In virtually all cases this is not necessary in order to identify and name a particular formation. In the case of the herbland formations most dominant plants have been described in terms of their family groups (the members of a family are made up of individual genera with similar characteristics). To assist in the naming of herbal plants and/or their genera, once again consult Part 3.

(N.B. Some formations are dominated by more than one genus. Where this occurs reference should be made to Appendices 1 and 2. Therein are listed the various combinations of dominant genera — referred to as co-dominant genera — and the formations which they dominate.)

Type of understorey In order to further narrow down the field of formation types reference is now made to the type of understorey that is found beneath the crowns or canopies of the dominant plants. The relationship between the understorey and the dominant plants which form the overstorey can be seen in figure 3.2. In the descriptions that follow the understorey is referred to as *substrata* in the tree and shrub formations. In the herbal formations the dominants and understorey plants, if any, are incorporated together as the *stratum*.

The understorey is divided into four main types with a couple of lesser types. These are:

- *Shrubby:* the understorey is composed of shrubby plants; may be called heaths if of a short, wiry or sclerophyll nature and also includes any short or tall (but less than dominant height) trees, tree ferns, etc. Grasses and other herbs may be present but are not conspicuous in the understorey. In some instances this shrubby understorey is divided into tall shrubby (over 2 m) and low shrubby (below 2 m).
- *Grassy:* the understorey is composed of grasses with very few or no shrubs present although there may be a few juvenile dominant plants. In addition other herbal plants such as sedges, rushes, etc., may be present. This also includes ephemeral plants that may occur after rain.
- *Layered:* this understorey is composed of a distinct shrub, low tree layer in combination with, generally tall, grasses. Layered understoreys are found in the northern, monsoonal and some tropical regions.

- *Hummock grass:* the understorey exhibits hummock grasses or spinifex, a common plant in many semi-arid and arid regions. In some places some grasses and ephemeral plants may be found.
- *Other types:* some formations have been described as having a closed understorey or herbal understorey. Closed forest understoreys are described as vine, vine-fern, fern and/or moss, all of which are self-explanatory.

Geographical location Unfortunately problems arise when there are two formations with the same name exhibiting the same understorey and dominant genus but that are represented by different species in widely spaced geographical areas. This problem can be overcome by referring to the formation as northern, southern, central, montane, alpine, temperate, etc., to indicate the general area where it is located, e.g. the formation known as the northern *Acacia* grassy tall shrublands which exhibits certain species is distinguished from the southern and central *Acacia* grassy tall shrublands which exhibits other species.

Finally where the same formation type is not extensive but is dominated by the same genus and exhibits similar understoreys but different species within roughly the same, overlapping or different geographical regions then the formation is referred to by number. For example, *Melaleuca* woodlands and low woodlands-1 is distinguished from *Melaleuca* woodlands and low woodlands-2.

Naming Formations

In the descriptions that follow each formation has a name, herein called a systematic name. This name is based on its structural features and one or more of its other features. The structural part of its name derives from those structural features already described and is set out in figure 3.1. Using this part of its name as a root then the other features can be added, where necessary, as prefixes. For example tall shrublands dominated by mulga (an *Acacia*) with a grassy understorey is referred to as an *Acacia* grassy tall shrubland. Because there are other such shrublands dominated by other species of the *Acacia* genus in northern Australia it is distinguished by being called southern and central *Acacia* grassy tall shrubland.

Details on how to recognise and name a

formation are given below. (N.B. Not all formations are named in this manner.)

Closed forest formations are distinguished by understorey type and/or some aspect of their floristics, e.g. deciduous, semi-deciduous and/or geographical criteria.

Open heath formations are distinguished by geographical criteria as expressed by climatic zones, e.g. tropical, wet temperate, dry temperate, alpine, etc., then by habitat type (expressed either as wet or dry), e.g. wet temperate wet and dry open heaths.

Non-vascular plant formations are named by the dominant genus (one instance) or by the dominant phyllum.

Vegetation formations of extreme, varied and altered habitats are named by genus (two instances) or habitat types, e.g. salt marshes, wetlands, etc.

Finally it should be noted that in formations dominated by species of eucalypts the word *Eucalyptus* has been dropped from the formation name.

How to Recognise and Name a Formation

There are a number of ways to do this. Consideration should be given as to how disturbed the formation is, i.e. is it 'natural', fairly intact or greatly disturbed?

METHOD ONE

This method is the most accurate and provides a means of systematically naming formations. It will help to have read the first two sections of this chapter. Step by step, the method is as follows.

1. Determine whether the formation is dominated by trees, shrubs or herbs, or whether it occurs in extreme, varied or altered habitats.
2. Determine the density or projective foliage cover of the dominant plants. It will be helpful to refer to figure 3.2. The Structure of Plant Formations, and figure 3.1. The Classification of Vegetation.
3. Determine the height of the dominant plants if trees or shrubs. See figure 3.3. How High is that Tree? — or simply guess. The heights of shrubs and herbs can be determined by comparing with one's own body height.

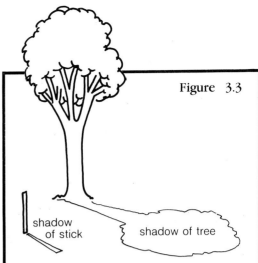

Figure 3.3

shadow of stick

shadow of tree

How High is that Tree?

1. Take a stick of known length, say 100 cm, and measure its shadow, say 60 cm.
2. Measure the shadow of the tree, say 800 cm, and multiply its length by the height of the stick (800 × 100 cm = 80 000 cm).
3. Next divide this figure by the stick's shadow length (80 000 ÷ 60 = 1333 cm approximately).
4. Converted to metres this gives the tree's height as 13.3 metres.

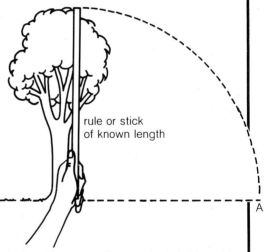

rule or stick of known length

A

1. Standing some distance back hold a stick at arms length so that it seems to be as high as the tree.
2. Pivot the stick so that it lies on the ground noting where the end of the stick lies (point A).
3. Measure or step out this distance between point A and the base of the tree. This distance is equivalent to the tree's height.

Vegetation of Australia — Major Types

Figure 3.5

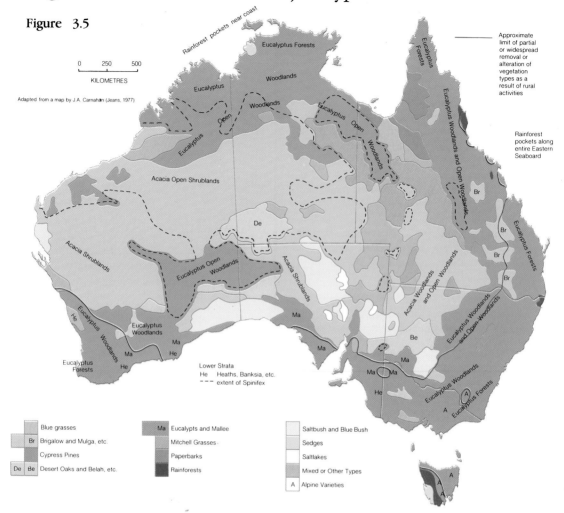

Adapted from a map by J.A. Carnahan (Jeans, 1977)

4. Using this information refer to figure 3.1 to obtain a broad description of the vegetation's formation. These 'broad descriptions' correspond to chapters 4 to 16.

5. Determine the genus of the dominant plants. (Note that this is not necessary for virtually all closed forests, closed scrubs and heaths, open heaths, non-vascular plant formations and extreme and varied formations.) If more than one genus appears dominant refer to Appendices 1 and 2 for possible combinations. If the genus is not immediately obvious then refer to Part 3 for descriptions of the dominant genera and families.

   The dominant genus of many herblands is difficult to determine. Refer to Part 3 to find out the differences between grasses (POACEAE family), sedges (CYPERACEAE family) and bulrushes (TYPHACEAE family), etc. If still having difficulties it may be necessary to refer to Appendix 3. Formations Arranged by Specific Habitats and Climatic Zones, in order to narrow down the number of possible alternatives. Further verification can be had by consulting figure 3.4. Vegetation of Australia-Major Formations and figure 3.5. Vegetation of Australia-Major Types.

6. Determine the understorey type. Note that it is necessary only for closed forests, formations dominated by species of *Eucalyptus* and *Acacia* and some *Casuarina* open woodlands. For the different understorey types see How Vegetation is Classified in this Book, this chapter. In some *Acacia* shrublands and open shrublands the height of the understorey plants should be considered (remember tall shrubs are over 2 m, low shrubs less than 2 m).

7. By now the plant formation name should be

Vegetation of Australia — Major Formations

Figure 3.4

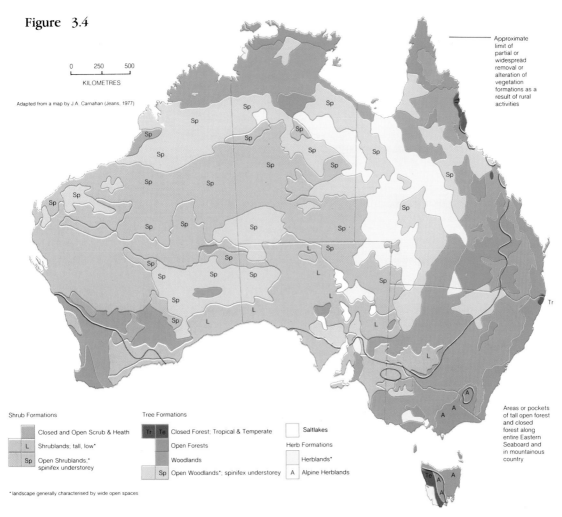

0   250   500
KILOMETRES

Adapted from a map by J.A. Carnahan (Jeans, 1977)

Approximate limit of partial or widespread removal or alteration of vegetation formations as a result of rural activities

Areas or pockets of tall open forest and closed forest along entire Eastern Seaboard and in mountainous country

Shrub Formations

	Closed and Open Scrub & Heath
L	Shrublands; tall, low*
Sp	Open Shrublands;* spinifex understorey

Tree Formations

Tr	Te	Closed Forest; Tropical & Temperate
	Open Forests
	Woodlands
Sp	Open Woodlands*; spinifex understorey

| | Saltlakes |

Herb Formations

| | Herblands* |
| A | Alpine Herblands |

* landscape generally characterised by wide open spaces

obvious and one can turn to the appropriate heading in the chapters that follow. Note that each chapter is named after the broad formation type, e.g. closed forests, open shrublands, etc. In some instances it will be necessary to give the derived formation name a geographical indicator, e.g. northern, subalpine, etc., in order to distinguish it from similar formations. If unsure then refer to Appendix 3. Attention is drawn to the section titled Interpreting the Formation Details at the end of this chapter.

An example of method one:
1. The formation is dominated by trees.
2. Estimated density is less than 10 per cent.
3. Tree height is less than 10 m but over 5 m.
4. Checking with figure 3.1, the broad formation type is a low open woodland.
5. The dominant tree appears to be a eucalypt.

Even if not sure one could go on to determine the understorey then, by referring to Appendix 3, narrow down the possibilities.
6. The understorey is composed of spinifex, i.e. hummock grass.
   Possible formation: (*Eucalyptus*) hummock grass low open woodland.

By referring to the appropriate heading in Chapter 7 Open Woodlands then one would see that the formation is also called a tree steppe, that it is located in semi-arid or arid country, that typical dominant species include the variable-barked bloodwood and that the area may be used for the extensive grazing of beef cattle. Note that the word *Eucalpytus* was written in brackets. This is to signify that the *Eucalyptus* genus, where dominant, has been dropped from the systematic name.

The Regions of Australia
Figure 3.6

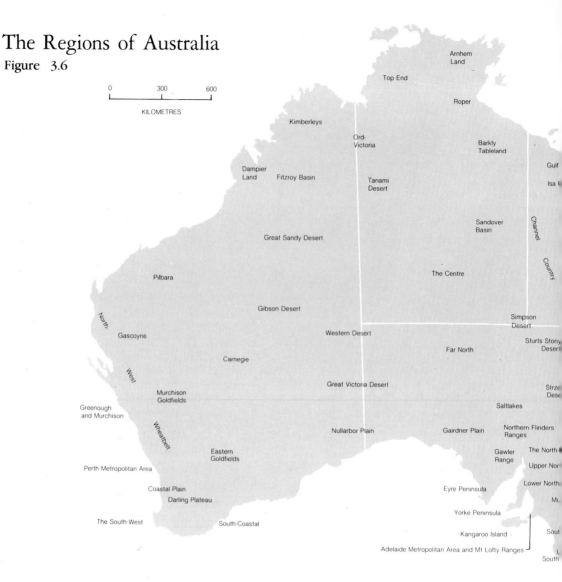

0   300   600
KILOMETRES

Arnhem Land
Top End
Roper
Kimberleys
Ord-Victoria
Barkly Tableland
Gulf
Dampier Land
Fitzroy Basin
Tanami Desert
Isa
Sandover Basin
Channel Country
Great Sandy Desert
Pilbara
The Centre
Gibson Desert
Simpson Desert
Gascoyne
Western Desert
Sturts Stony Desert
North
Far North
West
Carnegie
Great Victoria Desert
Strze Dese
Murchison Goldfields
Saltlakes
Greenough and Murchison
Wheatbelt
Northern Flinders Ranges
Eastern Goldfields
Nullarbor Plain
Gairdner Plain
Gawler Range
The North-
Perth Metropolitan Area
Upper Nor
Coastal Plain
Eyre Peninsula
Lower North
Darling Plateau
Mu
The South-West
Yorke Peninsula
South-Coastal
Kangaroo Island
Sout
Adelaide Metropolitan Area and Mt Lofty Ranges
South
Western Dis

METHOD TWO

This method is relatively easy to use. It assumes that one already knows the climatic zone in which the formation under consideration is located as well as whether the formation is dominated by trees, shrubs or herbs. One can start with a specific habitat or climatic zone as expressed in Appendix 3 and through a process of elimination derive a possible formation type. This process of elimination would leave one with a number of possible alternatives which could be reduced further by reading the lcoation description and landform types of each possible alternative and comparing these with the formation under consideration. This alternative may be useful if one does not know the dominant genus or when the formation has undergone some dramatic change such as land clearing, overgrazing, fire, etc.

With practise the recognition of formations becomes much easier. After a time one learns to recognise the *shapes* of formations and their constituent plants within each of the prevailing strata. The more one looks the easier it is to see these shapes. Furthermore, with experience, one can associate, even anticipate, formations with landforms within each of the climatic zones. Once this has been established in the mind's eye it is very easy to note the subtle variations in the landscape and to feel at ease within that landscape as these subtleties help nurture a familiarity and understanding of that landscape.

Interpreting the Formation Details

North Coast

North-East Highlands

Burdekin Basin

Central Coast

The Mid-West

Fitzroy Basin

Central Highlands

Burnett-Mary Basin

Maranoa

Darling Downs and Western Downs

Brisbane Metropolitan Area, Moreton and Gold Coast

Warrego-Paroo

Granite Belt

North-West Plains

Upper Darling

North-West Slopes

Northern Tablelands

North Coast

Western Plains

Central Western Slopes

Central Tablelands

Hunter Valley

Riverina

South-West Slopes

Sydney Metropolitan Area and Outer Sydney

Illawarra

Southern Tablelands

Snowy Mountains

South Coast

The North-East

Victorian Alps

Gippsland

East Gippsland

Melbourne Metropolitan Area and South-Central Victoria

North-West

The North-East

Midlands

East Coast

Central Plateau

The South-East

Once the possible formation has been recognised then all one needs to do is turn to the appropriate chapter heading, e.g. Closed Forests, Woodlands, etc., check through the index of formations listed there and then turn to the appropriate page.

On that page the possible formation will be described. The information regarding the formation is set out systematically so that one can readily determine location, habitat details, flora of the upper- and understoreys and any changes that may have occurred, particularly since European settlement.

The information has been set out as follows.

1. *Systematic name*: this name and its derivation has already been described under the heading The Naming of Formations, this chapter.

2. *Common name*: where applicable this name is one that is in common use, has been previously described in other texts by that name or includes a common plant name in order to help identification. A number after this name indicates that it is only one type of formation which, in combination with other similar types, is collectively known by one common name, e.g. mallee, mulga, etc.

3. *Location*: this is given in terms of climatic zones within each State or regions within a State. It serves to indicate the range of each formation type. For the location of climatic zones see figure 2.5 and for the location of regions see figure 3.6. Small or isolated examples of these formations may fall outside the locational range given.

4. *Habitat*: the habitat has been described under five headings and is included to help identify the particular type of country on which the formation is found, its altitudinal range and the climate it experiences. These factors are:
   a) *Landforms*: described either in broad, general terms, e.g. plains, downs, undulating country, hilly country or mountainous country, etc., where formations are extensive, or in more specific terms, e.g. valley slopes, ridges, sand-dunes, coastal cliffs, etc., where formations are small or restricted in size. For further information see Part 1, Chapter 2, Topography. Some landform types are defined in the Glossary.

b) *Soils:* as so many formations are dependent on soil types, specific soil names have been included where possible. For further details see Chapter 2, Soil.

c) *Altitude:* included to give an idea of the vertical range of formation sites. The figures should be taken as a rough guide. Heights are expressed in metres.

d) *Temperatures:* this section details the average temperatures to be experienced within the formation. They are not indicative of the extremes that plants and formations may sometimes endure. Summer includes the months of December, January and February in the temperate regions and from September to April inclusive in the tropical regions. Winter includes June, July and August in the temperate regions and June and July in the tropical regions. For further information see Chapter 2, Climate.

e) *Precipitation:* expressed in terms of average annual precipitation measured in millimetres. In some cases the timing of maximum precipitation and the likelihood of inundation or flooding is included. For the average annual rainfall and seasonal incidence of rainfall in Australia see figure 2.1.

5. *Upper stratum* or *strata:* this section describes the major or dominant genus present, its maximum height or range of heights and some typical species to be found. When more than one genus is dominant then this has been indicated. In extensive or widespread formations that exhibit different dominant species some indication has been given of their individual locations. Where emergents are common in the overstorey then the word strata has been used.

5. a) *Stratum:* in formations composed totally of herbal plants then only one layer has been described. This layer is assumed to include the dominant plant layer and any understorey or ground cover that may be present.

6. *Substrata:* this describes the understorey and the types of plants to be found there. It includes all vegetation below the canopy of the upperstorey dominants. In some cases there may be many layers, in others only one. Normally the description is subdivided into understorey and ground cover foliage.

7. *Transformations:* this section had to be included because very few formations outside the wilderness areas are either untouched or even intact. It accounts for any change to the naturally evolved formation caused by altered fire frequency and intensity, clear-felling and other forestry operations, flooding by dam works and resultant changes to downstream hydrology, land clearing for pastures and crops as well as mining and urban development and changes to the natural vegetation by grazing and trampling in rangelands (herein described as extensive grazing). The singular or combined influences of these changes will alter, often radically, the structure and floristics of the original or naturally evolved formation. In some places where secondary regrowth has followed after land disturbance the resultant formation may be of such an extent, or at least an obvious part of the landscape, that it has been described in terms of separate, individual formations. It is considered that any change wrought by Aboriginal peoples before European settlement is a natural change given that many European minds consider that the Aboriginals have lived in harmony with the prevailing climatic and ecological conditions for thousands of generations.

In addition, as a prelude to each 'formation chapter' there is an introductory section which provides an overview of the formations that follow. It has been included to give an idea of the major genera present, the location of these formations in a broad sense and, most importantly, a description which, when used in conjunction with figure 3.2 should simplify the identification of each major formation. Finally mention is made of the approximate total land area covered by, or once covered by, the major formations, the number of major alliances (groups of related species with the same structural characteristics) to be found and an approximation of the number of bird and mammal species that can (and must) occupy these habitats.

Ecotones

Because the classification of vegetation is less than perfect and because vegetation often exhibits gradual rather than dramatic changes from one area to another it is not always possible to accurately describe vegetation in terms of discrete formations. Vegetation should be thought of as a continuum wherein some elements of one formation gradually intermingle with elements of another formation so that the further each formation is apart from its neighbour then the more distinctive that particular formation will be.

That gradual change between two adjacent formations which displays elements of both types is called an ecotone. In some places the ecotone itself may be quite distinctive in which case it may well be designated a formation in its own right. In this text the formations described are considered to be 'pure', i.e. they do not contain elements in terms of structure or other features of adjacent formations. What this means is that some vegetated areas may be difficult to name in terms of formation and that some discretion is required when attempting to recognise and name formations.

Size of Formations

The question of ecotones leads on to the question, what is the size or scale of formations? Obviously the extensive formations such as woodlands, shrublands, etc., are very large; in fact many of these formations cover hundreds, if not thousands, of square kilometres as a continuous entity. Many other formations such as some wetlands, sedgelands and alpine types may be only a few metres across. The problem is, when does a formation exist in its own right rather that just being a part of an understorey of a more extensive formation? For example many open forests exhibit 'wetland-type' formations along stream banks, etc., even though the upperstorey trees may form a continuous canopy over the stream. There is no simple answer. The author's approach is to consider the formation to extend as far as the eye can see in extensive formations. Smaller formations are considered to exist in their own right if they form an obvious entity within a larger formation and are not covered by any upperstorey canopy. Thus the 'wetland-type' of formation given in the above example would not be considered a formation in its own right.

Problems of Generalising

One difficulty of a classification of this type is that when one generalises about formations, especially small ones that change from one type to another in a small area, there are difficulties in what to call a particular formation. Mention has already been made of ecotones whereby one formation grades into another. The problem is what does one call a formation that exhibits zones dominated by different plants on say, a sand-dune in the arid deserts. One way is to refer to it as an arid complex, as has been done in Chapter 16 Vegetation Formations of Extreme, Varied and Altered Habitats but this does not successfully deal with the problem.

To cite an example, on the sand-dunes of the Simpson Desert there are four distinct plant communities each located on a different part of the dune. The dune tops exhibit tangled cane grass as the dominant plant; below the tops are found a variety of ephemeral herbs, next, on the mid-slopes of the dune is hard spinifex while on the lower slopes and within the dune swales is a variety of dominant shrubs such as gidgee, mulga, hopbushes and so on; each of these may be locally dominant. A fifth community is a formation dominated by samphires around the margins of some saltlakes. The problem is whether each of these community formations should be considered individually as distinct formations or grouped together as a complex formation as the total distance between the four (or five) communities may cover only a few hundred metres. This text takes the first course, that of defining each formation individually by the dominant plant irrespective of the size so dominated. This problem equally applies to the zonation of plants around a pond or along a watercourse, across coastal sand-dunes, adjacent to coastal cliff-tops and on salt marshes, within mangroves, etc. When one is confronted with small formations exhibiting this type of zonation of dominant species reference should be made to the appropriate heading in Chapter 16.

Naming Plants

In this book plants have been named using common names rather than scientific ones. Scientific, or Latin names, have been used where no common name can be found. Because many plants have more than one common name the name selected is the one, in the author's opinion, most commonly used, either in general usage or by other authors. To overcome the confusion caused by using common names for plants attention is drawn to the index. It is felt that the use of common names is less intimidating to the general, and perhaps uninitiated, reader.

CLOSED FORESTS

Introduction

Closed forests or rainforests are characterised by dense foliage in their upper layers, a dark twilight world beneath and a general absence of eucalypt species. A rainforest is the most productive vegetation system in terms of numbers of species and sheer organic matter as measured by weight. The dense foliage, called the canopy, lies between 5 and 40 m above ground level and is normally so thick that very little sunlight penetrates to the lower levels. In many instances this layer is interspersed by taller trees, called emergents, which rise above the canopy level. These taller trees, as well as some canopy species, are supported by large buttress roots which rise from the soil like giant skirts.

Within and just below the canopy are numerous plants such as vines, epiphytic orchids, staghorns, etc., while lower down are many terrestrial ferns, more vines and all manner of plant life. This is at least true for the warm rainforests. In the cooler rainforests there are very few species below the canopy. Instead there are often great festoons of moss draped over branches, on fallen logs and on the ground.

On and near the ground the vegetation is thin due to the low light. Here lie young seedlings awaiting a break in the canopy so that sufficient light is available for them to continue their growth.

Closed forests require a variety of conditions for their survival. Basic to all such forests is the existence of a humid environment and the absence of bushfires. Humid environments depend on the degree of moisture availability, the direction of prevailing winds and the regular appearance of clouds to supply precipitation and to reduce solar radiation (the sun's 'heat') so as to reduce evaporation. Closed forests are also dependent on the water-holding and delivering capabilities of the soil. This means that richer, more friable soils such as those derived from basalt or shale are more likely to support closed forests. In some instances closed forests can survive on poorer soils by recycling nutrients from leaf litter and extracting nutrients and salts from the atmosphere.

Due to the high humidity of rainforest environments and their ability to produce rapid plant growth many of the leaves of rainforest species are a dark, glossy green with tips on their ends. It is thought that this arrangement allows water to rapidly run off the leaf so inhibiting the growth of fungi, etc., which otherwise may interfere with the leaf's function.

Closed forests also depend on an absence of bushfires for the species within these forests cannot survive them. This is due partly to the forest's nutrient supply being interrupted or destroyed and partly due to the plant's physical inability to cope. Even in areas of very low fire frequency, say every one hundred or more years, the closed forest will more than likely change into an open forest with resultant changes to its structure, dominant species type and number of species present, i.e. a complete change of habitat which influences all the plants and animals contained therein. This is a powerful argument against penetration of virgin rainforests by roads as instant access increases the chances of accidental or deliberate firing.

Given the appropriate conditions of humidity, soil type and absence of fire then closed forests can be found in a variety of terrains. In Australia these terrains are located in mountainous country and on some adjacent lowlands (virtually all of these have been cleared) within the high-rainfall districts where a constancy of water is assured. In drier areas such forests are restricted to narrow gullies, edges of watercourses or to southerly aspected hillslopes. They range from Cape York Peninsula to Tasmania, normally within 100 km of the coast. Minor areas are also found across the northern coastline. In all cases the range is segmented with stands as small as 1 ha. It has been estimated that rainforests once covered 0.9 per cent of the land area and are presently composed of 79 major alliances. Because of the diversity of genera which are found in the closed forests these formations, unlike the others described in this book (except the open heaths), are described geographically and by the nature of the understorey rather than by the dominant genera present within any one formation. Exceptions to the descriptions may occur. For a more detailed classification see Webb (Groves, 1981).

The closed forests support up to 115 species of birds (of which 49 are virtually restricted to it) and 31 species of mammals (12 of which are limited to this habitat). Closed forests are often referred to as scrubs, brush or jungle.

Tall Closed Forest Types

VINE TALL CLOSED FORESTS — tropical rainforests-1

Location: tropical humid coast of north Qld (North Coast: Ingham to Cooktown), minor areas south to Eungella Range.

Habitat: Landforms: coastal lowlands and adjacent hillslopes and mountains. Soils: kraznozems, alluvium, etc. Altitude: generally below 1000 m on basalt-derived soils. Temperatures: very warm to hot all year round. Precipitation: over 1200 mm with a definite summer maximum, no real dry season.

Upper strata: dominated by a variety of species which grow to different heights. Tallest are the emergents, trees which reach above the more or less continuous canopy. Emergent species include the silver silkwood, crowsfoot elm, milky pine, *Acacia* cedar and black bean. Some of these grow to 55 m. Below are the trees of the canopy which vary in height from 20 to 35 m or more. There are many species, two of which are *Endiandra toora* and *Apodytes brachystylis*. In a few localities this tall closed forest merges into a tall mangrove formation.

Substrata: below the canopy are numerous other woody species including the *Endiandra sankevana* and the scrub ironwood. As well there is a variety of palms such as the walking-stick palm and feather palm, numerous vines including the lawyer vine and other woody lianas as well as strangler figs and climbing aroids. The tall trees of the forest produce a surface on which epiphytes can grow. These include a variety of orchids as well as staghorns, elkhorns, birds nest ferns and tassel ferns. On the ground are various tree seedlings, ground ferns, ground orchids as well as wild ginger, cunjevoi and cordylines.

Transformations: many areas of tall tropical rainforest have been cleared for sugarcane farming and associated urban development. Other areas are at risk due to logging, road building and land development.

OTHER TALL CLOSED FORESTS

In some instances the emergent and canopy species of vine-fern closed forests and fern and/or moss closed forests may reach over 30 m. Should the canopy trees reach over this height they would then form tall versions of these forests.

Closed Forest Types

VINE AND SEMI-DECIDUOUS VINE CLOSED FORESTS — tropical rainforests-2

Location: tropical humid coast of north Qld (from Mackay to Cape York Peninsula).

Habitat: Landforms: hill and mountain slopes, tablelands; some coastal lowlands. Soils: kraznozems, etc. Altitude: generally below 1000 m. Temperatures: very warm to hot in summer, warm to very warm in winter. Precipitation: over 1200 mm with a definite summer maximum; a partial dry season in some areas, especially Cape York Peninsula.

Upper stratum: some species may be similar to those found in tall closed forests. Typical species of the tablelands include the Queensland kuari pine, silky oak, crowsfoot elm and red cedar among many others. In areas which experience a dry season some plants are semi-deciduous; species include the emergents silk cotton tree and *Ficus albipila*, both of which grow to 30 m, and the canopy species red sirrus, *Vitex acuminata* and Melville Island white beech among others.

Substrata: woody species in the understorey include *Ixora klanderana*, *Aglaia elaeagnoidea* and *Glycosmis pentaphylla* as well as numerous vines, orchids, ferns and palms. Generally the forest floor is relatively open.

Transformations: many areas have been cleared for sugarcane farming, tobacco cropping and dairying. Other areas are subjected to logging, clear felling and penetration by roads.

PALM-VINE CLOSED FORESTS — swamp rainforests

Location: tropical humid coast of northern Qld.

Habitat: Landforms: coastal lowlands subjected to seasonal inundation. Soils: various. Altitude: virtually at sea-level. Temperatures: see Tall Closed Forest Types. Precipitation: see Tall Closed Forest Types.

Upper stratum: dominated by palms including the feather palm (on basalt-derived soils) and the fan palm on infertile soils with vines (*Calamus* spp) common to both stands.

Substrata: represented by various sedges, etc. Lianas are common in the understorey.

Transformations: some areas have been cleared or otherwise altered.

Vine-fern closed forests −1: ground cover exhibits ferns and some mosses where the sun can penetrate; note the vines. (Cambewarra Mountain, South Coast, NSW)

Vine-fern closed forests −2: this forest exhibits elements of rainforest and tall open forest — the eucalypts in the background are brown barrel; in the foreground there is a blanket leaf (centre) a lilli-pilli to the left and a clematis-covered blue olive-berry to the right. (nr Club Terrace, East Gippsland, Vic.)

VINE-FERN CLOSED FORESTS-1 —
subtropical rainforests

Location: temperate east coast of NSW and southern and central Qld; tropical humid mountains of northern Qld.

Habitat: Landforms: coastal lowlands, hill and mountain slopes, upland areas. Soils: kraznozems, etc. (soils derived from basalt). Altitude: generally below 300 m in south and 1000 m in north within the temperate regions; generally above 1000 m in tropical regions. Temperatures: summers are very warm to hot, winters are cool to warm depending on altitude and latitude. Precipitation: over 1200 mm with a slight summer-autumn maximum in south and a summer maximum in north.

Upper strata: dominated by a variety of species in the emergent and canopy levels; in the tropical north emergents include a plum pine (*Podocarpus ladei*), rose silkwood and dogwood which grow to a height of 25 m. In central Qld the tulip oak, red cedar and a type of quandong (*Elaeocarpus foveolatus*) are (or were) common. Along gorges the white kurrajong and Illawarra flame tree are found. To the south are closed forests dominated by bunya pines and hoop pines which are allied with species such as red cedar, Morton Bay chestnut, crows ash, tulip oak, white beech and yellow wood among others. The southernmost versions of these forests exhibit the red cedar, coachwood, sassafras, yellow carabeen, giant stinging tree and Illawarra flame tree. Cabbage-tree palms are also fairly common in the south while Bangalow palms are found on alluvial soils in the central and northern districts.

Vine-fern closed forests −1: the canopy is a world of leaves, trunks and branches. (Cambewarra Mountain, South Coast, NSW)

Substrata: the understorey of these forests is composed of numerous vines or lianas, various palms, ferns and epiphytes such as orchids. Generally the ground layer is relatively sparse.

Transformations: many areas have been cleared for dairying, intensive grazing, urban development or have been selectively logged. There are virtually no lowland subtropical rainforests left save small isolated pockets on some farms and within reserves.

SEMI-DECIDUOUS VINE CLOSED FORESTS — tall monsoonal rainforests

See Semi-deciduous and deciduous low closed forests. This formation is a tall version of monsoonal rainforests located at more humid sites or experiencing a shorter dry season.

MONTANE VINE-FERN CLOSED FORESTS — cloud rainforests-1

See Montane vine-fern low closed forests.

VINE-FERN CLOSED FORESTS-2 — warm temperate rainforests

Location: temperate humid coast and adjacent ranges of southern NSW and eastern Vic.

Habitat: Landforms: sheltered gullies and southerly aspected slopes in hilly or mountainous country. Soils: various, generally those derived from basalt. Altitude: below 1200 m. Temperatures: summers are warm to very warm, winters are cool. Precipitation: over 1200 mm with a slight summer or autumn maximum.

Upper stratum: there are no emergents save for some eucalypts on the margins of rainforest gullies (see also Chapter 5, Tall open forests and open forests with a closed understorey). The canopy is less than 30 m high. Typical species include black-woods, kanookas, lilli-pillies, coachwoods, yellow carabeens, crab-apples and pinkwoods. Cabbage-tree palms may be present in some areas. In fact cabbage-tree palms are all that remain of these forests in some cleared paddocks that are presently used for dairying. Due to the overlap of certain species that are also found in subtropical rainforests these forests can be considered a southern or cooler version of subtropical rainforests even though they are somewhat depauperate in form, size and number of species.

Substrata: represented by a variety of lianas or by an abundance of tree ferns. Clematis is common in some areas. Normally the ground layer is relatively sparse.

Transformations: many areas have been subjected to selective logging and clear felling. Areas that have been cleared are used for the intensive grazing of beef cattle or for dairying; these pastures are sown with rye grass, clover, paspalum and kikuyu, etc.

FERN AND/OR MOSS CLOSED FORESTS — cool temperate rainforests

Location: temperate humid regions of western Tas.; minor pockets in southern Vic. and on the high tops of northern NSW and southernmost Qld.

Fern-moss closed forest: understorey exhibiting water ferns; ferns are common in wet habitats; the trees are blackwoods and paperbarks. (on Tidal River, Wilsons Promontory, Vic.)

Habitat: Landforms: hilly to mountainous country; sheltered gullies. Soils: various. Altitude: up to 1000 m in Vic. and Tas.; over 1000 m in NSW, Qld. Temperatures: summers are cool to mild, winters are cold to cool. Precipitation: over 1200 mm with a winter-spring maximum in the south.

Upper stratum: generally dominated by the deciduous beech (Tas. only) and myrtle beech (Tas. and mainland). Allies include the southern sassafras, blackwood, and in Tas., the King William pine. Generally the heights of the dominants are below 30 m. In some places the beech is absent; a few gullies in the hilly country of Vic. exhibit pure stands of southern sassafras; other sheltered gullies exhibit stands of cedar wattle, blackwood and silver wattle. These stands probably result from fires penetrating areas previously carrying beech forests. In northern NSW there are pure stands of coachwood occurring within stands of myrtle beech. In southern NSW pinkwood forests are found on cool mountain summits. Occasionally there may be emergents of the eucalypts mountain ash, alpine ash, brown barrel, etc.

Substrata: often the understorey is sparse. In some places there is a discontinuous shrub and fern layer represented by southern sassafras, the pine *Podocarpus alpina* and the soft tree fern. Otherwise, or as well, there are numerous mosses and lichens growing on fallen logs or draped across low branches. In Tas. some myrtle beech forests exhibit horizontal scrub, wiry bauera and the trees Tasmanian blackwood, Tasmanian laurel and leatherwood in the understorey.

Transformations: many of these forests are relatively undisturbed due to their relative inaccessibility though some are under threat by hydro-electricity works, mining and the penetration of roads.

SUBCLIMAX COOL TEMPERATE RAINFORESTS

Location: temperate humid regions of Tas.
Habitat: see Fern and/or moss closed forests.
Upper stratum: dominated by *Eucalyptus* emergents, generally over 30 m high. A typical species is the mountain ash. The canopy is absent.
Substrata: represented by the species myrtle beech, southern sassafras and celery-top pine.
Transformations: this forest is transitional between cool temperate rainforests and tall open forests, its structure and composition depending on the intensity and frequency of bushfires.

Low Closed Forest Types

SEMI-DECIDUOUS AND DECIDUOUS LOW CLOSED FORESTS — monsoonal rainforests

Location: monsoonal northern regions of Qld (Cape York Peninsula) and NT (Top End, Arnhem Land). Some references also include the Kimberley regions of WA.
Habitat: Landforms: along watercourses, around waterholes, sheltered gullies. Soils: various. Altitude: virtually at sea-level. Temperatures: very warm to hot all year. Precipitation: over 1200 mm in most places with a definite summer maximum.
Upper stratum: the canopy height is generally between 5 and 10 m although it may reach above 10 m in a few restricted localities thus forming a semi-deciduous or deciduous closed forest or a tall monsoonal rainforest. Species include dry season deciduous and semi-deciduous plants such as wild nutmeg, Indian beeches, umbrella tree, red-fruited kurrajong, white cheesewood, evodia, native kapok and various milkwoods. On the jungle fringes may be found native bamboo clumps, Melville Island white beeches, tuckerooes and kelumpangs.
Substrata: the understorey is composed of vines as well as various epiphytes and palms. Typical palms include the Carpentaria palm and pandanus. In some places the fan-leaved bloodwood and ghost gum may be seen. Tall grasses and cycads also may occur in the understorey.
Transformations: most stands are unaltered due to their relative inaccessibility. Stands vary between 2 and 20 ha in size.

MONTANE VINE-FERN LOW CLOSED FORESTS — cloud rainforests-2

Location: tropical humid coastal mountains of north Qld.
Habitat: Landforms: high, rocky tops of coastal mountain ranges. Soils: various; some derived from granite. Altitude: over 1200 m. Temperatures: summers are warm, winters are mild. Precipitation: up to 4000 mm with a summer maximum, no definite dry season.
Upper stratum: dominated by a tea-tree (*Leptospermum wooroonooran*), a relative of the camphor laurel (*Cinnamomum propinquum*) and the pimply ash. These trees form a canopy between 3 and 15 m high. The higher canopy, which constitutes a montane vine-fern closed forest occurs in sheltered pockets below the summits of these mountains.

Substrata: represented by *Alyxia orophila*, *Eugenia apodophylla* and *Drimys membranea* and also includes Australia's only native rhododendron. The bristly tree fern is also found here.
Transformations: virtually unaltered.

VINE-FERN LOW CLOSED FORESTS-1 —
dry rainforests

Location: see Vine-fern closed forests-1.
Habitat: similar to Vine-fern closed forests-1 except limited to upland areas, narrow ridge-tops and/or on poorer soils. Generally over 300 m in altitude in southern areas.
Strata: a depauperate version of vine-fern closed forests with fewer species present. Canopy height is generally between 4 to 10 m. Generally these low closed forests are drier than their equivalent taller formations so are often known as dry rainforests. Typical species of dry rainforests include the hoop pine and crows ash.
Transformations: see Vine-fern closed forests.

VINE-FERN LOW CLOSED FORESTS-2 —
low warm temperate rainforests

A depauperate version of vine-fern closed forests-2 found at the climatic or edaphic limits of this formation. (See also Chapter 5, Tall open forests or open forests with a closed understorey.)

FERN AND/OR MOSS LOW CLOSED FORESTS — low cool temperate rainforests

Location: temperate humid regions of western Tas.
Habitat: Landforms: high mountain valleys and gullies. Soils: various. Altitude: around 1000 m. Temperatures: summers are cool, winters are cold. Precipitation: up to 3000 mm with a winter-spring maximum; no dry season.
Upper stratum: dominated by a variety of species including the deciduous beech and various pines such as the celery-top pine, King William pine and pencil pine. In some places these pines may dominate. (See also Chapter 5, *Athrotaxis* open forests and low open forests.)
Substrata: tree ferns, heaths and wiry bauera are found in the understorey.
Transformations: relatively intact.

PISONIA LOW CLOSED FORESTS — *Pisonia* rainforests

Location: tropical humid islands off Qld coast.

Habitat: Landforms: coral cays, etc. Soils: sandy, etc. Altitude: virtually at sea-level. Temperatures: summers are very warm and humid, winters are warm. Precipitation: over 1000 mm with a summer maximum.
Upper stratum: dominated by the pisonia tree which grows to a height of 10 m and has a large, spreading crown. Allies include the sandpaper fig and various other deciduous rainforest species.
Substrata: due to the spreading nature of the dominant the understorey and ground layer is sparse.
Transformations: some areas are undisturbed; other areas may have been cleared for development purposes.

Scrub Types

HOOP PINE SCRUBS

Location: temperate humid coastal districts of northern NSW and Qld.
Habitat: similar to vine-fern closed forests-1 except located on sandy soils.
Stratum: dominated by pure stands of hoop pine. Such stands are very rare and limited in size.

SOFTWOOD SCRUBS — vine thickets

Location: temperate humid and subhumid regions of central and southern Qld.
Habitat: Landforms: undulating to hilly country. Soils: clayey. Altitude: generally below 400 m. Temperatures: summers are hot, winters are mild to warm. Precipitation: over 600 mm with a summer maximum.
Upper stratum: dominated by Queensland bottle trees and bonewood, each of which may dominate its own type of scrub, i.e. bottle-tree scrubs and bonewood scrubs. Eucalypt emergents such as the coolabah, Coolwarra box and mountain coolabah may be present.
Substrata: lianas are common and there may be a thick shrub layer, typically the broad-leaf leopard tree and scrub or brush wilga. The ground layer is generally sparse.
Transformations: some areas have been cleared for intensive grazing and cropping.

CYCLONE SCRUBS

Location: tropical humid coastal districts of northern Qld.

Habitat: similar to vine tall closed forests; these forests are regularly subjected to cyclonic winds or they represent cyclonic wind damage.

Strata: typical of vine tall closed forests except that where vegetation has been damaged by cyclones secondary regrowth of vines and other woody species is common. Secondary regrowth species include the large-leaved stinging tree and the sarsparilla.

Transformations: such formations have rarely existed for longer than 50 years although the evidence of extensive vine growth remains.

Tree Thicket Types

Black gidgee or (northern) blackwood Found in restricted localities in tropical semi-arid (sub-humid) Qld; forms thickets on some floodplains, e.g. Cape, Suttor and Belyando rivers. (See also Chapter 5, North-eastern *Acacia* open forests and low open forests-1.)

Bulwaddy Found as thickets in the tropical semi-arid regions of the NT. The plant is found on sandy or gravelly laterites and grows to a height of 3.5 m. The understorey is bare. Precipitation is generally a little less than 400 mm.

Gidgee Found mainly in tropical and temperate semi-arid Qld. Occasionally forms thickets on the drier margins of *Acacia* low open forests. (See also Chapter 5, North-eastern *Acacia* open forests and low open forests-1.)

Lancewood Located in tropical semi-arid and temperate subhumid regions of Qld and NT where it occasionally forms extensive thickets. In Qld these thickets are found in the brigalow regions in areas *free* of brigalow. (See also Chapter 5, North-eastern *Acacia* open forests and low open forests-1.)

Leichhardt pine located along riverbanks in the monsoonal regions of NT. In some places it forms dense stands some 10 to 30 m high.

Mangroves See Chapter 16, Other Natural Types: mangrove formations.

Melaleucas In some places, adjacent to streams, *Melaleucas* or paperbarks form dense thickets. In northern Australia trees may reach over 30 m.

Palm groves Found in some restricted areas within the monsoonal and tropical subhumid regions. Typical species include the walking-stick palm, Millstream fan palm and red-leaved palm. Rather than occurring as single trees these palms may form dense clumps or groves which are separated by open spaces.

River she-oaks Commonly found on stream banks and on mid-stream bars in temperate humid regions of the east. In the early stages of growth these trees form very dense tree thickets. As mature trees some areas exhibit a dense formation supporting small vines, etc.

Saplings Within the more humid regions secondary regrowth on cleared or otherwise destroyed land may form dense tree thickets, especially during the earlier stages of growth. Typical species include those from the *Eucalyptus* and *Acacia* genera, among others.

Screw palms These may form dense thickets in coastal, estuarine and riverine locations in monsoonal and tropical humid regions. (See also Chapter 6, Other Types: *Pandanus* and *Terminalia* woodlands and low woodlands.)

Chapter Five

OPEN FORESTS

Introduction
Eucalyptus Types
Shrubby tall open forests — wet schlerophyll forests-1, Grassy tall open forests — wet schlerophyll forests-2, Layered tall open forests, Tall open forests on the margins of some rainforests, Tall open forests with a herbal understorey, Tall open forests and open forests with a closed understorey — mixed forests, Tall open forests and open forests on poor soils in wet areas, Shrubby and heathy open forests — dry sclerophyll forests, Grassy open forests, Layered open forests, Shrubby and heathy low open forests — (low) dry sclerophyll forests, Grassy low open forests, Layered low open forests, Subalpine low open forests

Other Types
North-eastern *Acacia* open forests and low open forests-1 — the brigalow (etc.), North-eastern *Acacia* open forests and low open forests-2, Other *Acacia* low open forests — wattle stands, *Casuarina* open forests and low open forests-1 — belah/buloke forests, *Casuarina* open forests and low open forests-2 — she-oak forests, *Callitris* open forests and low open forests — cypress pine forests, *Melaleuca* open forests and low open forests — paperbark (swamp) forests, *Banksia* open forests and low open forests — banksia forests, *Athrotaxis* open forests and low open forests — Tasmanian pine forests, *Agonis* open forests — willow-myrtle forests

Introduction

Open forests are common throughout the humid regions of Australia; these regions lie within 200 km of the coast. Most open forests are dominated by varieties of eucalypts, particularly those of the *Monocalyptus* subgenus; these include the stringybarks, peppermints and ashes.

Shrubby tall open forest understorey: note the tree ferns, shrubs and low trees and the smooth unbranched trunks of the mountain grey gum dominants; the misty appearance is due to drizzle. (Mt Cole, Central Victorian Hills, Vic.)

Due to these forests covering such a range of habitats and climatic regimes there are great variations in terms of heights, structures and species present in the upper- and understoreys. Not all open forests are dominated by eucalypts, other genera include *Casuarinas*, *Callitris* species, *Melaleucas* and *Acacias* among others.

The eucalypt open forests can be subdivided into two types, those found in moist areas and those found in drier areas. The moist open forests are in the main represented by very tall species although they do include some low trees such as snow gums. These moist forests are found on good soils in areas which receive good rains. In some places they could be considered as a transitional forest between rainforests and the drier type of open forests. These forests are characterised by a lack of hard-leaved shrubs in the understorey, the rapid growth of dominants, and they are relatively free from fire. The rapid growth is in part a survival mechanism for most of these species are otherwise unable to cope with the major conflagrations. Nonetheless intense fires at intervals greater than 25 years are necessary for many dominants to regenerate. In lower rainfall areas where soils are good and there is an occasional low intensity fire, the understorey is normally grassy. At altitude these moist open forests are characterised by grassy understoreys although tree growth is retarded by the prevailing colder conditions.

The drier open forests exhibit different characteristics. They have to cope with a low nutrient supply for they are located on poorer soils or on soils that do not have good moisture-retaining abilities; they have an uncertain supply of water, due in part to there being a distinct dry season or at least a period when rainfall is reduced and, last but not least, they have to cope with a regular or irregular fire regime. As a consequence of these factors the understorey possesses a high frequency of nitrogen-fixing plants, especially after fires, and other plants which assist in the nutrient production and intake for the forest's trees. Consequently these forests are of shorter stature than their moister counterparts (except in upland areas) and they exhibit many hard-leaved shrubs in their understorey. Again where cold temperatures are prevalent and there is a shorter growing season there is a corresponding reduction in tree height. In places of extreme environmental stress as regards a regular water supply, such as in the monsoonal regions of Australia's north, some species have adapted to the long dry season by being deciduous or partly deciduous so as to retain their moisture. (More information regarding how eucalypts cope with environmental stresses is given under the notes on the *Eucalyptus* genus in Part 3.)

The other open forest genera are limited in extent. It is thought that the cypress pine (*Callitris* spp) and she-oak (*Casuarina* spp) forests do not adapt to fire as well as most eucalypts do but there is evidence to suggest that they are well adapted to cope. Regeneration in these cases is by seed. In the brigalow (*Acacia* sp.) forests, which locally cover extensive areas, there are a number of environmental stresses to be coped with. These include a variability in precipitation throughout the year and from one year to the next, high summer temperatures and consequently high evaporation and a wide daily range of temperature in wintertime. A feature of brigalow forests is that there is no single formation type but a variety of forests, each with its own stable community. Variations within communities depend to a large extent on changes in rainfall and on fire frequencies.

Open forests are lighter than closed forests beneath their canopies because the foliage of the dominants is not as dense and the trees are more widely spaced. Within these forests the crowns of trees are often small compared to their height, due in part to the fact that the crowns generally touch each other thus restricting the space for lateral growth. Many open forests cover extensive areas, particularly in hilly and mountainous country. In Australia open forests once covered approximately 5.2 per cent of the land area and are presently composed of 194 major alliances. The sclerophyll (eucalypt) forests are home to 116 species of birds (12 must live there) and 53 species of mammals (4 of which must live there).

Shrubby tall open forest understorey exhibiting a diversity of secondary-level trees: blanket leaf, musk daisy-bush, hazel pomaderris, blackwoods and tree ferns; the dominants are southern blue gums. (on Tarwin River west branch, Gippsland, Vic.)

Eucalyptus Types

SHRUBBY TALL OPEN FORESTS — wet sclerophyll forests-1

Location: throughout the humid lands of NSW, Vic., south-east Qld, southernmost WA and Tas. Minor areas in north-east Qld.

Habitat: Landforms: normally hilly to mountainous country, gullies. Soils: podzolic soils, kraznozems, alluvial soils. Altitude: below 1200 m. Temperatures: summers are mild to very warm, winters are cool to mild in south. Precipitation: normally greater than 1000 mm.

Upper stratum: dominated by eucalypts over 30 m high. Maximum heights are generally over 60 m, and may reach 100 m. Typical east coast forest species include blackbutt, coast grey box, white mahogany, swamp mahogany, woollybutt tallowwood, silver-top ash, Gympie messmate, and grey gum. Nearer to and on the tablelands are found the mountain grey gum, shining gum, eurabbie, brown barrel, mountain gum, manna gum, and narrow-leaved peppermint. In Vic. and Tas. the shining gum, eurabbie, mountain ash, mountain gum, alpine ash, brown barrel and Tasmanian blue gum are common. In WA these forests are dominated by the karri, red tingle, Western Australian blackbutt, and marri.

In rare circumstances brush box (*Tristania* sp.) allies itself with and may even co-dominate with the eucalypts Sydney blue gum, blackbutt and red mahogany. Within the eastern coastal ranges the turpentine (*Syncarpia* sp.) may form alliances with various eucalypts, e.g. red bloodwoods, etc. In some places they form pure stands, e.g. sheltered gullies, below southerly facing cliffs or on the edge of closed forests.

Substrata: the understorey of some of these forests is composed of a dense growth of low trees and tall shrubs. Typical species include the silver wattle, forest oak, burrawangs, and yellow pittosporum along the east coast; blackwood, sassafras and stinkwood in the south-east; and karri she-oak, willow myrtle and various banksia species in WA. In some east and south-east forests tree ferns are common. Generally these ferny understoreys are found in forests whose dominants are over 40 m tall and grow on richer soils, e.g. mountain ash forests. The ground cover is composed of shrubs, herbs and ferns. Common ferns include the creeping shield fern and bracken, etc.

Transformations: in some areas these forests have been removed and replaced by introduced crops (potatoes, peas, maize, etc.), sown pastures (rye grass, white clover, etc.) or clear-felled for lumber. Other areas have been selectively logged. Particularly destructive fires may devastate these forests, in some instances replacing the forest with, for example, *Acacia* low open forests. In clear-felled areas regrowth appears as stunted trees, closely spaced and of poor form with a ground layer of discarded crown branches and limbs. The combination of discarded timber and dense volatile foliage on the regrowth, occurring as it does in the most bushfire prone areas of Australia, has created a significant fire hazard.

GRASSY TALL OPEN FORESTS — wet sclerophyll forests-2

Location: see Shrubby tall open forests (except WA).

Habitat: see Shrubby tall open forests: generally found at the upper altitudinal limit of shrubby tall open forests, especially in Vic. and Tas.

Upper stratum: see Shrubby tall open forests.

Substrata: a predominance of tussock grasses with or without a shrub layer. Generally the understorey is clear and park-like. (See also Tall open forests and open forests on poor soils in wet areas.)

Transformations: see Shrubby tall open forests.

Shrubby tall open forest understorey displaying the trunks of mountain ash and a dense cover of tree ferns. (Strzelecki Ranges, Gippsland, Vic.)

Shrubby tall open forest remnant: this forest is a dismal shadow of its former self, having been subjected to fierce forest fires; the understorey is choked with secondary growth. (nr Cape Cornella, the South-East, Tas.)

Shrubby tall open forest ground cover and substrata: luxuriant due to high rainfall and the prevailing moist environment. (nr Mt Worth, Gippsland, Vic.)

LAYERED TALL OPEN FORESTS[*]

Location: restricted sites in Arnhem Land and other areas in the NT.

Habitat: presumably on 'good' soils, low altitude; temperatures hot all year; precipitation greater than 1000 mm with a definite summer maximum.

Upper stratum: unsure of species.

Substrata: composed of a shrub layer and grasses over 2 m high.

Transformations: formation probably intact.

TALL OPEN FORESTS on the margins of some rainforests

Location: pockets throughout the humid east coast ranges of NSW and Qld.

Habitat: see Shrubby tall open forests.

Upper stratum: dominated by a variety of genera over 30 m tall. Typical species include turpentine, brush box, hoop pine, and the eucalypts rose gum, tallowwood, cadaga and flooded gum, as well as some other rainforest trees. In some instances brush box may form pure stands near rainforests. This formation is generally considered to be an ecotone (i.e. a transition between rainforests and tall open forests) but due to the presence of some species which are restricted to this habitat this could be considered a formation in its own right.

Substrata: the understorey may display some rainforest species or a low tree-tall shrub layer typical of tall open forests.

Transformations: as for Shrubby tall open forests.

[*] This formation has been mentioned in some texts, generally as a passing reference without description.

Open forest with a closed understorey: many features of a vine-fern closed forest are present in the understorey including lianas, epiphytes and ferns, etc.; the overstorey is dominated by eucalypts. (Bamarang, South Coast, NSW)

TALL OPEN FORESTS with a herbal understorey

Location: along the Murray River (NSW–Vic. border).
Habitat: Landforms: floodplain. Soils: alluvium, seasonally or periodically flooded. Altitude: below 200 m. Temperatures: summers are very warm to hot, winters cool to mild. Precipitation: above 400 mm with a slight winter maximum.
Upper stratum: dominated by river red gums up to 42 m high.
Substrata: composed of a mixture of herbal plants including grasses, sedges and forbs. The substrata is irregularly flooded.
Transformations: since control of river flow has been implemented there has been a change in the flood periodicity with consequent change to the riverine forest habitat. (See also Chapter 16, Freshwater wetland formations.)

TALL OPEN FORESTS AND OPEN FORESTS with a closed understorey — mixed forests

Location: see Shrubby tall open forests and Shrubby and heathy open forests (not in WA)
Habitat: Landforms: moist, sheltered gullies, hillslopes with a sheltered aspect. Other features: see Shrubby tall open forests.
Upper stratum: dominated by a variety of eucalypts including the spotted gum, red bloodwood, etc. which occasionally grows over 30 m high. Other genera may also be present, for example

Shrubby open forest: dominated by spotted gums and red bloodwood; the understorey exhibits burrawangs and bracken. (Bamarang, South Coast, NSW)

the sandpaper fig, the brush box and so on. Occasionally these non-eucalypt species, where present, form a lower tree stratum.
Substrata: the understorey exhibits species typical of subtropical, warm temperate or cool temperate rainforests depending on location. In warmer localities lianas are common along with a variety of trees and shrubs. Often the ground is covered with ferns.
Transformations: see Shrubby tall open forests. This formation is restricted in size and distribution and due to its topographic location does not necessarily merge into either a closed forest or tall open forest.

Shrubby open forest four months after a severe bushfire: initial regrowth of the dominant trees comes from epicormic buds under the bark. (nr Mt Clear, Snowy Mountains, ACT)

TALL OPEN FORESTS AND OPEN
FORESTS on poor soils in wet areas

Location: see Shrubby tall open forests (not in WA).

Habitat: Landforms: see Shrubby tall open forests. Soils: less fertile types, e.g. sandstones, etc. Altitude: below 1200 m. Temperatures: see Shrubby tall open forests. Precipitation: around 1000 mm.

Upper stratum: dominated by eucalypts between 20 and 60 m high. Typical species include the manna gum and mountain ash in southern regions and the spotted gum and tallowwood in northern regions. Generally these tall open forests have an open park-like feel to them, due in part to the spacing of the trees. In some circumstances such a spacing may constitute a tall woodland, e.g. overmature stands.

Substrata: the understorey on poor soils is characterised by wattles and forest she-oaks in low tree or tall shrub form. In spotted gum forests the burrawang may be common.

Transformations: see Shrubby tall open forests.

SHRUBBY AND HEATHY OPEN
FORESTS — dry sclerophyll forests

Location: widespread throughout the humid country of NSW, Vic., SA, WA and Tas. A small area exists in southernmost Qld. Minor extensions into the subhumid regions.

Habitat: Landforms: undulating, hilly and mountainous country. Soils: solodic types, podzolic types, calcareous sands and other less common varieties. Altitude: generally below 1200 m. Temperatures: summers are mild to hot, winters are cold to humid. Precipitation: 500 to 800 mm with winter maximums in south and summer maximums in north.

Upper stratum: dominated by eucalypts between 10 and 30 m tall. Typical species of the east coast include the scribbly gum, white mahogany (depauperate type), red bloodwood, forest red gum, grey ironbark, white stringybark and spotted gum. Further inland, trees include the red stringybark, red box, apple box, and varieties of peppermint. In drier coastal habitats and on the inland side of the tablelands red ironbark, broad-leaved peppermint and broad-leaved red ironbark are found. In southern Vic. and parts of SA the manna gum and messmate stringybark (depauperate types) associate with the brown stringybark. In WA these forests are represented by jarrah, marri, yate and tuart. In some east coast areas, particularly the Outer Sydney, Central and South Coast regions of NSW, eucalypts are allied with and may even co-dominate with the smooth-barked apple (*Angophora* sp.) and, to a lesser extent, the rough-barked apple. Poorly drained areas may exhibit grey she-oak (*Casuarina* sp.) co-dominant with eucalypts, particularly the swamp mahogany.

Substrata: the understorey is composed of a distinct shrub, sometimes tree, layer of sclerophyllous plants. Common plants include banksias, wattles, grasstrees, she-oaks, hakeas, grevilleas, etc. There may be a discontinuous grassy layer composed of the following types; wallaby, *Poa* and kangaroo grasses. The shrub layer varies according to soil fertility. Some shrubby open forests exhibit a shrub layer similar to adjacent tall open forests or woodlands; others, primarily on sandy soils, exhibit a heathy understorey with virtually no grasses. In WA forests the shrubs are accompanied by small trees with virtually no grasses.

Transformations: extraction of timber by selective logging and clear-felling; establishment of exotic pine plantations, mainly Monterey pine. Some areas partially or completely cleared for intensive grazing of sheep and beef cattle. Altered fire regimes and introduced herbaceous species have changed the forest's substrata in many places. In WA the spread of dieback disease and the extraction of bauxite have altered, changed or destroyed (and will continue to do so) the jarrah forests along parts of the Darling Range. For effects of clear-felling see Shrubby tall open forests.

GRASSY OPEN FORESTS

Location: mainly found in the humid country of south-eastern and central Qld. Minor areas in subhumid northern NSW and western Vic.

Habitat: Landforms: undulating and hilly country. Soils: primarily soloths and solodic type soils; podzolics. Altitude: generally below 900 m. Temperatures: summers very warm to hot, winters cool in south and mild in north. Precipitation: 500 to 800 mm with winter maximums in south and summer maximums in north.

Upper stratum: dominated by eucalypts between 10 and 30 m tall. Typical dominants include the brown and messmate stringybarks in Vic. and the narrow-leaved red ironbark in Qld. At the drier margins of this forest type in Qld the narrow-leaved red ironbark may co-dominate with the white cypress pine (*Callitris* sp.). Other eucalypt species in the north include the red ironbark, carbeen, forest red gum, lemon-scented gum and Queensland white stringybark.

Substrata: characterised by a distinctive herbaceous layer with few or no shrubs. Grasses are typified by the tussocky wallaby, kangaroo and *Poa* grasses.

Transformations: many areas cleared and sown with introduced species, e.g. subterranean clover and rhodes grass, and intensively grazed by beef cattle and sheep.

(N.B. after a major fire some shrubby open forests may appear to be 'grassy' until the shrub layer redevelops.)

LAYERED OPEN FORESTS

Location: within the monsoonal lands of northern Qld, WA and NT.

Habitat: Landforms: generally undulating to flat. Soils: typically red and yellow earths among others. Altitude: generally below 400 m. Temperatures: summers are hot to very hot, winters are mild to very warm. Precipitation: generally above 1000 mm with a definite summer maximum.

Upper stratum: dominated by eucalypts between 10 and 30 m tall. Most common species include the Darwin stringybark and Darwin woollybutt as well as various bloodwoods. Lesser trees include the northern cypress pine, ironwood and nutwood. In some instances the northern cypress pine (*Callitris* sp.) may form an alliance with the Darwin stringybark, producing a distinctive forest stand.

Substrata: characterised by a layer of tall shrubs and low trees *and* a layer of tall tropical grasses up to 2 m high. Whilst all is moist and green during the 'wet' season the long and hot 'dry' season dries-off the tall grasses and causes many of the woody species to lose their leaves. Common understorey plants include the sand palm and native pear. After the 'knock-em down' rains, usually in April, the tall grasses appear bent and broken within the understorey.

Transformations: many areas are subjected to grazing of beef cattle; also the understorey may be burned towards the end of the 'dry' season to promote the growth of grasses for stock feed.

SHRUBBY AND HEATHY LOW OPEN FORESTS — (low) dry sclerophyll forests

Location: on the margins of, or within, the shrubby open forests previously mentioned.

Habitat: see Shrubby and heathy open forests; in some places soils may be rocky or infertile and precipitation may be lower. At altitude temperatures may be lower but precipitation may be higher.

Upper stratum: some species already described in Shrubby and heathy open forests may be of such a stature that they form low versions of these forests. In some areas, such as on sandstone or quartzite outcrops, other species may occur, for instance the Grampians gum, brown stringybark, Wadbilliga ash, etc. Then again infertile soils may support species of naturally low height such as the pink gum and shining peppermint. In the Sydney area (NSW) the scribbly gum is common in the bushland around the city.

Substrata: the understorey is represented by a variety of shrubs and herbs; the shining peppermint and scribbly gum typically have a heathy understorey.

Transformations: some areas are intact due to their relative inaccessibility.

Grassy low open forest: the ground cover is composed of tussock grasses; the low shrub, probably Scotch broom, is invading the understorey. (nr Polblue Swamp, Northern Tablelands, NSW)

GRASSY LOW OPEN FORESTS

Location: on the margins of, or within, the grassy open forests previously mentioned.

Habitat: see Grassy open forests; precipitation may be lower or the ground may be periodically waterlogged.

Upper stratum: some species already described in Grassy open forests may be of such a height so as to form a low version of this forest. Another species includes the mountain swamp gum found in the montane country of south-eastern Australia.

Substrata: see Grassy open forests. In swampy areas forbs and sedges may be common in the understorey.

Transformations: see Grassy open forests.

LAYERED LOW OPEN FORESTS

A shortened version of Layered open forests. See appropriate heading.

SUBALPINE LOW OPEN FORESTS

Location: subalpine regions of NSW, Vic., Tas. and ACT.

Habitat: Landforms: upper mountain and upland valley slopes, ridges. Soils: alpine humus soils, lithosols, etc. Altitude: over 1200 m in north; over 600 m in Tas. Temperatures: cool to mild summers; very cold to cold winters. Precipitation: generally over 1000 mm with usually a winter-spring maximum.

Upper stratum: dominated by a variety of eucalypts including the snow gum, black sallee, spinning gum, Tasmanian snow gum and cider gum. In some places these low open forests grade into shrubby open scrubs or low subalpine woodlands.

Grassy open forest: dominated by spotted gums growing on a steep hillside overlooking the Shoalhaven River; the soil here is clayey. (nr Grassy Gully, South Coast, NSW)

Shrubby low open forest dominated by messmate stringybarks and exhibiting a tall shrubby understorey of tea-tree: this formation is located on a stabilised sand-dune; tree height is about 6 m. (Corner Inlet, Gippsland, Vic.)

Substrata: varies; dense stands may have a sparse ground layer while more open stands exhibit tussocky grasses. Other areas may display shrubs and heaths.

Transformations: relatively undisturbed in some areas. Other areas may be seasonally grazed (Vic. and Tas.) or have been destroyed by hydro-electricity works.

Other Types

NORTH-EASTERN *ACACIA* OPEN FORESTS AND LOW OPEN FORESTS-1 — the brigalow (etc.)

Location: primarily within the subhumid lands of south-eastern and central Qld; also far northern subhumid NSW and the 'wetter' semi-arid country of central and southern Qld.

Habitat: Landforms: downs, low hills and undulating plains. Soils: solodic soils, grey clays, black earths, alluvial soils among others; many soils exhibit gilgais or melon holes. Altitude: generally below 500 m. Temperatures: hot summers, cool to warm winters. Precipitation: around 600 mm, mainly summer maximums, although variable season to season.

Upper stratum: dominated by brigalow standing up to 15 m tall. Other dominants include yarran, bendee and blackwood in areas of scattered brigalow; rosewood and lancewood which form quite dense stands in areas virtually free of brigalow; and the eucalypts bimble box, yapungah and coolabah which commonly form alliances with the brigalow or form emergents above the brigalow (etc.) canopy. In addition the brigalow may co-dominate with belah (*Casuarina* sp.), bottle tree (*Brachychiton* sp.), Queensland ebony (*Bauhinia* sp.) and the white cypress pine (*Callitris* sp.). Within the brigalow *low* open forest gidgee may be present. Gidgee often forms pure stands, with brigalow acting as a barrier between it and the surrounding grasslands. (See also Chapter 6, *Acacia* low woodlands.) On the driest margins of the brigalow lands, and on poorer soils, these open forests may constitute low open forests. Other *Acacias* in the brigalow country include the black gidgee or blackwood, which form open forests in the Cape, Suttor and Belyando river basins. Emergents such as the coolabah may be present.

Substrata: the understorey varies depending on the soil types. In the southern and central brigalow regions the tall shrubs, wilga and sandalwood are common. Here the herbaceous layer is ephemeral. Usually there is a scattering of lesser shrubs. The

Subalpine low open forest: understorey with low prostrate shrubs; the dominants are snow gums. (Howitt High Plains, Victorian Alps, Vic.)

brigalow-belah communities also have a scattering of shrubs and a sparse grass layer. In the northern brigalow regions yellow wood is a common shrub which may even co-dominate with brigalow (i.e. *Acacia* and *Terminalis* open forests). Other shrubs include emu bushes and *Carissa* spp. At the fringes of this community grasses are common. Within the *Acacia* and *Eucalyptus* and the *Acacia* and *Callitris* communities there may be a variety of smaller sclerophyllous shrubs, particularly *Acacia* species and a variety of grasses including spear grass, love grass, kangaroo grass and blue grass among others.

Transformations: Most areas have been cleared and given over to cropping or sown with exotic grasses such as rhodes grass and buffel grass, and used for the intensive grazing of animals. In the gidgee areas budda regrowth is common.

NORTH-EASTERN *ACACIA* OPEN FORESTS AND LOW OPEN FORESTS-2

Location: the tropical and north-eastern temperate subhumid/semi-arid country of north-eastern Australia (including small areas in the NT).

Habitat: Landforms: plains and downs, low hills and gentle slopes. Soils: either coarse-textured soils, e.g. lithosols, lateritic podzolic and lateritic red-yellow earths (bendee, lancewood formations) or fine-textured soils (gidgee formations). Altitude: generally below 400 m. Temperatures: summers are hot to very hot, winters are warm. Precipitation: generally over 700 mm with a definite summer maximum.

Upper stratum: dominated by various species of *Acacias* up to 10 m tall. Typical species include lancewood, bendee, mulga and gidgee. At the wetter margins these plants may reach 15 m thus forming an *Acacia* open forest. Bendee and lancewood often co-dominate. Bendee also allies itself with mulga, *A. petraea* and *A. aprepta*. In some places eucalypts of boxes, ironbarks and bloodwoods emerge above the canopy. In addition there are minor areas dominated by such *Acacias* as the currawong, womal, bowyakka, *A. sparsiflora*, *A. petraea* and rosewood.

Substrata: a few shrubs and grasses are present though often the understorey is sparse. Generally lancewood and bendee has a few scattered shrubs and a sparse grass layer of mainly kerosene grasses. Kangaroo grass may be present in the wetter areas. The gidgee understorey displays emu bushes with wilga in the south and *Terminalia oblongata* in the north. For mulga understories see appropriate headings in Chapter 10 Shrublands.

Transformations: these formations may be used for the extensive grazing of beef cattle. At the wettest margins in Qld these formations have been recently replaced with sown pastures of buffel grass, rhodes grass and panic grasses. In cleared gidgee areas budda regrowth is common.

OTHER *ACACIA* LOW OPEN FORESTS — wattle stands

In some humid regions (and perhaps some subhumid ones) may be seen dense stands of bipinnate wattle trees which, if extensive enough, form low open forests. Generally these wattles are found on disturbed land in a variety of situations, e.g. hillsides, riverflats, etc., usually on land formerly occupied by shrubby tall open forests. Disturbance of these prior formations would have been due to land clearing or bushfires of such severity that the original formation failed to re-establish itself. A typical plant is the black wattle.

CASUARINA OPEN FORESTS AND LOW OPEN FORESTS-1 — belah/buloke forests

Location: See North-eastern *Acacia* open forests and low open forests-1.

Habitat: as for North-eastern *Acacia* open forests and low open forests-1.

Upper stratum: dominated by *Casuarinas* between 9 and 15 m tall. Within the southern and central brigalow forests, belah and buloke may dominate locally. In some places buloke co-dominates with narrow-leaved red ironbark and bimble box. (See also Chapter 6, *Casuarina* woodlands and low woodlands.)

Subalpine low open forest: dominated by spinning gums with a low shrubby or heathy understorey. (Dargo High Plains, Victorian Alps, Vic.)

Substrata: the belah open forests are characterised by a scattering of shrubs with an ephemeral grass layer. The buloke open forests exhibit a variety of sclerophyllous shrubs with a range of grasses.

Transformations: as for North-eastern *Acacia* open forests and low open forests-1.

CASUARINA OPEN FORESTS AND LOW OPEN FORESTS-2 — she-oak forests

Location: primarily at littoral and riverbank sites along the south-eastern, eastern and northern coasts of Australia. Also at rock sites elsewhere.

Habitat: Landforms: exposed situations such as coastal cliffs, old dunes, subcoastal rocky outcrops, along riverbanks and on mid-stream bars, swampy areas. Soils: lithosols, alluvial soils; sandy soils among others. Altitude: generally below 800 m. Temperatures: vary. Precipitation: generally above 500 mm.

Upper stratum: dominated by varieties of *Casuarina* between 4 and 30 m tall. Typical species include drooping she-oak, grey she-oak, river she-oak, swamp she-oak and coast she-oak. Often she-oaks will co-dominate with the coast banksia and silver banksia along the south-eastern and eastern seaboards. (See also Chapter 6, *Casuarina* woodlands and low woodlands.) On some rocky outcrops a shrubby form of she-oak, the scrub oak may form an open scrub some 2 to 6 m tall.

Substrata: normally characterised by a diversity of shrubs, heaths and herbs in coastal locations and along estuaries; sparser cover in more exposed situations; sedges, etc., in swamps.

Transformations: due to the limited size of these formations many are still intact although some are often totally cleared for urban development along the coast.

CALLITRIS OPEN FORESTS AND LOW OPEN FORESTS — cypress pine forests

Location: see North-eastern *Acacia* open forests and low open forests-1; also within the drier subhumid country of NSW (as small isolated stands), and along the wet monsoonal coast and inland of northern Australia.

Habitat: as for North-eastern *Acacia* open forests and low open forests-1.

Upper stratum: dominated by the white cypress pine within the areas listed above, and the black cypress pine on rocky outcrops and well-drained sandy soils. Pure stands, in the forms of open and low open *forests* are of limited extent (see also

Chapter 6, *Callitris* woodlands and low woodlands), but the *Callitris* and *Eucalyptus* alliance is rather more common. Typical co-dominant eucalypts include the bimble box, narrow-leaved red ironbark and narrow-leaved box. In northern Australia pure stands of northern cypress pine are found, especially on the offshore islands.

Substrata: generally characterised by a variety of grasses including spear grasses and love grasses. Sclerophyllous shrubs may be present in cypress pine-eucalyptus formations.

Transformations: subjected to selective logging for timber. Other areas cleared for sheep and cattle grazing. The presence of shrubs in the understorey would appear to indicate a reduction in bushfires since European settlement.

MELALEUCA OPEN FORESTS AND LOW OPEN FORESTS — paperbark (swamp) forests

Location: within the coastal and subcoastal country of monsoonal northern Australia; also small pockets along the temperate humid coasts of NSW and south-west WA.

Habitat: Landforms: coastal floodplains (northern Australia); dune swales elsewhere. Soils: grey clays particularly, among others; soils generally waterlogged and occasionally covered by water up to 1 m deep. Altitude: below 50 m. Temperatures: warm to very hot summers, cool to very warm winters. Precipitation: up to 1500 mm during wet season (northern Australia); over 800 mm elsewhere.

Upper stratum: dominated by *Melaleucas* up to 25 m tall. In northern Australia typical *Melaleucas* include the silver paperbark, blue paperbark, and yellow-barked paperbark, among others; the weeping tea-tree may grow in pure stands up to 40 m tall, so forming a *Melaleuca* tall open forest. In NSW the broad-leaved paperbark dominates, while in WA the swamp paperbark is most common. See also Chapter 4, Tree Thicket Types: *Melaleucas*.

Substrata: depends on habitat. In drier areas emu bushes and other shrubs along with varieties of Mitchell grasses may be found in northern Australia. In wetter and other areas aquatics and sedges are common.

Transformations: Most areas are probably intact.

BANKSIA OPEN FORESTS AND LOW OPEN FORESTS — banksia forests

Location: various coastal locations along the south-eastern and eastern seaboards. Also on the coastal plain of WA.

Habitat: Landforms: sandy lowlands, dunes and 'sandy' cliffs. Soils: sandy types. Altitude: near sea-level. Temperatures: vary; tempered by coastal location. Precipitation: varies.

Upper stratum: dominated by banksias up to 16 m tall, though most are less than 10 m. Typical species include the coast banksia in eastern regions. Some areas exhibit a *Banksia* and *Casuarina* co-dominant formation. In WA a variety of *Banksia* species dominate, a common species is the giant banksia. (See also Chapter 6, *Banksia* woodlands and low woodlands.)

Substrata: characterised by numerous shrubs, and grasses and heaths.

Transformations: many areas cleared for urban development or sown pastures.

ATHROTAXIS OPEN FORESTS AND LOW OPEN FORESTS — Tasmanian pine forests

Location: humid (western) districts of Tas.

Habitat: Landforms: rugged mountain country, edges of lakes and tarns. Soils: lithosols, etc. Altitude: 100 to 900 m. Temperatures: cool summers, cold winters. Precipitation: 1200 mm to 2500 mm.

Upper stratum: dominated by the King William pine and pencil pine. Though normally associated with cool temperate rainforests they may form small pure stands in high rainfall areas, groves beside lakes and tarns, or ally themselves with the Tasmanian snow gum and cider gum (*Eucalyptus* spp) in subalpine areas. (See also Pine and/or beech low woodlands.)

Casuarina *open forest: dominated by river she-oaks with grasses and sedges in the understorey; this forest runs along riverbanks. (Kangaroo River, South Coast, NSW)*

Substrata: represented by various shrubs and herbs.

Transformations: some areas affected by hydro-electricity works, etc.

AGONIS OPEN FORESTS — willow-myrtle forests

Location: western temperate humid coast of WA (south of Gardner River).

Habitat: Landforms: coastal lowlands behind dunes. Soils: sandy. Altitude: sea-level to 10 m. Temperatures: summers are hot, winters are mild. Precipitation: 500 to 900 mm with a winter maximum.

Upper stratum: dominated by the willow-myrtle (locally known as the WA peppermint), which grows to 16 m high. In open forests it generally forms pure stands. In some places the density is such that closed forests, woodlands or low woodlands are formed. In woodland formations it is often allied with the giant banksia (*Banksia* sp.).

Substrata: the understorey is quite open. Shrubs include the rayflower *Anthoceris littorilis* and the wattle *Acacia decipiens* among others. The herbs include *Lepidosperma gladiatum* and *Anthocarpus preissii*.

Transformations: some areas relatively undisturbed, others cleared for urban development and coastal grazing.

WOODLANDS

Introduction
Eucalyptus Types
Tall woodlands, Shrubby woodlands — subhumid woodlands,
Grassy woodlands — savanna woodlands-1, frontage woodlands, Layered woodlands
Shrubby low woodlands — semi-arid woodlands, Grassy low woodlands — savanna
woodlands-2, frontage woodlands, Layered low woodlands, Hummock grass low
woodlands, Subalpine low woodlands, Grassy very low woodlands, Hummock grass
very low woodlands

Other Types
North-eastern *Acacia* woodlands and low woodlands — brigalow woodlands (etc.),
Southern *Acacia* shrubby and grassy low woodlands — weeping myall/western
myall/ironwood woodlands, *Casuarina* woodlands and low woodlands —
belah/buloke/drooping she-oak woodlands, *Callitris* woodlands and low woodlands —
cypress pine woodlands, *Melaleuca* woodlands and low woodlands- 1 — paperbark
woodlands, *Melaleuca* woodlands and low woodlands- 2 — paperbark swamp woodlands,
Banksia woodlands and low woodlands — banksia woodlands, Pine and/or beech low
woodlands, Mixed low woodlands and tall shrublands, Other woodlands and low
woodlands — *Adansonia, Agonis, Brachychiton, Excoecaria, Geijera-Flindersia, Grevillea,
Hakea, Heterodendrum, Lysiphyllum, Melaleuca-* 3, *Myoporum, Nypa, Pandanus* and *Terminalia*
woodlands and low woodlands

Callitris *woodland: dominated by cypress pines and, unusually, a collection of shrubs; this woodland
occurs on a formation called calcrete. (nr Goondooloo, Upper South-East, SA)*

Introduction

Woodlands are characterised by a park-like appearance. They are composed of many different species, the most common belonging to the *Eucalyptus* genus. Of all the eucalypts in Australia up to 80 per cent are found in woodlands. Eucalypt woodlands are mainly composed of members of the *Blakella*, *Corymbia* and *Symphomyrtus* subgenera, i.e. ghost gums, bloodwoods, grey gums, red gums, grey boxes and ironbarks, etc. Other woodlands are dominated by *Acacias*, *Casuarinas*, *Callitris* species, *Melaleucas*, *Banksias* and so on. A characteristic of woodlands is the fact that trees have a depth of crown which is equal to or greater than the length of the bole.

Woodlands are more commonly found in drier areas than the open forests consequently the main woodland areas occupy the subhumid regions. In some places woodlands are found on or near the coast, generally in areas that receive a moderately low rainfall or on particularly sandy soils. Normally the following situation applies; as one moves inland from a humid coastal region (with its pockets of closed and moist open forests and expansive areas of dry open forests) towards drier regions there is a general decrease in tree height and an increase in the space between the trees. To carry on to the driest margins of treed formations the spacing would further increase along with a reduction in tree height until one entered the open woodlands and various scrubs and shrublands. Of course there are exceptions to this. Some woodlands penetrate the arid interior along the riverbanks and floodplains of the inland rivers.

Because of the diversity of woodland types it is difficult to generalise about the factors that influence them. Generally they occupy regions that may experience extended droughts, high summer temperatures, cold, frosty mornings in winter and irregular, low intensity fires. Such fires are normally of low intensity due to the wide spacing of the trees. In upland areas woodland trees must also endure severe cold or snow conditions.

The presence of understorey species varies from place to place depending on soil types, changes to fire intensity and frequency and reliability of rainfall. In many woodlands the understorey is grassy. In infertile or rocky areas the understorey is often shrubby. Shrubby understoreys are also found where regrowth has occurred after a fire and the frequency of fires has been reduced by human intervention. The result is that the understorey may possess a secondary tree layer or a thick scrub which effectively blocks out the light for future seedlings or a grassy ground cover to develop. Should such woodlands be exposed to further fires then the intensity and severity of those fires will be increased, perhaps to the point that the dominant trees will be unable to regenerate because of their inability to cope with such environmental stress.

Due to the increased spacing between trees in woodlands as compared to open forests the shape of the tree is often quite pendulous. This is because the crowns do not touch so lateral growth is not restricted. This pendulous nature is further enhanced by the trees' lower stature. Woodlands in Australia once accounted for approximately 22.6 per cent of the land area and some 225 major alliances. Along with the brigalow forests and open woodlands they house some 323 species of birds (128 must live here) and 135 species of mammals, 49 of which are virtually confined to these formations.

Eucalyptus Types

TALL WOODLANDS

Location: generally near the climatic limits of, or within, overmature stands of shrubby tall open forest.
Habitat: see Chapter 5, Shrubby tall open forests.
Upper stratum: dominated by various species of overmature eucalypts over 30 m tall. In places the tall open forests of WA may exhibit tall woodland formations.* A few species have formed tall woodlands in their own right, e.g. the Queensland western white gum of the Darling Downs.
Substrata: see Shrubby tall open forests.
Transformations: see Shrubby tall open forests.

SHRUBBY WOODLANDS — subhumid woodlands

Location: within the subhumid lands of NSW, northern Vic., southernmost Qld and eastern Tas.; the southern subhumid/semi-arid country of WA and SA.
Habitat: Landforms: generally undulating country, downs. Soils: red-brown earths, yellow earths, solodised solonetz and solodic soils, red earths, etc. Altitude: up to 1200 m on the tablelands. Temperatures: hot to very hot summers, cool to mild winters. Precipitation: generally between 400 and 600 mm in the eastern regions, and down to 200 mm in WA.

* e.g. tuart woodlands near Busselton, the South-West, WA.

Upper stratum: dominated by eucalypts up to 30 m tall. Typical species include yellow box, Blakely's red gum, white gum, grey box and stringybarks in NSW; river red gum, swamp gum, manna gum, apple box and grey box in Vic. and parts of SA. The sugar gum is found in various parts of SA, generally in alliance with the long-leaved box. At higher altitudes swamp gum, candlebark and snow gum are major species in the eastern mainland region. In WA wandoo, and York gum in alliance with the jam tree (*Acacia* sp.), are common in the more humid areas. In the drier areas salmon gum, brown mallett, Dundas blackbutt and Dundas mahogany are prominent. In a few inland localities the rough-barked apple (*Angophora* sp.) allies with grey box.

The understorey may exhibit a moderate growth of wattles, she-oaks and cypress pines. These tall shrubs and trees may be of such a density and height as to co-dominate with the eucalypts. For instance the buloke and belah (*Casuarina* sp.) may co-dominate with grey box, belah also forming alliances with yellow gum. The white cypress pine (*Callitris* sp.) co-dominates with grey box and bimble box; and in the Mt Lofty Ranges yellow gum allies itself with the golden wattle (*Acacia* sp.).
Substrata: lower shrubs and trees include wilga, sandalwood, warrior bush, kurrajong and wattles in the eastern regions, and varieties of saltbush in the drier WA woodlands. Normally the grass layer is poorly developed.
Transformations: very few areas, except in the dry woodlands of WA, are undisturbed. Most areas have been greatly modified, cleared, for wheat or other crop production, or sown with exotic herbs such as subterranean clover or medic grasses for intensive grazing. On the drier margins extensive sheep grazing is common, especially in the eastern States. In these drier regions it seems very likely that since the first European settlement shrubs have replaced grasses due to a reduction in the number of bushfires. In NSW many shrubby woodlands, now virtually useless for extensive sheep grazing, are being cleared for cropping. Often these clearings are far in excess of the recommended maximum area to be cleared within that particular region of the State.

GRASSY WOODLANDS — savanna woodlands-1, frontage woodlands

Location: the subhumid regions of northern NSW and southern and central Qld. Also along many ephemeral watercourses of the inland. Minor areas in subhumid western Vic. and southern SA.

Shrubby woodland: dominants unknown, possibly bimble box; the shrubs include mulga, emu bushes, etc.; a grass layer is present. (nr Byrock, Upper Darling, NSW)

Grassy woodland: dominated by candlebark? The creekline supports a row of wattles; note the red patches on the newly exposed bark, a common feature on some gums during the summer. (Oolans Ford, Southern Tablelands, NSW)

Grassy woodland understorey supporting a ground cover of sedges: this land is occasionally flooded; some trees have a mallee habit. (Little Desert, Wimmera, Vic.)

Habitat: Landforms: undulating country, plains and downs; floodplains and frontage country. Soils: red-brown earths, black earths, solodised solonetz, alluvial soils, etc. Altitude: generally below 500 m. Temperatures: hot to very hot summers, generally mild to warm winters. Precipitation: 400 to 600 mm in most areas; generally with summer maximums; lesser amounts along semi-arid watercourses.

Upper stratum: dominated by eucalypts up to 30 m tall. Generally tree heights are below 20 m and may be less than 10 m (see Grassy low woodlands). Typical species include narrow-leaved ironbarks, Thozet's box and bimble box. The 'frontage country', that area subjected to occasional flooding, exhibits stands of river red gum, black box and coolabah. Alliances with the white cypress pine (*Callitris* sp.) are common in some areas. In southern areas typical species include the river red gum, yellow gum and peppermint box, occasionally in alliance with moonah (*Melaleuca* sp.).

Substrata: Characterised by grasses and other herbs with an absence of shrubs. Typical grasses include kangaroo grass and spear grass.

Transformations: many areas exhibiting this formation have been cleared for the sowing of crops; sown with exotic pastures; or extensively grazed by sheep and beef cattle. In some areas the tussocky grass ground layer has been unintentionally replaced by barley grass, native burrs and some shrubs. In many places there has been an increase in the number of shrubs due to a reduction and control of wildfires.

Eucalyptus and Callitris *grassy woodland: dominated by white cypress pine and bimble box; cypress pines often co-dominate with eucalypts in the subhumid inland. (nr Meadow Glen, Western Plains, NSW)*

Shrubby woodland: dominated by salmon gums and exhibiting low shrubs of grey bush; these woodlands are unusual for being so tall in an area of very low rainfall (around 250 mm). (nr Newmans Rocks, Eastern Goldfields, WA)

Grassy woodland: this woodland has been partly cleared to promote pasture growth; it has also promoted the growth of Paterson's curse. (nr Abercrombie River, Central Tablelands, NSW)

Hummock grass low woodland: dominated by snappy gums with an understorey of spinifex; this dry rocky region receives downslope runoff after summer rain. (Wittenoom Gorge, Pilbara, WA)

Shrubby low woodland: this woodland survives in an arid area by utilising runoff from the low granite ridge; surrounding it is a small ephemeral herbland; trees are pale bloodwoods. (The Granites, Corner Country, NSW)

LAYERED WOODLANDS

Location: throughout the southern monsoonal northern semi-arid country of Qld, WA and NT.
Habitat: As for layered open forests but with reduced precipitation, or poorer soil fertility, etc.
Upper stratum: dominated by eucalypts up to 30 m tall. Generally woodland tree heights are 10 to 15 m. Species typical of those mentioned in Chapter 5, Layered open forests. See also Layered low woodlands.
Substrata: As for Layered open forests. Occasionally soft spinifex is present in the ground layer.
Transformations: As for Layered open forests.

SHRUBBY LOW WOODLANDS — semi-arid woodlands

Location: temperate subhumid, semi-arid regions of central and northern NSW and southern and central Qld.
Habitat: Landforms: undulating plains, downs, low ridges. Soils: various; often with a sand component. Altitude: 100 to 500 m. Temperatures: summers are hot, winters are mild to warm. Precipitation: 250 to 750 mm with a summer maximum in the north.
Upper stratum: dominated by a variety of *Eucalyptus* species less than 10 m tall. At the driest margins these woodlands grade into open woodland/shrubland formations. Dominants include the bimble box in northern NSW and Qld. Bimble box forms alliances with a variety of other genera including budda (*Eremophila* sp.) on red earths, white cypress pine (*Callitris* sp.) and tumbledown gum on sandy soils and belah (*Casuarina* sp.) and wilga (*Geijera* sp.) on clayey soils. Further south bimble box merges with mulga along drainage lines and is surrounded by pure stands of silver-leaved ironbark.

Substrata: there is a great diversity to the shrubby understorey. Typical species include emu bushes, whitewood, wilga, yarran, umbrella wattle, ironwood (*Acacia* sp.), warrior bush, kurrajong, wild orange, hopbushes and *Cassias*. The ground layer exhibits different grasses; spear grasses in the south, blue grasses (*Bothriochloa* spp) in the central regions and kerosene grasses throughout.
Transformations: most areas subjected to extensive grazing by beef cattle and sheep. Recently large pockets have been cleared for cropping in the Western Division of NSW.

Grassy woodland remnant: this woodland has been over-cleared; many years' grazing, plus the effects of droughts and flooding rains will result in soil erosion and the probable loss of good grazing land. (nr Lake George, Southern Tablelands, NSW)

GRASSY LOW WOODLANDS — savanna woodlands-2, frontage woodlands

Location: tropical semi-arid regions of Qld, WA and NT as well as along the watercourses of northern and eastern tropical and temperate arid and semi-arid regions.
Habitat: Landforms: floodplains, riverflats, downs. Soils: alluvium, red and yellow earths, clayey soils. Altitude: generally below 500 m. Temperatures: summers are hot to very hot, winters are warm. Precipitation: generally between 300 and 750 mm; less in arid areas.
Upper stratum: dominated by a variety of eucalypts up to 10 m tall. Typical species include the silver-leaved box and variable-barked bloodwood across northern Australia; the river red gum, yapunyah, black box and coolabah on the floodplains of the Darling and eastern Lake Eyre drainage systems and the silver-leaved box, coolabah, ghost gum and pale bloodwood on the floodplains or frontage country of the northern rivers.

Substrata: represented by a variety of grasses including blue grass (*Dichanthium* spp), brown top and Mitchell grass among many others. On the floodplains other herbs and forbs may be present.

Transformations: most of these formations are utilised for the extensive grazing of beef cattle (in the north) and sheep (in the south).

LAYERED LOW WOODLANDS

Location: throughout the tropical semi-arid regions of Qld, WA and NT.

Habitat: Landforms: plains and downs, low hills. Soils: various. Altitude: generally below 400 m. Temperatures: summers are very hot, winters are warm to hot. Precipitation: 300 to 600 mm with a definite summer maximum.

Upper stratum: dominated by eucalypts up to 10 m tall. Species include the snappy gum, silver-leaved box, western box in the west; Gilbert River box, Browns box, coolabah, Normanton box, inland yellow jacket and various ironbarks in the east. The Gilbert River box may form alliances with the ironwood (*Erythropleum* sp.).

Substrata: the understorey is represented by a variety of tall shrubs including whitewood, beef-wood, quinine bush in western regions and supplejack, quinine bush, bean tree, billygoat plum, hopbushes and various wattles in the eastern regions. In the south-east budda often occurs with Browns box and ironbarks. The grass layer includes kerosene grasses as well as blue grasses (*Dichanthium* and *Bothriochloa* spp).

Transformations: most areas are subjected to extensive grazing by beef cattle.

HUMMOCK GRASS LOW WOODLANDS

Location: tropical semi-arid regions in northern Australia.

Habitat: Landforms: plains, downs, low ridges, rocky outcrops. Soils: various. Altitude: generally below 400 m. Temperatures: summers are very hot, winters are warm to hot. Precipitation: below 400 mm with a definite summer maximum.

Upper stratum: dominated by the variable-barked bloodwood, snappy gum and silver-leaved ironbark. At the driest margins this formation may grade into a low open woodland.

Substrata: the ground layer exhibits species of spinifex as well as kerosene grasses. (For further information see Chapter 14, *Trioda* and *Plectrachne* open hummock grasslands.)

Transformations: may be subjected to extensive grazing by beef cattle.

SUBALPINE LOW WOODLANDS

Location: subalpine areas of NSW, Vic., Tas. and ACT.

Habitat: Landforms: valley sides, mountain slopes and tops. Soils: various including lithosols. Altitude: over 1200 m on the mainland and 600 m in Tas. Temperatures: summers are cool to mild, winters are very cold to cold. Precipitation: up to 2000 mm.

Upper stratum: dominated by the snow gum on the mainland and the Tasmanian snow gum in Tas. Other species include the black sallee and cider gum. (See also Chapter 9, Shrubby open scrubs-3.) At the limits of tree growth, i.e. near the tree line, these species may display a very low and contorted form thus forming a subalpine very low woodland.

Substrata: the understorey generally exhibits *Poa* species of tussock grasses although there may be patches of alpine heath, etc.

Transformations: some areas are occasionally subjected to summer grazing by beef cattle.

Grassy low woodland in an arid area: the dominants here are 3 to 4 m high, the ground cover little more than cropped brown stalks; after floods or rains growth would be prodigious. (Bulloo River floodplain, Bulloo, Qld)

GRASSY VERY LOW WOODLANDS

Location: tropical semi-arid northern Australia (Leichhardt River, Qld to Ord River, WA).

Habitat: Landforms: undulating plains, low stony ridges. Soils: lithosols, clayey soils. Altitude: generally below 400 m. Temperatures: summers are very hot, winters are warm to very warm. Precipitation: 300 to 600 mm with a definite summer maximum.

Upper stratum: dominated by the eucalypts silver-leaved box on clayey soils and snappy gum on low stony ridges. Tree heights range from 2 to 4 m.

North-eastern Acacia *low woodland: dominated by brigalow?; the understorey exhibits a variety of tall and low shrubs and grasses. (nr Talwood, Western Downs, Qld)*

In some places this formation may grade into an open woodland. Supplejack (*Ventilago* sp.) may ally with silver-leaved box in the wetter areas.

Substrata: there is a grassy understorey represented by various species.

Transformations: many areas are subjected to extensive grazing by beef cattle.

HUMMOCK GRASS VERY LOW WOODLANDS

Location: tropical semi-arid northern regions of WA.

Habitat: Landforms: stony slopes and ridges. Soils: lithosols. Altitude: below 300 m. Temperatures: summers are very hot, winters are very warm to hot. Precipitation: 300 to 600 mm (approx.) with a definite summer maximum.

Upper stratum: dominated by the Wandi ironbark which grows to a height of 2 to 4 m.

Substrata: represented by hummock grass with occasional occurrences of love grasses and golden-beard grasses. (For further information see Chapter 14, *Trioda* and *Plectrachne* open hummock grasslands.)

Transformations: some areas may be subjected to extensive grazing by beef cattle.

Other Types

NORTH-EASTERN *ACACIA* WOODLANDS AND LOW WOODLANDS — brigalow woodlands (etc.)

Location: tropical semi-arid and temperate sub-humid Qld with minor extensions into northern NSW.

Habitat: Landforms: plains, downs, low hills. Soils: clayey. Altitude: generally below 500 m. Temperatures: summers are hot, winters are mild to warm or very warm. Precipitation: 350 to 600 mm with a definite summer maximum.

Upper stratum: dominated by a variety of *Acacias* up to 15 m tall. Towards the drier country this formation may grade into a low open woodland. Typical species include brigalow, blackwood (*A. argyrodendron*), bendee, gidgee and boree (*A. tephrina* syn. *A. cana*). Boree is generally associated with gidgee. Mulga trees may be prominent towards the drier margins. Another species, lancewood, is often found on dry stony hilltops; this may occur as a shrubby plant.

Substrata: normally the understorey is composed of shrubs although gidgee and bendee may have a grassy understorey. Typically the shrub layer includes emu bushes, *Terminalia oblongata* and *Carissa ovata*. The boree understorey also includes inland rosewood, whitewood, leopardwood in the wetter areas and emu bushes in the drier areas. Normally there is a ground layer with kerosene, Mitchell and *Sporobolus* grasses in the moister areas and *Bassia* species in the drier areas.

Transformations: many areas are subjected to extensive grazing by beef cattle. In a few places these formations may have been cleared for cropping and sown pastures.

North-eastern Acacia *low woodland: dominated by gidgee with a grassy understorey; there are some minor shrubs. (nr Cunnamulla, Warrego-Paroo, Qld)*

SOUTHERN *ACACIA* SHRUBBY AND GRASSY LOW WOODLANDS — weeping myall/western myall/ironwood woodlands

Melaleuca *low woodland: found in damp places as a rule; these cadjeputs grow in the bed of the Ashburton River, a river which experiences incredible floods from cyclonic rains; flooding would easily cover the tops of the trees. (Nanutarra, Pilbara, WA)*

Location: throughout the semi-arid/subhumid regions of southern and south-eastern Australia, minor areas elsewhere.

Habitat: Landforms: floodplains, undulating plains. Soils: alluvial soils, grey, brown and red calcareous soils, clayey soils. Altitude: generally below 300 m. Temperatures: summers are hot, winters are mild to warm. Precipitation: 250 to 550 mm with a definite winter maximum in the south.

Upper strata: dominated by the weeping myall (mainly on the inland plains of NSW), western myall (mainly between Port Augusta, SA and the WA border) and ironwood (Cobar-Bourke districts of NSW). Each grows to a height of 10 m. Weeping myall is often allied with inland rosewood (*Heterodendrum* sp.) and eumong (*Acacia* sp.). Occasionally there may be eucalypt emergents of bimble box and coolabah. Western myall is

Southern Acacia *grassy low woodland: dominated by weeping myall, a common species on the clay plains of subhumid/semi-arid eastern inland Australia. (nr Coonamble, North-West Plains, NSW)*

Southern Acacia *shrubby low woodland: dominated by western myall with saltbushes in the understorey. (nr Skull Tanks, Gairdner Plain, SA)*

normally allied with sugarwood (*Myoporum* sp.) and belah (*Casuarina* sp.). Another dominant is *Acacia pruinocarpa*, a species found in the Gascoyne region of WA.

Substrata: varies. The western myall understorey includes saltbushes, bluebushes, and to the north, emu bushes. (For further information see Chapter 10, *Atriplex, Chenopodium* and *Maireana* low shrublands.) The weeping myall understorey exhibits Mitchell and blue grasses (*Dichanthium* spp) in the north and spear, wallaby and windmill grasses in the south. Ironwood formations exhibit emu bushes and various grasses.

Transformations: most areas are extensively grazed by sheep; in the Riverina, NSW, the understorey of old-man saltbush has been almost entirely replaced with barley grass since the advent of grazing.

CASUARINA WOODLANDS AND LOW WOODLANDS — belah/buloke/drooping she-oak woodlands

Location: primarily in the semi-arid south-west of NSW; also as scattered formations in semi-arid and subhumid south-eastern Australia; minor areas in WA.

Habitat: Landforms: undulating to flat; around granite outcrops (WA). Soils: solonised brown soils, red-brown earths, grey, brown and red clays. Altitude: generally below 400 m. Temperatures:

hot to very hot summers, cool to mild winters. Precipitation: 350 mm or less with a winter maximum.

Upper stratum: dominated by belah in the drier areas, and drooping oak and buloke in the wetter areas. Tree height is generally between 5 and 15 m. Often these species co-dominate with other genera. For instance, belah commonly allies itself with the inland rosewood (*Heterodendrum* sp.) while buloke may be found with the white cypress pine (*Callitris* sp.) or the grey box (*Eucalyptus* sp.). Other less common alliances of belah include sugarwood (*Myoporum* sp.), wilga (*Geijera* sp.), slender cypress pine (*Callitris* sp.), various *Acacias* and leopardwood (*Flindersia* sp.). Occasionally belah will ally itself with white cypress pine and wilga in a single formation. The drooping she-oak may form solitary formations or may be found with moonah (*Melaleuca* sp.). Around the base of granite outcrops the rock she-oak may be found growing on coarse sands.

Substrata: the understorey may be composed of low shrubs, particularly in areas supporting grey box. These shrubs include the co-dominants mentioned above (though they are not always co-dominant) as well as false sandalwood, black wattle, pearl bluebush and black bluebush. Other woodlands may display a grassy understorey with virtually no shrubs. Typical grasses include spear grass, kangaroo grass, etc.

Transformations: much of the subhumid woodlands have been cleared or altered to accommodate cropping and sown pastures. The grassy semi-arid woodlands are extensively grazed by sheep with resultant changes to the grassy layer. This has led, in some instances to a sparse ground layer and the increase of *Bassia* species (burrs).

CALLITRIS WOODLANDS AND LOW WOODLANDS — cypress pine woodlands

Location: primarily on the subhumid/semi-arid margins of south-eastern and eastern Australia. Also small areas in WA. and in the rain-shadow valleys of the Snowy River in southern NSW, eastern Vic.

Habitat: Landforms: generally undulating to flat. Soils: found on sandy soils. Altitude: generally below 500 m. Temperatures: summers are hot to very hot, winters are mild to warm. Precipitation: up to 600 mm or more in the north; down to 400 mm in the south-east; and less in the arid country.

Upper stratum: the most common *Callitris* species is the white cypress pine which generally forms low woodlands in alliance with a variety of other genera, though small pure cypress pine woodlands may be found. Typical co-dominants include horse mulga (*Acacia* sp.) in WA, and elsewhere include the wilga (*Geijera* sp.), sugarwood (*Myoporum* sp.), cooba, mulga (*Acacia* spp), buloke and belah (*Casuarina* sp.), also belah with wilga; the rough-barked apple (*Angophora* sp.) in the north; and most commonly the eucalypts bimble box, grey box and narrow-leaved ironbark. In some instances these latter species grade into open forests. In the Snowy River area cypress pines co-dominate with various eucalypts.

Substrata: these woodlands normally exhibit a grassy understorey with virtually no shrubs. In some cypress pine-eucalypt woodlands there may be a dense shrubby layer composed of emu bushes, warrior bush, wilga, etc.

Transformations: most woodlands are subjected to extensive grazing by sheep in the south and beef cattle and/or sheep in the north. It seems likely that the presence of shrubs in the understorey is in direct response to a reduction in the number of bushfires experienced since European settlement.

MELALEUCA WOODLANDS AND LOW WOODLANDS-1 — paperbark woodlands

Location: primarily in northern Qld adjacent to the Gulf of Carpentaria and on the Cape York Peninsula.

Habitat: Landforms: coastal plains. Soils: earthy sands, etc. Altitude: below 100 m. Temperatures: warm to very hot throughout the year. Precipitation: around 500 mm or less, with a definite summer maximum.

Upper stratum: dominated by paperbarks. These trees have a low stature, between 4 and 7 m, though they may grow to 20 m under ideal conditions. *Melaleucas* may co-dominate with the bean tree (*Bauhinia* sp.) in semi-arid areas. Other species, though not necessarily co-dominants, include the whitewood (*Atalaya* sp.), the emu apple (*Owenia* sp.), the beefwood (*Grevillea* sp.), the ironwood (*Erythrophleum* sp.) as well as some bloodwoods (*Eucalyptus* sp.) and some *Terminalia* species. (See also *Melaleuca* woodlands and low woodlands-2 and Other woodlands and low woodlands.)

Substrata: composed of a shrubby-herbaceous layer. Shrubs include mimosa and *Capparis* species. Grasses are typically the kerosene and goldenbeard grasses. Some areas may exhibit soft spinifex.

Transformations: these woodlands are subjected to extensive grazing by beef cattle.

MELALEUCA WOODLANDS AND LOW WOODLANDS-2 — paperbark swamp woodlands

Location: varies; typically found in the humid and subhumid country of southern and eastern Australia.

Habitat: Landforms: low, often swampy, environments; watercourses, etc., dry creekbeds in inland areas. Soils: podzols, etc., often waterlogged or with impeded drainage. Altitude: varies. Temperatures: vary. Precipitation: varies.

Upper stratum: dominated by a variety of paperbarks, principally white paperbark and swamp paperbark in the southern regions; dwarf paperbark (generally a small, stunted and twisted plant) and broad-leaved paperbark in the northeastern regions and inland paperbark in the inland regions. In some instances the formation may be of such density that it forms an open forest, open scrub or closed scrub. (See also Chapter 5, *Melaleuca* open forests and Chapter 9, *Melaleuca* [closed and] scrubs.)

Substrata: varies, depending on the nature of the site. If particularly swampy then a variety of grasses and sedges may be present.

Transformations: some areas may be cleared for cropping and intensive grazing.

BANKSIA WOODLANDS AND LOW WOODLANDS — banksia woodlands

Location: coastal plain of south-west WA, littoral situations in eastern Vic. and NSW.

Habitat: Landforms: sandy coastal plains (WA), dunes and 'sandy' cliff-tops in NSW and Vic. Soils: siliceous sands. Altitude: below 100 m. Temperatures: very warm to hot summers, mild winters. Precipitation: 500 to 900 mm with a definite winter maximum in WA; over 700 mm elsewhere.

Upper stratum: dominated by species of *Banksia* up to 12 m high. Typical species in WA include orange banksia in wetter areas, holly-leaved banksia with *B. attenuta* in drier areas, and *B. attenuta* with firewood banksia in the driest of areas. Here the dominants range from 3 to 10 m in height. Further north firewood banksia grades into open scrubs. In some places in the wetter southern areas there may be an alliance with the WA she-oak (*Casuarina* sp.) and pricklybark (*Eucalyptus* sp.). In the eastern States the principal species are the coastal banksia, old-man banksia and wallum.

Substrata: a large variety of shrubs, predominantly heaths. The blackboy (*Xanthorrhoea* sp.) is common amongst the heaths of WA. The heath

Southern Acacia *shrubby low woodland: dominated by* A. pruinocarpa*?; this woodland occurs along the watercourse of the Gascoyne River. (south of Kumarina, Gascoyne, WA)*

understorey is often closed in littoral situations.

Transformations: some areas have been preserved or remained unaltered. Other areas have been cleared for urban expansion or given over to sown pastures.

PINE AND/OR BEECH LOW WOODLANDS

Location: subalpine areas of Tas.; often adjacent to subalpine low open forests and subalpine low woodlands.

Habitat: Landforms: fringes of glacial lakes, watercourses, gullies, etc. Soils: various. Altitude: up to 1200 m. Temperatures: summers are cool to mild, winters are cold to very cold. Precipitation: up to 2000 mm.

Upper stratum: dominated by a variety of genera. Deciduous beech (*Nothofagus* sp.) often allies with King William pine (*Athrotaxis* sp.), a short version of celery-top pine (*Phyllocadus* sp.) and the shrubby pines (*Dismela archeri* and *Microstrobus niphophilus*). These pines are found near lakes, streams and on the edge of low open forests and woodlands. In some places the density of vegetation may constitute a low open forest. (See also Chapter 5, *Athrotaxis* open forests and low open forests.)

Substrata: the understorey exhibits a variety of shrubs, heaths, grasses and forbs. Typical species include the Tasmanian waratah, waxberries (snowberries), cheeseberries and pandanus grass.

Transformations: some areas are virtually unaltered; in other areas habitats have been lost due to raising the level of lakes in connection with hydro-electricity schemes, flooding by the same, forestry projects and mining.

MIXED LOW WOODLANDS AND TALL SHRUBLANDS

Location: temperate semi-arid region of NSW (Western Plains north-west of Cobar).

Habitat: Landforms: undulating plains, low rocky ridges. Soils: red loams, sandy loams. Altitude: around 200 m or so. Temperatures: summers are hot, winters are mild to warm. Precipitation: 250 to 350 mm.

Upper stratum: dominated by a variety of low trees and tall shrubs. These include ironwood, yarran and mulga (*Acacia* spp), white cypress pine (*Callitris* sp.), budda (*Eremophila* sp.), leopard-wood (*Flindersia* sp.), inland rosewood (*Heterodendrum* sp.), wilga (*Geijera* sp.) as well as various *Cassias* and hopbushes (*Dodonea* spp). In some places the bimble box (*Eucalyptus* sp.) occurs as an emergent.

Substrata: many of the above species may be of such a height that they constitute part of the understorey. The grass layer is represented by kerosene grasses.

Transformations: most areas are subjected to extensive grazing by sheep. It is probable that the preponderance of shrubs in this formation is a direct response to the reduction in, and control of, the number of bushfires since European settlement.

OTHER WOODLANDS AND LOW WOODLANDS

Throughout Australia there are other low woodlands characterised by different genera to those listed above. Though these woodlands are of limited extent they may be locally prominent as pure stands; more commonly these woodlands form co-dominant formations with those genera already discussed.

Other woodlands include the following.

Adansonia woodlands — northern baobab woodlands. Though widespread and common throughout the Kimberley and Ord-Victoria regions of northern Australia the northern baobab generally occurs as an emergent tree in woodland formations. In a few localities it may be thought of as forming a woodland (or open woodland).

Agonis woodlands and low woodlands See Chapter 5, *Agonis* open forests.

Brachychiton low woodlands — desert kurrajong woodlands. Desert kurrajongs occasionally form small belts or groves, particularly in the arid regions of central Australia, and the semi-arid parts of south-west WA. Generally it is allied with, and is surrounded by, low mallee open scrub.

Excoecaria low woodlands — gutta percha woodlands. These low woodlands are located in grey or brown clays subject to occasional flooding (adjacent to coolabah woodlands), and on coastal mudflats in the tropical northern regions. The

Casuarina *low woodland: exhibiting belah as the dominant and saltbush in the understorey. (nr Lake Everard Stn, Gairdner Plain, SA)*

Heterodendrum *low woodland: these low trees of inland rosewood dominate a saltbush understorey; the trees' flat crown bases are due to cropping by sheep. (nr Lake Everard Stn, Gairdner Plain, SA)*

Flindersia *low woodland: this leopardwood woodland has a widely spaced shrub layer of bramble wattle in the understorey; the ground cover is ephemeral. (nr Glen Cowrie Stn, Upper Darling, NSW)*

understorey is represented by blue grasses and beard grasses.

Geijera-flindersia **low woodlands** — wilga/leopardwood woodlands. The wilga and leopardwood are often found together in the northern subhumid/semi-arid country of NSW, especially along the Bogan and Macquarie Rivers. They may also form alliances with other genera, e.g. *Acacia, Casuarina, Callitris*, etc., in woodland formations.

Grevillea **low woodlands** — beefwood woodlands. Beefwood woodlands are not large within themselves, but may be locally common over extensive areas of eastern semi-arid inland Australia. They commonly occur on low rocky hills, and adjacent to non-perennial streams or small riverflats. Often there is a shrubby layer composed of *Acacia, Eremophila* species, etc. Beefwood occasionally co-dominates with wilga, bean tree, whitewood and needlewood.

Hakea **low woodlands** — needlewood woodlands. Needlewood occasionally co-dominates with the beefwood (*Grevillea* sp.). Though not a prominent tree, needlewood is widely scattered throughout much of the temperate arid and semi-arid lands of Australia. In the north-eastern inland regions the needlewood may form alliances with inland rosewood on sandy soils. Another species, the corkwood, forms alliances with various genera throughout the semi-arid and arid inland.

Heterodendrum **low woodlands** — inland rosewood woodlands. Inland rosewood is commonly found as a co-dominant with belah, cypress pine, mallee eucalypts, western myall and needlewood throughout much of the subhumid/semi-arid country of south-east Australia.

Lysiphyllum **low woodlands** — bean tree/Queensland ebony woodlands. The bean tree forms pure stands in semi-arid northern Qld, though it commonly forms alliances with tea-tree (*Melaleuca* sp.), whitewood (*Atalaya* sp.), beefwood (*Grevillea* sp.), the screw palm (*Pandanus* sp.), and various semi-deciduous eucalypts such as the smooth-stemmed bloodwood and white gum. The Queensland ebony generally allies itself with brigalow (*Acacia* sp.) and wilga (*Geijera* sp.) formations in central eastern Qld.

Melaleuca **woodlands and low woodlands-3** — moonah woodlands. Moonah woodlands and low woodlands are found in scattered areas throughout southern SA, often allied with varieties of eucalypts and occasionally drooping she-oak (*Casuarina* sp.). Generally they exhibit a grassy understorey.

Myoporum **woodlands and low woodlands** — sugarwood woodlands. Sugarwood low woodlands are located in the semi-arid and subhumid country of southern and south-eastern Australia, particularly in eastern SA, north-western Vic. and the far south-west of NSW. Pearl blue bush often occurs in the understorey.

Nypa **woodlands** Dominated by the mangrove palm which is found along the McIvor and Herbert Rivers, north Qld. The habitat is one of brackish waters on tidal estuaries. Generally the stands, which occupy small areas, are monospecific, although a few mangroves may be present.

Pandanus **low woodlands** These woodlands often occur adjacent to streams and watercourses of monsoonal and humid northern Australia, and also along coastal and estuarine locations along the Qld and northern NSW coasts. A typical species is the screw palm. (See also Chapter 4, Tree Thicket Types.)

Terminalia **low woodlands** — nutwood and other woodlands. Nutwood low woodlands are found throughout monsoonal and tropical semi-arid northern Australia (except Qld), occasionally as pure stands, but more commonly within layered woodlands. Okari formations are commonly found in coastal locations above the high-water mark in tropical northern Australia. Other species of *Terminalia* woodlands include the billygoat plum, *T. aridicola, T. oblongata* and *T. platyphylla*. Alliances include the ironwood (*Erythrophleum* sp.) and supplejack (*Ventilago* sp.).

Chapter Seven

OPEN WOODLANDS

Introduction
Eucalyptus Types
Shrubby low open woodlands — includes Pindan, Shrubby and heathy low open woodlands — tree heaths, Grassy low open woodlands — tree savanna, Hummock grass low open woodlands — tree steppe, Low open woodlands with a mixed sub-strata, Grassy very low open Woodlands

Acacia Types
Southern *Acacia* low open woodlands — western and weeping myall open woodlands, North-eastern *Acacia* low open woodlands, *Acacia* grassy low open woodlands — Georgina gidgee open woodlands, etc., *Acacia* hummock grass low open woodlands — ironwood open woodlands

Other Types
Allocasuarina hummock grass low open woodlands — desert oak open woodlands, *Casuarina* shrubby low open woodlands — belah open woodlands, *Casuarina* shrubby and grassy low open woodlands — drooping she-oak open woodlands, *Callitris* low open woodlands — cypress pine open woodlands, Other open woodlands and low open woodlands

Introduction

Open woodlands can be thought of as an extension of woodlands. Here the trees are further spaced, often to such an extent that the understorey appears more dominant in the landscape. Tree genera are basically the same as woodlands. Eucalypts and *Acacias* predominate in most formations although other types are locally important. Normally open woodlands grade into woodlands on their wetter margins, their habitats being more severe and only marginally suitable for tree growth. This severe habitat is due to low annual precipitation rates, periods of extended droughts, high evaporation rates and, in some instances, especially in more humid regions, an inability of soil to retain moisture or poor soil fertility. It is thought that fire may also play a part in determining the formation of open woodlands.

Depending on the spacing of trees open woodlands may appear to be dominated by the plants in the understorey and should perhaps be classified accordingly. Such appearances are reinforced by the fact that the trees of most open woodlands are low in height. Nonetheless the tree stratum is generally conspicuous, though sparse. In those places where the tree layer is inconspicuous, i.e. there is a considerable distance between each tree, then perhaps the formation could be referred to as a shrubland or herbland, as the case may be. In this instance any trees present would be called emergents.

Most open woodlands do not exhibit the pendulous crowns of woodland trees as the crowns themselves are often straggly and open. The formations are often extensive, covering many dry inland plains. They are presently composed of 102 major alliances and once covered 5.8 per cent of the land area.

Shrubby and heathy low open woodland: occupying a small, rocky habitat on the edge of a precipice; away from the cliff the trees increase in stature and density; the understorey exhibits grass trees. (Bungonia Caves, Southern Tablelands, NSW)

Eucalyptus Types

SHRUBBY LOW OPEN WOODLANDS — includes Pindan

Location: on the semi-arid and arid margins of eucalypt woodlands of northern Australia.

Habitat: Landforms: plains and downs, rocky outcrops. Soils: earthy sands, lithosols, etc. Altitude: generally below 300 m; up to 600 m in the Centre, NT. Temperatures: very hot summers, warm winters. Precipitation: down to 150 mm with a definite summer maximum.

Upper stratum: dominated by eucalypts between 5 and 10 m tall. Typical species include the variable-barked bloodwood and some species typical of adjacent woodlands and low woodlands. Ghost gums may be seen in the Centre, NT. Further north supplejack (*Ventilago* sp.) may associate with the variable-barked bloodwood.

Substrata: characterised by an understorey of tall shrubs such as the Pindan wattle (in WA) or low shrubs elsewhere.

Transformations: some areas are used for the extensive grazing of beef cattle.

SHRUBBY AND HEATHY LOW OPEN WOODLANDS — tree heaths

Location: on various rocky tablelands, typically sandstone, in the humid and subhumid regions, e.g. Blue Mountains, NSW.

Habitat: Landforms: rocky tablelands and outcrops. Soils: lithosols, etc. Altitude: up to 1200 m. Temperatures: vary, depends to some extent on altitude. Precipitation: generally above 600 mm.

Shrubby low open woodland: unidentified dominants forming an overstorey above a wide variety of shrubs including mulga, emu bushes, etc.; the ground is covered with a blaze of ephemeral everlastings. (nr Paynes Find, Murchison Goldfields, WA)

Upper stratum: dominated by a variety of eucalypts such as scribbly gums as well as some that may exhibit a mallee habit (see Chapter 9, Shrubby open scrubs-3). Often the eucalypts co-dominate with various *Banksia* species.

Substrata: characterised by a variety of dwarf shrubs and some heaths. Species include the waratah, grass trees, mountain devils, she-oaks, (see Chapter 9, Wet temperate wet and dry open heaths). Near rocky outcrops and streams there may be a wet heath-sedge community (see Chapter 9, Sedge-like heaths).

Transformations: many areas are still intact; other areas have been cleared for urban development, etc. The intensity and frequency of fires appears to influence the nature of this formation.

GRASSY LOW OPEN WOODLANDS — tree savanna

Location: on the arid and semi-arid margins of eucalypt woodlands throughout northern and central Australia; also on the frontage country of many inland streams and watercourses.

Habitat: Landforms: plains and downs; floodplains and some undulating country. Soils: alluvial soils, red-brown earths, etc. Altitude: generally below 500 m. Temperatures: hot to very hot summers, warm to very warm winters. Precipitation: down to 150 mm with a summer maximum in the north.

Grassy low open woodland: dominants unknown; the ground cover is composed of kerosene grasses and ephemerals; in the background is a riverine woodland. (Ashburton River floodplain, North-West, WA)

Southern Acacia low open woodland: exhibiting western myall; the understorey, originally saltbush, has been totally cleared. (old Koonalda Stn Roadhouse, Nullarbor Plain, SA)

Grassy low open woodland: dominants unknown; these widely spaced eucalypts occupy the edge of a dry lake bed. (Poppita Lake, Lower Darling, NSW)

Upper stratum: dominated by eucalypts up to 10 m tall. Species are similar to those found in adjacent low woodlands. Typical species are the coolabah on frontage country and, further south, the black box.

Substrata: characterised by grasses, some of which may be ephemeral, with perhaps a scattering of shrubs. Frontage country, which is subjected to occasional flooding, displays a profusion of grasses and forbs after such an event.

Transformations: many areas are subjected to extensive grazing by beef cattle and sheep.

HUMMOCK GRASS LOW OPEN WOODLANDS — tree steppe

Location: throughout much of semi-arid and arid Australia, particularly in the western two-thirds of the continent. Often this formation merges into other arid formations such as those dominated by *Acacias*.

Habitat: Landforms: sand plains, sand-dunes, stony hills. Soils: earthy sands, siliceous sands, lithosols. Altitude: generally below 600 m. Temperatures: hot to very hot summers, mild to very warm winters. Precipitation: down to 150 mm with a slight summer maximum in the north.

Upper stratum: dominated by low, scattered eucalypts such as the variable-barked bloodwood and marble or desert gum. (See also Chapter 6, Hummock grass low woodlands.)

Substrata: exhibits varieties of hummock grasses such as soft spinifex and feathertop spinifex in northern regions and hard spinifex in southern regions. Where this formation merges into shrublands there may be some tall shrubs in the understorey.

Transformations: extensive beef cattle grazing occurs on the periphery of this formation in northern and central areas; other areas remain unaltered.

LOW OPEN WOODLANDS with a mixed substrata

Location: parts of the monsoonal north especially Arnhem Land, NT.

Habitat: Landforms: dissected sandstone tablelands. Soils: lithosols. Altitude: below 300 m. Temperatures: hot throughout the year. Precipitation: over 600 mm with a definite summer (wet season) maximum.

Upper stratum: dominated by a scattering of low eucalypts.

North-eastern Acacia *low open woodland: though the grove shown here is not open the distribution of these lancewoods is generally more exposed; these dominants are about 2 m tall. (Carters Range, Channel Country, Qld).*

Substrata: a very sparse covering of shrubs and hummock grasses interspersed with areas of bare rock.

Transformations: virtually intact.

GRASSY VERY LOW OPEN WOODLANDS

See Chapter 6, Grassy very low woodlands.

Acacia Types

SOUTHERN *ACACIA* LOW OPEN WOODLANDS — western and weeping myall open woodlands

Location: throughout the semi-arid and arid regions of south-eastern Australia.

Habitat: Landforms: plains and downs, valleys of range country; floodplains (weeping myall). Soils: calcareous sandy soils (western myall), alluvial soils (weeping myall). Altitude: generally below 300 m. Temperatures: hot to very hot summers, mild winters. Precipitation: less than 300 mm with a definite winter maximum in the north.

Upper stratum: dominated by the western myall either in pure stands or in alliances with mulga, sandhill mulga, dune wattle and umbrella mulga (*Acacia* spp) or belah (*Casuarina* sp.). On the alluvial soils, particularly within the Murray-Darling river basin, weeping myall is found, often in pure stands.

Substrata: the understorey of western myall is nearly always low shrubs of saltbush and bluebush; the weeping myall understorey exhibits a variety of grasses.

Transformations: many of these formations are extensively grazed by sheep.

NORTH-EASTERN *ACACIA* LOW OPEN WOODLANDS

A dry country version of the woodlands dominated by bendee and boree. The ground layer in boree low open woodlands generally exhibits Mitchell grass. See Chapter 6, North-eastern *Acacia* woodlands and low woodlands.

ACACIA GRASSY LOW OPEN WOODLANDS — Georgina gidgee open woodlands, etc.

Location: within the semi-arid and arid regions of northern and north-eastern Australia.
Habitat: Landforms: plains and downs. Soils: grey, brown and red clays among others. Altitude: below 400 m. Temperatures: hot to very hot summers, mild to very warm winters. Precipitation: below 350 mm with a summer maximum.
Upper stratum: dominated by low trees (sometimes shrubs) of Georgina gidgee, mimosa and boree. In a few restricted localities around the Simpson Desert grows waddywood, a rare species.
Substrata: varies from area to area. In the wetter areas there may be Mitchell grass in the understorey; drier areas display ephemeral grasses and forbs after rain or there may be a covering of spinifex.
Transformations: many areas are used for the extensive grazing of beef cattle and, to a lesser extent, sheep.

ACACIA HUMMOCK GRASS LOW OPEN WOODLANDS — ironwood open woodlands

Location: primarily — the arid regions where the borders of SA, WA and NT meet; other occurrences further afield.
Habitat: Landforms: plains and downs. Soils: many types. Altitude: up to 600 m. Temperatures: very hot summers, mild to very warm winters. Precipitation: up to 250 mm with a slight summer maximum.
Upper stratum: dominated by the ironwood (*Acacia* sp.). Typically this species occurs as scattered trees often in association with mulga and Georgina gidgee though in a few places it may produce a unique formation. In the driest areas it may be of shrubby form.
Substrata: either spinifex or bare ground covered with ephemerals after rain.
Transformations: most areas are unused although some extensive beef cattle grazing may occur in the wetter areas.

Hummock grass low open woodland: dominated by snappy gums with a spinifex understorey; this semi-arid montane valley is 700 m above sea-level. (Hamersley Plateau, Pilbara, WA)

Other Types

CASUARINA SHRUBBY LOW OPEN WOODLANDS — belah open woodlands

Location: restricted mainly to the southern semi-arid regions of SA with minor extensions in south-western NSW; within *Casuarina* low woodlands.
Habitat: Landforms: plains and downs. Soils: calcareous sandplain soils. Altitude: below 300 m. Temperatures: hot summers, mild winters. Precipitation: below 300 to 500 mm with a winter maximum.
Upper stratum: dominated by belah which may be locally common. Often forms alliances with mulga and western myall.
Substrata: the understorey is composed of various shrubs including emu bushes, saltbushes, bluebushes and shrubby forms of inland rosewood.
Transformations: subjected to extensive grazing by sheep.

CASUARINA SHRUBBY and GRASSY LOW OPEN WOODLANDS — drooping she-oak open woodlands

Location: within the rain shadow of the Mt Lofty Ranges, along parts of the eastern gulf coasts and within parts of the Flinders Ranges, SA.
Habitat: Landforms: undulating country, downs, steep hillsides. Soils: red-brown earths, etc. Altitude: generally below 450 m. Temperatures: hot summers, cool to mild winters. Precipitation: below 300 mm with a winter maximum.

Upper stratum: dominated by the drooping she-oak.

Substrata: the understorey varies from place to place. Often there is a ground cover of tussock grasses including wallaby grass and spear grass. On steep hillslopes the twiggy daisy-bush (*Olearia*) may be found.

Transformations: some areas are subjected to grazing by sheep.

ALLOCASUARINA HUMMOCK GRASS LOW OPEN WOODLANDS — desert oak open woodlands

Location: between the ranges of arid central Australia, i.e. far northern regions of SA, central eastern regions of WA and the south-west of NT.

Habitat: Landforms: sandplains. Soils: earthy sands, etc. Altitude: up to 600 m. Temperatures: hot to very hot summers, mild to very warm winters. Precipitation: below 250 mm with a slight summer maximum.

Upper stratum: this formation is dominated by the desert oak, which often forms small groves.

Substrata: characterised by hard spinifex. Other ground cover plants include some tussock grasses and, after rain, ephemerals.

Transformations: virtually unaltered except in the wetter areas. In these places the ground cover may be fired to induce young green growth.

Callitris *low open woodland: exhibiting white cypress pines overlying tussock grasses. (Bunyeroo Valley, Flinders Ranges, SA)*

CALLITRIS LOW OPEN WOODLANDS — cypress pine open woodlands

Location: various locations throughout semi-arid and arid temperate Australia; minor areas in subhumid lands.

Hakea *low open woodland: this very sparse woodland occupies an interdunal depression; the dominant tree is corkwood, about 3 to 4 m high; the ground cover is spinifex, a few of which are seeding. (nr Barradale, Norh-West, WA)*

Habitat: Landforms: rocky ranges, ridges and steep hillslopes. Soils: lithosols. Altitude: up to 1000 m. Temperatures: hot summers, mild to warm winters Precipitation: generally below 400 mm.

Upper stratum: dominated by the white cypress pine. Trees are of good form in the more fertile areas, e.g. hillslopes of the Flinders Ranges SA, or may exhibit a twisted, gnarled form when colonising extensive rocky ground. The gnarled and distorted form of these trees is due to the impoverished soil found in the joints, cracks and chasms that it occupies. In some places mallee eucalypts are found.

Substrata: where there is extensive soil cover various tussock grasses form the understorey otherwise the ground exhibits bare rock with a few stunted bushes and grasses occupying the cracks.

Transformations: some areas are extensively grazed by sheep, otherwise the formation is unaltered.

OTHER OPEN WOODLANDS AND LOW OPEN WOODLANDS

A few genera, as listed in Chapter 6, Other woodlands and low woodlands may be of such density as to constitute an open woodland form of those woodlands. Throughout the central and western arid regions various species of *Acacias* (mulga, ironwood, etc.), some eucalypts and *Allocasuarina* species (desert oaks, etc.) together with some of the genera listed in Other woodlands and low woodlands produce low open woodlands, generally in alliance with each other. Of these open woodlands the needlewood and corkwood (*Hakea* spp) are common dominants. Another common dominant, in the Great Sandy Desert, is the desert walnut (*Owenia* sp).

Chapter Eight

CLOSED SCRUBS AND HEATHS

Introduction
Closed scrubs — includes shrub swamps, Montane closed scrubs, Other closed scrubs, Closed heaths — includes wet deserts, Shrubby thickets

Closed scrub occupying a coastal headland: this grades into a closed heath near the cliff-top; the dominant plant is paperbark; there is no understorey though grass patches occur where the canopy is broken. (Aireys Inlet, Western Districts, Vic.)

Introduction

Closed scrubs and heaths are shrubby formations characterised by dense foliage. These formations are subdivided into scrubs, dominated by shrubs over 2 m tall, and heaths, dominated by shrubs less than 2 m tall. They are found on either infertile or waterlogged sites, generally within the coastal or montane regions. Typical areas include headlands, back-swamps on riverflats, upland swamps or boggy ground behind sand-dunes, etc. In most cases these formations are subjected to various environmental stresses such as salt spray off the ocean, strong winds or regular inundation. As a rule strong salt-laden winds effectively sheer plants thus inhibiting growth; in these localities a closed heath would be expected.

Closed scrubs and heaths are often dominated by tea-trees and paperbarks. In addition closed heaths may also include varieties of banksias, hakeas, she-oaks, etc. It has been thought that closed scrubs are relatively fire-free or have at least escaped fire for a sufficiently long time in order to be called closed scrubs, unlike closed heaths, which are subjected to the occasional fire hence their stature remains relatively short. Also these heaths may be shortened by 'wind shearing'.

Beneath the canopy of these formations the light is less intense than would be experienced in more open formations, consequently the understorey is undeveloped or lacking. Normally the canopy is a tangle of twisted branches, stems and leaves while the ground is often bare. In Australia closed scrubs and heaths represent a miniscule land area, especially away from the coast, and are composed of approximately 86 major alliances.

Closed scrub: dominated by paperbarks with sedges in the foreground; this locality is always damp and regularly inundated. (nr Spearwood, Coastal Plain, WA)

CLOSED SCRUBS — includes shrub swamps

Location: in various coastal and subcoastal regions, particularly in the humid, subhumid and monsoonal regions; also in some temperate subhumid/semi-arid areas subject to winter rains.

Habitat: Landforms: behind coastal dunes, adjacent to swamps, sheltered coastal valleys. Soils: sandy soils, peats, etc; soils often waterlogged. Altitude: virtually at sea-level (see also Montane closed scrubs). Temperatures: vary. Precipitation: generally high; formation may be subjected to periodic flooding.

Upper stratum: dominated by shrubs over 2 m tall. Common species include the coastal tea-tree in sandy areas and the swamp paperbark in swampy areas. Virtually all closed scrubs are represented by tea-trees (*Leptospermum* spp) or paperbarks. (*Melaleuca* spp). Other species include the manuka tea-tree, mountain pepper, scented paperbark and silver banksia. (See also Chapter 9, *Melaleuca* [closed and] open scrubs.)

Substrata: the understorey is often bare due to the density of the upper stratum although there may be a few shade-tolerant grasses and sedges forming a sparse ground cover.

Transformations: due to the waterlogged nature of swamps and the fragility of dune systems this formation is generally unaltered except in areas of urbanisation. In tropical and temperate humid regions the introduced plant, lantana may form closed scrubs in some gullies and clearings.

MONTANE CLOSED SCRUBS

Location: see Chapter 9, Montane open heaths.

Habitat: see Montane open heaths; montane closed scrubs are found within montane open heaths adjacent to streams and other watercourses.

Upper stratum: dominated by species of tea-tree (*Leptospermum* spp) and some *Acacias* such as the silver wattle. In some places alpine baeckea forms dense thickets.

Substrata: species of boronias and *Prostanthera* are found in the understorey.

Transformations: due to their limited size and situation most formations are probably still intact.

Closed scrub understorey: the dominant and virtually only plant is tea-tree which occupies the swale behind a beach foredune. (Seven Mile Beach, South Coast, NSW)

OTHER CLOSED SCRUBS

In some places the *Eucalyptus* open scrubs (mallees) may be of such density that they produce closed scrub formations. See the appropriate open scrub formations. Likewise *Acacia* and *Casuarina* open scrubs may occasionally form closed scrubs.

CLOSED HEATHS — includes wet deserts

Location: in various coastal and subcoastal areas, particularly in the humid, subhumid and monsoonal regions.

Habitat: Landforms: behind and on top of coastal dunes, on coastal hillsides and headlands, on lowlands and hill country with infertile sandy or waterlogged soils. Soils: often sandy. Altitude: generally near sea-level although up to 600 m in some places. Temperatures: vary. Precipitation: generally high, especially in the 'wet deserts' of Cape York Peninsula, Qld.

Upper stratum: dominated by shrubs or heaths less than 2 m tall. Typical plants include varieties of tea-trees, paperbarks, wattles, dwarf she-oaks and jacksonias, each of which may be locally dominant. In the 'wet deserts' of Cape York Peninsula the dominants are represented by the tea-tree *Leptospermum fabrica* allied with *Fenzlia obtusa* along with various other shrubs. (For further information on 'wet deserts' see Chapter 9, Tropical and subtropical wet and dry open heaths.)

Substrata: often the understorey is bare although there may be a few shade-tolerant grasses and sedges.

Transformations: due to the nature of their environment many closed heaths are still relatively intact except in areas of concentrated urbanisation. In some cases closed heaths which remain free from fire may form into closed scrubs.

SHRUBBY THICKETS

The following plants often occur as dense thickets or low, dense clumps within other more extensive formations.

Acacia rostellifera Found north of Dongara, WA, on sand-dunes; grows to 6 m.

Bauera **scrub** Found in Tas, beneath or adjacent to some fern and/or moss closed forests.

Berrigan or long-leaved emu bush May occur as clumps in some low open woodlands and open shrublands.

Conkerberry Forms low dense thickets up to 2 m high throughout tropical semi-arid regions with extensions into the monsoonal and arid parts. Found mainly on sandy soils.

Grevillea gordoniana Found along the temperate semi-arid coast south of Shark Bay, WA. Forms very dense bushy clumps with branches close to the ground. See also Chapter 9, *Banksia* open scrubs.

Horizontal (scrub) Found in Tas. beneath or adjacent to some fern and/or moss closed forests. Grows to a height of 6 m. This plant forms a tangled mass of branches which is virtually impenetrable.

Shrubby thicket: lignum occupying a riverbank; such thickets are common along many inland streams and within seasonal swamps. (Wilson River, Channel Country, Qld)

Lignum Common on the floodplains of inland watercourses as a tangled sprawling mass of branches and stems. Grows to 3 m. Black box is common in the overstorey, in southern areas.

Melaleuca cardiophylla This plant is found on the coastal limestones in rocky situations in the south-west of WA. Grows to over 4 m.

Nitre bush Forms low clumps within black box woodlands and samphire low shrublands in some semi-arid areas. See also Chapter 10, *Nitraria* low shrublands.

Nitre goosefoot Forms low clumps within black box woodlands and some low shrublands in some semi-arid areas.

Samphires Often form low dense thickets up to 1 m high in samphire low shrubland formations. See also Chapter 10, Samphire low shrublands.

Wait-a-while Forms shrubby thickets in the subhumid/semi-arid belah-cypress pine woodlands of NSW.

Acacia-Casuarina *closed scrub: under ideal conditions various 'broom-type' wattles and she-oaks form dense thickets; the species here appears to be A. resinomarginea with a eucalypt to the left. (south of Paynes Find, Murchison Goldfields, WA)*

Chapter Nine

OPEN SCRUBS AND HEATHS

Introduction
Eucalyptus Types
Shrubby open scrubs-1 — mallee-1, Shrubby open scrubs-2 — mallee-broombush, Shrubby open scrubs-3 — wet mallee, Grassy open scrubs — mallee-2, Hummock grass open scrubs — mallee-3

Other Types (excluding Heaths)
Acacia and *Casuarina* open scrubs — broombush thickets, *Acacia* Hummock grass open scrubs, *Melaleuca* (closed and) open scrubs — broom plains, *Banksia* open scrubs — scrub heaths, *Casuarina* low open scrubs, *Atriplex, Chenopodium* and *Maireana* low open scrubs, *Nitraria* low open scrubs, Samphire low open scrubs, Other low open scrubs

Heath Types
Tropical and subtropical wet and dry open heaths — wet desert/wallum, Wet temperate wet and dry open heaths, Dry temperate wet and dry open heaths, Alpine and Subalpine open heaths, Bog heaths, Sedge-like heaths, Montane open heaths, Spinifex heaths

Introduction

Open scrubs and open heaths are formations composed of shrubby plants characterised by having many stems rather than one supporting a relatively low and fairly open canopy. They are subdivided into scrubs when over 2 m tall or heaths when less than this height. Although the height is arbitrary there are other characteristics which more readily differentiate scrubs from heaths.

The open scrubs are typified by plants dominated in the main by eucalypts which exhibit what is known as a mallee habit. Other open scrubs are also represented by various *Acacias, Banksias,* and *Melaleuca* species. Dealing with the eucalypts first the term mallee has two meanings. Firstly it refers to a growth form, secondly it refers to a community of plants dominated by mallee eucalypts. A mallee eucalypt grows from a lignotuber, a swelling rootstock from which grow branches which splay outward to form a flattened canopy. The number of branches seems to be influenced by the frequency of bushfires and by soil type. Few fires and/or better soils produce less but quite firm branches; these shrubs are called bull mallees. Many fires and/or poorer soils produce many small, flexible branches and these mallees are referred to as whipstick mallees.

Mallees are located in the winter rainfall belt of the subhumid/semi-arid regions of southern Australia and are generally found on old sand-dune formations. These regions experience cool winters and hot, dry summers. A result of occupying such dune country is that there is an alternative pattern to mallee formations. This pattern corresponds to bull mallees occupying the intervening dune flats or swales and whipstick mallees occupying the old dune ridges. This variation would seem to be in response to variations in soil type between dunes and swales.

The mallee formation exhibits a variety of understoreys depending on precipitation amounts, soil types and fire periodicity. Most mallees display a variety of low shrubs or heaths, some display grasses while on the poorer soils and in the more arid regions hummock grasses or spinifex may be present.

Except in the driest of areas mallee communities are quite dense, often to the point where their crowns are touching and perhaps interlocking. Though they can withstand some clearing and thinning an excess of this can lead to severe soil erosion and degradation, and a corresponding loss of nutrients. This was clearly brought home by the giant dust storm which covered Melbourne during the latter part of the 1979–83 drought when tonnes of soil passed through the city from the drought-stricken Wimmera and Mallee regions of Victoria. It is hoped that the lesson was learnt by those who would clear the remaining mallee areas of New South Wales for crop production, a mallee region whose reliability of rainfall is considerably less than those mallee regions to the south and south-west. In total mallees provide habitats for some 12 species of birds and a variety of mammals, most of which could not live elsewhere.

In some places mallee eucalypts are not the only dominants. A species of *Melaleuca*, the broombush also exhibits a mallee habit and forms small mallee communities either on its own or in alliance with some eucalypt mallees. Not all mallees are found within the southern sub-humid/semi-arid winter rainfall belt. In some humid and subhumid montane and tableland regions eucalypts that have experienced regular fires, especially those in heathy areas, may also exhibit mallee habits. These shrubs, which also grow from rootstocks, exhibit many short-lived stems. These mallees of the humid-subhumid regions are commonly known as wet mallees. Of the remaining open scrub genera their forms are not referred to as mallees although it is possible that fire and impoverished soils may well be responsible for their characteristic form.

So much for the open scrubs. Open heaths, dominated as they are by relatively low shrubs, present a totally different structure in their formations. The heights of the dominants are low (less than 2 m) and the formation is distinguished by a lack of trees or tall shrubs (except in tree heaths and mallee heaths, both of which could be considered as a transition between heathy open forests/woodlands or shrubby open scrubs and open heaths). Heaths are distinguished by an enormous number of species, in some cases as many per unit area as would be found in some tropical rainforests. The thing about heaths is that the number of species present at any one time is closely linked to the periodicity and intensity of previous fires. The other thing about heaths is that they respond more to soil types than to the prevailing climatic conditions. Nonetheless heaths are generally found in the humid and subhumid regions of Australia as well as some northern monsoonal areas.

Heaths are basically of two types. The so-called wet heaths occupy seasonally waterlogged soils which are generally sandy soils overlying impermeable clays. The other type, found on sandy soils, and in most cases located in drier areas, is the dry or sand heath. In both cases impoverished sandy soils are common. It is unusual then that such poor soils can support such a diversity of plant life. The answer lies in the fact that most heath community families possess root nodules which contain certain bacterium capable of fixing nitrogen, so forming the organic compounds required by the plants.

Fire is also important in heath communities. Although nitrogen is lost during a fire seeds of the members of heath families, lying dormant in the soil, are cracked by the heat and germinated by the first rains. These seedlings grow quickly and renew nutrients that, once they have died, will be used by other members of the heath community. In addition fire makes available other nutrients to the plants through ash dissolving into the soil moisture. Also not all plants are killed by fire, many are capable of renewing themselves from rootstocks.

Needless to say the ecology of heaths is much more complicated than this. In addition to there being so many species in these communities not all of them are present at the same time.

The number of species per unit area varies depending on the period since the last fire. Throughout Australia there are approximately 3700 species of plants in open heath formations or where heaths are found in the understorey of other formations. Of these approximately half are found in the south-west of Western Australia and one-fifth are located in the sandstone country surrounding Sydney. Consequently it is difficult to generalise heath formations simply by the dominant genera present as has been done in all other formations, save the closed forests. For this reason the heath formations that follow are described geographically. The heaths are home to 20 species of birds (3 must live here) and 22 species of mammals, all of which can live elsewhere.

In Australia the open scrubs once accounted for approximately 7.7 per cent of the land area and some 77 major alliances while the open heath formations once accounted for 1.5 per cent of the land area and some 75 major alliances.

Shrubby open scrub −1: the shrub layer here is low, and occasionally absent due to the nature of the soil; there are many small outcrops of calcrete; the dominant shrubs are yorrell and red mallee. (nr Swan Reach, Murray, SA)

Eucalyptus Types

SHRUBBY OPEN SCRUBS-1 — mallee-1

Location: on the subhumid/semi-arid margins of south-western NSW, north-western Vic., southern SA and south-western WA.

Habitat: Landforms: low, slightly undulating country. Soils: solonised brown earths, etc. Altitude: below 400 m. Temperatures: hot summers, cool to mild winters. Precipitation: generally between 270 and 450 mm with a definite winter maximum.

Upper stratum: dominated by species such as the white mallee, soap mallee, red mallee and yorrell. Heights range between 3 and 6 m. Taller eucalypt trees such as the bimble box may grow in suitable locations. This formation is replaced by cypress pine low woodlands on deep sandy soils. Other areas may exhibit belah-inland rosewood low woodland for-mations. In some instances red mallee may form alliances with sugarwood (*Myoporum* sp.).

Substrata: dominated by a variety of shrubs. Towards the wetter margins and in areas dominated by soap mallee the shrub layer may be dense. In the drier margins the shrub layer is less dense and includes species such as tea-tree, cypress pines and a variety of wattles. Patches of bare ground are common.

Transformations: much of this type of mallee has been cleared for wheat and cereal cropping and intensive sheep grazing. Introduced pasture species include the medics.

SHRUBBY OPEN SCRUBS-2 — mallee-broombush

Location: virtually limited to the Big Desert, Vic., and the Ninety Mile Desert and parts of the Eyre Peninsula, SA.

Habitat: as for Shrubby open scrubs-1, but on sandy soils.

Upper stratum: dominated by yellow mallee between 2 and 4 m high.

Substrata: mainly broombush with areas of needle bush and other varieties of *Acacia* and *Hakea*. Herbs and grasses are rare. In some places broombush produces its own unique formation; see *Melaleuca* (closed and) open scrubs.

Transformations: many areas have been cleared for cropping of wheat and cereals, and the grazing of sheep.

Shrubby open scrub −2: this scrub of yellow mallee has an understorey virtually limited to broombush. (Ninety Mile Desert, Upper South-East, SA)

SHRUBBY OPEN SCRUBS-3 — wet mallee

Location: throughout the humid mountainous areas of NSW, Vic., Tas. and the ACT including subalpine habitats; minor areas in Qld.

Habitat: Landforms: either exposed, rocky, windswept montane or subalpine areas including ridges and exposed slopes; or rocky tableland surfaces, e.g. sandstone country around Sydney, NSW. Soils: lithosols. Altitude: generally over 1000 m on the mainland and 600 m in Tas. Temperatures: summers are mild to very warm, winters are very cool to cold in montane areas, milder elsewhere. Precipitation: up to 2000 mm in montane areas, otherwise generally over 800 mm.

Upper stratum: dominated by mallee forms of *Eucalyptus*. Typical montane species include the black gum, mountain grey gum, narrow-leaved sallee, Kybean mallee, narrow-leaved peppermint, etc., on the mainland and the black gum and swamp gum, etc., in Tas. In subalpine areas the snow gum and Tasmanian snow gum often take on mallee form and are the dominant species. In other areas, e.g. some sandstone tablelands, species include yellow-top ash, Port Jackson mallee and Blue

Mountain mallee. In Qld the mallee *E. codonocarpa* is found in high-rainfall areas.

Substrata: the shrub layer is exemplified by species of *Banksia* and *Grevillea*, etc. Grasses may be found in the open spaces. For substrata of snow gum and Tasmanian snow gum subalpine formations see Chapter 5, Subalpine low open forests.

Transformations: due to the nature of the topography of these formations most areas are virtually unaltered. Exceptions include those areas used for hydro-electricity works and 'alpine' ski resorts.

GRASSY OPEN SCRUBS — mallee-2

Location: at the wetter margins of *Eucalyptus* open scrub formations in the temperate subhumid regions of southern Australia.

Habitat: Landforms: slightly undulating country. Soils: solonised brown soils, etc., with 'heavy' subsoils. Altitude: below 400 m. Temperatures: summers are hot, winters are cool to mild. Precipitation: up to 450 mm.

Upper stratum: includes a variety of species including the red mallee. Often the species becomes single stemmed as it merges into grassy woodland. Most dominants reach 8 m in height, although greater heights are reached in some localities.

Substrata: represented by a layer of tussock grasses such as spear grass and wallaby grass. Some shrubs may also be present.

Transformations: this formation has been widely cleared for the cropping of wheat and the grazing of sheep. Sown pastures include medics and lucerne.

Shrubby open scrub −3: due to the extreme environment these snow gums exhibit a low mallee-like shape; the ground cover is composed of prostrate heaths. (Charlottes Pass, Snowy Mountains, NSW)

Acacia–Casuarina *open scrub: occupying a rocky hilltop; the she-oaks present are unidentified; the shrub on the right is a wattle; these plants are about 2.5 m tall. (Mt Burgess, Eastern Goldfields, WA)*

HUMMOCK GRASS OPEN SCRUBS — mallee-3

Location: at the driest margins of some southern open scrub formations.

Habitat: as for Shrubby open scrubs-1, but on deep sandy soils or hard rocky soils.

Upper stratum: the red mallee is normally present. Dominants are generally of low stature. (See also Chapter 10, Hummock grass tall shrublands.)

Substrata: the ground layer exhibits species of spinifex. For further information see Chapter 14, *Trioda* and *Plectrachne* open hummock grasslands.

Transformations: generally unchanged, though some areas may be extensively grazed by sheep.

Other Types (excluding Heaths)

ACACIA AND *CASUARINA* OPEN SCRUBS — broombush thickets

Location: within the southern temperate sub-humid/semi-arid regions of WA.

Habitat: Landforms: widespread on sandplains; minor areas on rocky hills and ranges. Soils: sandy types, lithosols, laterites. Altitude: up to 600 m. Temperatures: hot summers and mild winters. Precipitation: 250 to 500 mm with a definite winter maximum.

Upper stratum: dominated by various species of wattles (*Acacia* spp) and/or she-oaks (*Casuarina* spp) with the she-oaks dominating in the drier regions. Typical wattles are *Acacia resinomarginea* and *A. neurophylla*. Typical she-oaks include *Casuarina acutivalvis, C. corniculata* and *C. campestris*. Density of the dominants varies from a closed formation (*Acacia* and *Casuarina* closed scrub) to open formations (*Acacia* and *Casuarina*

tall shrublands and tall open shrublands). As this formation is subjected to frequent fires the heights of the dominants depend on the period since the last fire as the plants regenerate from seed. Shortly after fire the dominants will be less than 2 m thus forming a low scrub but will reach 3 to 5 m if left unburned. (See also Chapter 10, Mixed tall shrublands-3.)

Substrata: virtually absent in the closed formations. Low shrubs such as banksias, hakeas and *Isopogons* with tussock grasses are found in the more open formations.

Transformations: subjected to fire which destroys the formation. In the more humid areas many formations have been cleared for wheat cropping and the intensive grazing of sheep.

ACACIA HUMMOCK GRASS OPEN SCRUBS

Location: south-west of the Pindan country of WA (south of the Broome district).

Habitat: Landforms: low undulating country. Soils: earthy sands, etc. Altitude: below 100 m. Temperatures: summers are very hot to extremely hot, winters are very warm to hot. Precipitation: ranges from 350 to 550 mm with a definite summer maximum.

Acacia-Casuarina *open scrub: often occurs in shallow valley bottoms thus receiving the benefit of runoff; the dominant wattles are unidentified; there are a few low shrubs and grasses in the more exposed sections of the understorey. (east of Norseman, Eastern Goldfields, WA)*

Upper stratum: dominated by species of *Acacia*, especially the Pindan wattle. Dominants are usually over 2 m high.

Substrata: the ground layer is represented by hummock grasses such as spinifex. (For further information see Chapter 14, *Trioda* and *Plectrachne* open hummock grasslands.)

Transformations: subjected to extensive grazing by beef cattle. It is possible that the dominant shrub layer has increased in density due to this grazing.

MELALEUCA (CLOSED AND) OPEN SCRUBS — broom plains

Location: principally in the subhumid/semi-arid country of northern NSW, southern Qld, SA and WA.

Habitat: Landforms: slightly undulating country. Soils: those with impeded drainage, clayey soils. Altitude: up to 300 m. Temperatures: hot summers, cool to mild winters. Precipitation: around 600 mm with a slight summer maximum in the north.

Upper stratum: dominated by the *Melaleuca* species broom. Other tall species (*Acacia*, etc.) also present. In places it may be so dense that it forms a closed scrub. Broom (or broombush) commonly produces distinctive formations or alliances with mallee, i.e. mallee-broombush (see Shrubby open scrubs-2).

Substrata: quite dense, composed of grasses and forbs.

Transformations: some areas are harvested for brush-fencing. Other areas previously grazed or cleared for crops or pastures.

BANKSIA OPEN SCRUBS — scrub heaths

Location: temperate semi-arid coastal regions of WA (south of Freycinet Estuary).

Habitat: Landforms: coastal lowlands. Soils: red and red-brown soils. Altitude: up to 150 m. Temperatures: summers are very hot, winters are warm. Precipitation: around 250 mm with a slight winter maximum.

Upper stratum: dominated by *Banksia ashbyi* which grows to a height of 6 m. Co-dominants include *Grevillea gordoniana* and near the coast *Hakea stenophylla* and dune wattle. In some places this formation grades into a *Banksia* shrubland.

Substrata: the understorey is composed of numerous shrubs and heaths including the fringe-myrtle *Calytrix brevifolia* and *Micromyrtus imbricata*.

Transformations: most areas are undisturbed.

CASUARINA LOW OPEN SCRUBS

See *Acacia* and *Casuarina* open scrubs.

ATRIPLEX, CHENOPODIUM AND *MAIREANA* LOW OPEN SCRUBS

See Chapter 10, *Atriplex, Chenopodium* and *Maireana* low shrublands.

NITRARIA LOW OPEN SCRUBS

See Chapter 10, *Nitraria* low shrublands.

SAMPHIRE LOW OPEN SCRUBS

See Chapter 10, Samphire low shrublands.

OTHER LOW OPEN SCRUBS

Other low open scrubs are found in different locations, particularly along the coast where plants may be subjected to wind pruning-salt spray. For further information see Chapter 16, Coastal cliff formations and Coastal dune formations.

Note that it is not always desirable to refer to all short stature scrub plants as heaths as not all these plants exhibit heath-like features.

Heath Types

TROPICAL AND SUBTROPICAL WET AND DRY OPEN HEATHS — wet desert, wallum, etc.

Location: along parts of the tropical and temperate humid coasts of eastern Australia north of Coffs Harbour, North Coast region, NSW; including Cape York Peninsula, Qld.

Habitat: Landforms: undulating lowlands, coastal headlands; hilly country in north Qld. Soils: various sandy and gleyed soils. Altitude: generally below 200 m; 300 to 600 m in Cape York Peninsula. Temperatures: summers are hot and humid, winters are warm in the south and very warm in the north. Precipitation: generally over 800 mm with a pronounced summer maximum; 1500 to 1700 mm in Cape York Peninsula.

Upper stratum: dominated by a complexity of heath types represented by species of *Banksia*, *Grevillea*, *Leptospermum*, *Acacia*, *Kunzea* and *Zanthorrhoea*, etc. Dominant heights are normally below 2 m. In many places these heaths merge into tree heaths and heathy open forests dominated by scribbly gums, bloodwoods, stringybarks, swamp mahoganies, swamp oaks, etc. In some areas these heaths may grade into closed heaths or heathlands. In Cape York Peninsula the 'wet' deserts are represented by *Sinoga lysicephata* which forms open heaths 0.5 to 1.5 m high. Various other herbs and grasses are present. For further information on wet deserts see Chapter 8, Closed heaths.

Substrata: often absent. In some places a few varieties of sedges and perennial tussock grasses may be found. Grasses are more prominent in wet heaths.

Transformations: many areas are virtually unaltered. Close to centres of population considerable areas have been cleared and sown with exotic legumes and grasses. Species sown include Rhodes grass, paspalum, Kenya clover, etc. Pastures are generally intensively grazed by beef cattle.

WET TEMPERATE WET AND DRY OPEN HEATHS

Location: along parts of the temperate humid coasts of southern Vic., northern and north-western Tas. (including Bass Strait islands) and south-western WA; there are also discontinuous minor areas along the NSW coast and on the adjacent sandstone tablelands.

Habitat: Landforms: undulating coastal lowlands, dissected sandstone tablelands, coastal headlands. Soil: various sandy and gleyed soils; in sandstone country there is often a clay subsoil close to the surface. Altitude: generally below 200 m; may be higher in sandstone country. Temperatures: summers are mild in the south to very warm in the north, winters are generally very cool to mild. Precipitation: above 700 mm with winter maximums in the south; otherwise evenly distributed.

Upper stratum: dominated by shrubs and heaths less than 2 m high. Dominants include swamp paperbarks, drooping she-oaks, tea-trees and dwarf honeysuckle or silver banksia. Grass trees are common. In many places the heaths grade into tree heaths.

Substrata: commonly exhibits a dense heath layer up to 1 m tall. Species include examples of the *Epacris, Sprengelia* and *Leucopogon* genera as well as varieties of woody legumes. In the wet heaths some grasses may be present.

Transformations: some areas remain unaltered. In other places the heaths are lightly grazed, primarily by beef cattle, in areas where grasses are present. Often these areas are fired to promote improved grazing conditions. Other areas have been

Wet temperate wet open heath: these heaths are located where ground water comes close to the surface due to an impermeable layer of rock just blow the surface; they are normally boggy; species here include a wide variety of stunted shrubs, grasses, sedges, etc. (nr Timboolina Hill, Southern Tablelands, NSW)

cleared and sown with exotic grasses and legumes such as perennial rye grass and white clover. Many heaths of the east coast have been cleared for urban development.

DRY TEMPERATE WET AND DRY OPEN HEATHS

Location: within parts of the subhumid country of Vic.; subhumid areas of SA, especially the Upper South-East, Lower South-East and Murray regions, and Kangaroo Island; along the subhumid coasts of southern and south-western WA, and the Stirling Ranges, WA.

Habitat: Landforms: undulating coastal lowlands and sandplains, coastal headlands and some inland mountainous areas. Soils: sandy soils in the east; infertile lateritic (sandy) soil in WA. Altitude: generally below 250 m; up to 1000 m in the Stirling Ranges and the Grampians. Temperatures: summers are very warm to hot, winters are cool to mild. Precipitation: ranges from 400 to 800 mm with a definite winter maximum.

Upper stratum: dominated by low shrubs and heaths about 1 m high. In the east dominant species include the prickly tea-tree, silver banksia, desert banksia, tea-tree and fringe-myrtle. In WA the following genera are represented: *Acacia, Melaleuca, Hakea, Banksia, Grevillea* among many others. Grass trees are common. In some areas these heaths grade into tree heaths, heathlands, mallee heaths and open forests. Dry temperate open heaths

Dry temperate dry open heath: these occur in moderately dry areas on deep sands whose nutrient status is low; the heaths are short and wiry although some species may rise to dominance, in this case the grass trees. (nr Jurien, Coastal Plain, WA)

can be further subdivided into wet heaths, wet heaths on saline soils, and sand heaths. In SA wet heaths are found on seasonally waterlogged soils and exhibit grass trees, needle bush, banksia and varieties of *Casuarina*. Wet heaths on saline soils are dominated by slender honey-myrtle in alliance with *Hakea rugosa*. Sand heaths, found on deep sandy soils, exhibit those species characteristic of wet heaths or a she-oak/tea-tree alliance.

Substrata: often exhibits a dense layer of shrubs up to 50 cm tall. Grasses are rare or absent.

Transformations: many areas, particularly in WA, are virtually unaltered although there is considerable pressure to open these lands for grazing. Other areas have been cleared and sown with exotic grasses and legumes for the moderately intensive grazing of beef cattle and sheep.

ALPINE AND SUBALPINE OPEN HEATHS

Location: limited to upland regions of NSW, Vic., ACT and Tas.; especially those areas which carry snow on the ground for at least one month of the year.

Habitat: Landforms: mountain-tops, upland plateaux, high valleys, 'high plains' and adjacent slopes. Soils: lithosols, alpine humus soils, etc. Altitude: generally above 1500 m in NSW, 1400 m in Vic. and 900 m in Tas.; lower altitudes on exposed summits. Temperatures: summers are cool, winters are very cold to cold. Precipitation: ranges from 750 mm to over 2500 mm.

Upper stratum: dominated by a variety of shrubs, generally of low height. In damp localities such as those adjacent to bogs the following genera are represented: *Epacris* and *Kunzea*. In rocky environments, particularly Tas., numerous genera are present, e.g. *Oxylobium, Podocarpus, Acacia, Hovea, Kunzea, Baeckia, Callistemon* and so on. One plant unique to Tasmanian wet alpine environments is the cushion plant. This plant is often accompanied by smaller plants of various types including the coniferous *Dismelma* and *Microstrobus* shrubs and the prickly richea. In some places this formation may grade into an alpine heathland.

Wet temperate dry open heath: these present a bewildering array of plant species, the types present depending on the period since the last fire; the ground is generally dry, the heaths short and wiry; note the eucalypt sapling on the left. (Barren Grounds, Southern Tablelands, NSW)

Alpine open heath: occupying a north-facing rocky hillslope; many species are represented, all of them short in stature; a dwarf open heathland can be seen top right beneath the snow patch. (nr Blue Lake, Snowy Mountains, NSW)

Montane open heath: dominated by a stunted form of she-oak which is in flower; this heath occurs on a shallow soil at about 800 m in altitude; a few eucalypts occur as emergents. (nr Gundillion, Southern Tablelands, NSW)

Bog heath: dominated by sphagnum moss (not clearly visible) and Carex (?) sedges; these formations are located in very boggy valley bottoms, often at high altitudes. (Polblue Swamp, Northern Tablelands, NSW)

Substrata: due to the density of growth and the low profile of these heaths the understorey is usually absent. A variety of grasses, including snowgrass may be present in this formation, though not as an understorey.

Transformations: most heath areas are unsuitable for grazing though they are prone to disturbance by firing, and trampling by cattle in those areas where grazing is permitted.

BOG HEATHS

See Chapter 15, *Spaghnum* mosslands.

SEDGE-LIKE HEATHS

Location: isolated areas within humid and sub-humid environments.

Habitat: Landforms: in rocky environments subjected to water seepage (along some cliff-tops, bases of cliffs, etc.); adjacent to small streams, bogs, etc. Other features: vary.

Stratum: dominated by various small heaths with a mixture of sedges, rushes, grasses and other herbs. Some typical species include tussock sedges, sundews, peabushes, varieties of *Grevillea* and *Xyris ustulata*. Formations are of restricted size.

Transformations: many areas remain unaltered. Other areas may be affected by alterations to surrounding formations.

MONTANE OPEN HEATHS

Location: on the slopes of the taller mountain ranges and tablelands of NSW, Vic., Tas. and the ACT.

Habitat: Landforms: mountain and tableland slopes, often adjacent to subalpine areas. Soils: lithosols; poorly drained soils, etc. Altitude: generally between 1000 and 1500 m on the mainland; 600 and 900 m in Tas. Temperatures: summers are mild to very warm, winters are very cold to cool. Precipitation: up to 2000 mm with a winter-spring maximum in the south.

Upper stratum: dominated by a variety of species. On the mainland taller shrubs include the dwarf she-oak as well as species of *Banksia, Acacia, Grevillea, Hakea* and *Persoonia*. Many species are similar to those of subalpine heaths. Interspersed with the heaths may be areas of tussock grasslands. In Tasmania extensive montane heaths are found. Taller shrubs include the *Callistemon viridiflorus*, Tasmanian laurel and wiry bauera. Tasmanian montane heaths are often interspersed with button grass and wiry rush sedgelands (see Chapter 13, *Gymnoschoenus* tussocky sedgelands and *Restio* herblands).

Substrata: characterised by numerous species including some subalpine forbs. Species include willow herbs, eyebrights, triggerplants, pea-flowers and a variety of grasses and cypresses.

Transformations: many areas are unaltered and the formations are relatively intact.

SPINIFEX HEATHS

Location: south-western semi-arid temperate regions of WA.

Habitat: Landforms: sandplains, generally adjacent to saltlakes. Soils: earthy sands. Altitude: 400 to 500 m. Temperatures: summers are very hot, winters are mild. Precipitation: below 300 mm with a winter maximum.

Stratum: dominated by a variety of 'heathy' plants mixed with spinifex.

Transformations: generally unaltered.

SHRUBLANDS

Introduction

Shrublands are formations whose upper stratum is dominated by many-stemmed plants called shrubs. There are two varieties of shrublands; tall shrublands which exhibit shrubs over 2 m tall and low shrublands whose dominants are less than 2 m tall. Shrublands are widespread over much of inland Australia particularly within the semi-arid and some arid regions.

Shrublands are found on a variety of soils. Soil types, combined with the timing and quantity of precipitation determine to some extent the type and genus of the dominant plants. Substrata species are also determined by these features. In all cases the condition and presence of particular plants and formations is greatly dependent on the intensity and severity of stock grazing.

Most of Australia's shrublands are dominated by various *Acacia* species, the most common and widespread being mulga. Mulga is found in areas receiving less than 300 mm rainfall throughout the year. It occurs on a variety of soils and in a variety of alliances. Generally the soils have a hardpan beneath the surface. The root systems of mulga are composed of two 'layers'. One layer lies just below the surface and collects light falls of rain. The other layer is near the hardpan where heavier rainwater, after soaking through the sandy or loamy upper surface, accumulates. Here the low root branches collect moisture and nutrients long after the upper levels have dried up.

The regeneration of mulga appears as 'steppe'-sized plants within the understorey of the formation rather than as a gradation of different sizes. This is due to regeneration occurring in bursts, each burst representing a period when conditions were just right for seedlings to survive. For this to happen there needs to be late summer rains for flowers to set any quantity of seeds and for follow-up rains the following spring otherwise the seedlings will die during the hot summer. On average these rains coincide once every nine years. Hence the stepped appearance of regenerating plants.

Consequently mulga shrublands are located in those areas which receive both summer and winter-spring rains although neither may occur in any one year.

The understorey of mulga and other *Acacia* shrublands varies from place to place. In the northern regions the growth may be quite dense (almost an open scrub) with the plants displaying many whipsticks. The density of growth may exclude the development of shrubs. In other places where the dominants are spaced more widely there may be quite a density of shrubby growth. The ground cover is often grassy although where grazing has occurred the grass layer will probably be sparse or replaced by short-lived ephemerals which are very colourful after rain.

In the drier mulga country mulga occupies irregular lines which follow the contours of the land. This Wanderrie country, as it is known in Western Australia, is explained more fully under the heading: Southern and central *Acacia* grassy tall shrublands, in this chapter.

The tall shrublands, because they occupy the semi-arid and arid regions, have to endure low and erratic rainfall, extended droughts, high summer temperatures and very high evaporation rates. To make the best use of the limited precipitation the shape of the mulga plant is such that half the rain falling on the crown is collected and channelled down the branches and stem. Also the leaves of many desert plants are such that the tiny holes in their surface close completely thus preventing moisture loss through transpiration. Further to this some plants, during extended droughts, will remain dormant so totally ceasing the use of water.

Other shrubland dominants include mallee eucalypts (see the introduction to Chapter 9 Open Scrubs and Heaths), *Banksias* and various members of the CHENOPODACEAE family. These latter plants are the principal members of the low shrublands, commonly called the shrub steppes. The *Acacia* and *Eucalyptus* shrublands and open shrublands provide habitats for 133 species of birds, with 12 virtually confined to the habitat, and 29 species of mammals.

The low shrublands are located throughout the southern semi-arid and arid regions of Australia. Many species, but not all, grow in salty soils. Those that do have mechanisms for eliminating salts or at least maintaining a correct balance of the different salts within the plants. These low shrublands are subjected to the same environmental stresses and conditions as indicated for the tall shrublands.

Many of the low shrublands are grazed by stock and in some places this grazing has been severe on the plant communities. Overgrazing leads to a deterioration of the habitat. Not only do the compact shrubs with their densely packed branches reduce wind erosion but they also stop less palatable plants such as burrs, etc., from taking over. Around each plant is a small hummock of soil while between the plants are small bare areas. These areas often support a variety of ephemeral plants. The shrub steppes are occupied by 25 bird species (with one restricted to the area) and 12 species of mammals.

Shrublands may be subjected to fire given sufficient fuel. Widespread fires are more likely in areas that have experienced above average rainfall and where grasses have reached their maximum development. In the eucalypt (mallee) shrublands the dominants are able to regenerate from underground root stocks. *Acacia* shrublands, particularly mulga, are able to regenerate from hard long-lived seeds providing a fire is followed by good rains. Occasionally regeneration results in mulga growing so densely that understorey grasses are shaded out.

The tall shrublands appear almost park-like after good seasons with the tall shrubs interspersed by areas of grasses, ephemeral flowers or low shrubs. Nonetheless they lack the dense, pendulous foliage of woodland trees. During dry times these shrublands, especially in grazing areas, look barren with the nearly bare red soil separating the dormant, dead-looking, shrubs. The low shrublands present vast horizons for there is rarely a tree or shrub to break the horizon. The tall shrublands and open shrublands (see Chapter 11) once accounted for some 10 to 25 per cent of the land area, depending whose figures one takes into consideration. Together they are composed of 80 major alliances.

The low shrublands, and this does not include coastal salt marshes which are also composed of similar chenopod shrubs, once covered 6 per cent of the land area and are composed of some 58 alliances.

Shrubby tall shrubland: the foreground exhibits broombush amongst other shrubs; the upperstorey shrubs visible in the background are yellow mallee some 3 m high. (Ninety Mile Desert, Upper South-East, SA)

Eucalyptus Types

SHRUBBY TALL SHRUBLANDS — (semi-) arid mallee

Location: throughout the temperate subhumid/ semi-arid regions of southern Australia.

Habitat: Landforms: low, slightly undulating country; southern sand-dune country. Soils: solonised brown soils, etc. Altitude: generally below 300 m. Temperatures: summers are hot, winters are cool to mild. Precipitation: generally below 300 mm with a winter maximum.

Upper stratum: dominated by red mallee, ridge-fruited mallee and gilja, etc., in the eastern regions, often in alliance with sugarwood (*Myoporum* sp.), inland rosewood (*Heterodendrum* sp.) and cypress pines (*Callitris* spp). In WA some other mallee species are present, such as the white mallee, yellow mallee and Tammin mallee. Typical dominant heights are between 4 and 9 m.

Shrubby tall shrubland: dominated by bull mallee versions of yorrell and red mallee some 6 to 7 m high; the understorey is blue bush. (nr Yalata, Nullarbor Plain, SA)

Substrata: In wetter areas the understorey exhibits a variety of shrubs including the desert cassia and black bluebush. In drier areas mallee saltbush and bladder saltbush are common. Varieties of wattle may also be present.

Transformations: some areas may be unaltered, particularly in WA. Other areas are subjected to extensive grazing by sheep while a few fringe areas have been cleared for cereal cropping or sown with exotic pastures.

GRASSY TALL SHRUBLANDS

See Chapter 9, Grassy open scrubs; a shrubland version of this formation normally found in drier locations.

HUMMOCK GRASS TALL SHRUBLANDS — arid mallee -1

Location: in parts of the tropical semi-arid and arid inland centred near the WA/SA/NT borders and within the southern regions of the NT and adjacent regions in QLD; including the Channel Country.
Habitat: Landforms: sandplains, sand-dunes; lower slopes of jump-ups or flat-top hills. Soils: siliceous sands, etc. Altitude: around 500 m. Temperatures: very hot summers, warm winters. Precipitation: below 250 mm.
Upper stratum: dominants include the blue mallee and the Sturt Creek mallee each of which reaches a height of 2 to 4 m. In jump-up country Normanton box is found on the lower slopes.
Substrata: virtually limited to spinifex; some other small shrubs (including *Acacias*) may be present. For further information see Chapter 14, *Trioda* and *Plectrachne* open hummock grasslands. In the Normanton box country spinifex is generally found higher up the slope.
Transformations: most areas unused or extensively grazed by beef cattle.

EUCALYPTUS AND ACACIA MIXED TALL SHRUBLANDS

Location: within the arid regions of SA and WA (Gibson and Great Victoria Deserts).
Habitat: Landforms: interdunal corridors of sand-dune country. Soils: sandy. Altitude: up to 600 m or so. Temperatures: summers are very hot, winters are mild to warm. Precipitation: down to 150 mm.
Upper stratum: dominated by a mixture of *Eucalyptus* and *Acacia* species. These include the Kingsmill mallee and blue mallee as well as *A. helmsiana*, *A. pachyacra*, *A. grasbyi* and sandhill mulga. Other tall plants include various *Hakeas*, *Grevilleas* and emu bushes. Mulga is rare.
Substrata: represented by hummock grasses, mainly hard spinifex. The spinifex, *Plectrachne*

schinzi, occurs on deeper sands. (For further information see Chapter 14, *Trioda* and *Plectrachne* open hummock grasslands.)
Transformations: formations are virtually unaltered.

Acacia Types

ACACIA TALL SHRUBBY TALL SHRUBLANDS — mulga shrublands-1

Location: widespread in the temperate semi-arid and arid regions of Australia.
Habitat: Landforms: slightly undulating and dissected shield plains, some rocky rises. Soils: red and brown hardpan soils, etc. Altitude: up to 500 m. Temperatures: summers are hot to very hot, winters are mild to warm. Precipitation: below 200 mm.
Upper stratum: dominated by mulga up to 5 m tall. Other *Acacias* may also be present including bastard mulga and turpentine mulga. Occasionally eucalypt emergents may be present, typically bimble box in the higher rainfall eastern areas.
Substrata: this formation exhibits a well-developed understorey of shrubs which includes emu bushes, hopbushes, and *Cassias*. Emu bushes may grown up to 3 m high.
Transformations: many areas are subjected to extensive grazing by sheep and beef cattle which has, in some instances, drastically altered the formation.

ACACIA LOW SHRUBBY TALL SHRUBLANDS — mulga shrublands-2

Location: in the temperate semi-arid and arid regions; generally adjacent to the *Atriplex, Chenopodium* and *Maireana* low shrublands.
Habitat: Landforms: undulating to flat country. Soils: various; solonised brown soils. Altitude: generally below 400 m. Temperatures: hot summers, mild to warm winters. Precipitation: generally below 250 mm.
Upper stratum: dominated by mulga, horse mulga and nealie up to 5 m high. In some places this formation may grade into an open shrubland. Nealie forms pure stands in the Lower Darling region of NSW.
Substrata: characterised by low shrubs including varieties of saltbush and bluebush, primarily black bluebush. In nealie areas some *Grevilleas* may be present.
Transformations: subjected to extensive grazing by sheep and beef cattle. Some areas exhibit changes

to the original formation and areas of bare ground as a result of overgrazing.

ACACIA HEATHY TALL SHRUBLANDS

Location: restricted areas on the margins of temperate semi-arid regions of south-western WA.
Habitat: Landforms: undulating plains. Soils: various. Altitude: around 400 m. Temperatures: summers are hot, winters are mild to warm. Precipitation: 200 to 300 mm with a winter maximum.
Upper stratum: dominated by the *Acacia resino-marginea* which occurs at the margins of other *Acacia* shrublands.
Substrata: composed of low heath-like shrubs.
Transformations: not known.

NORTHERN *ACACIA* GRASSY TALL SHRUBLANDS

Location: throughout the tropical arid regions of north-west Qld and eastern NT.
Habitat: Landforms: undulating plains, downs. Soils: red earths, clayey soils. Altitude: 150 to 500 m approx. Temperatures: summers are hot to very hot, winters are warm. Precipitation: 200 to 250 mm with a summer maximum.
Upper stratum: dominated by Georgina gidgee. In many places this formation grades into tall open shrubland.
Substrata: composed of Mitchell grass species on the downs. In better drained areas there may be a sparse shrub layer composed of *Cassias* and emu bushes. For further information see Chapter 13, *Astrebla* tussock grasslands.
Transformations: many areas are unaltered. Other areas are subjected to extensive grazing by beef cattle.

SOUTHERN AND CENTRAL *ACACIA* GRASSY TALL SHRUBLANDS — mulga shrublands-3A

Location: widespread throughout the semi-arid and arid regions of temperate Australia.
Habitat: Landforms: generally slightly undulating lowlands and plains; also some interdunal areas of the southern deserts. Soils: red earths, red earth sands, etc. Altitude: up to 500 m or so. Temperatures: hot to very hot summers, mild to warm winters. Precipitation: from below 150 to 400 mm.
Upper stratum: dominated by mulga throughout most regions, replaced by horse mulga, occasionally in alliance with sandhill mulga, in the south and

Southern and central Acacia *grassy tall shrubland on a rocky hillside: mulga is the dominant shrub but in this locality its form is stunted and gnarled; the understorey grasses are sparse and a few ephemeral herbs can be seen. (Dolo Range, Far West, NSW)*

west. Other *Acacia* types include turpentine mulga and bastard mulga. Mulga grows in dense stands in some areas, each stand being separated by bare patches. Stands are aligned to the contours of the land in such a way that rain falling on the bare patches is directed towards the stands. In WA areas exhibiting these mulga stands are often referred to as Wanderrie country.
Substrata: the type of understorey depends on the soil to a great extent. Generally there is a grassy understorey which is widely distributed. Typical species include the love grasses and/or various ephemeral grasses and forbs. The ephemeral grasses fluctuate with seasonal conditions. Consequently during dry times the grassy substratum may be absent. On rocky ground this formation may exhibit a variety of shrubs, typically species of *Acacia*, *Cassia*, hopbushes and emu bushes.
Transformations: many areas are virtually unaltered. In less arid regions this formation is subjected to extensive grazing by beef cattle and sheep; in some places grazing has destroyed the formation and the ground is bare and unproductive.

ACACIA HUMMOCK GRASS TALL SHRUBLANDS — mulga shrublands-3B

Location: within the tropical semi-arid regions of WA, i.e. Hamersley Ranges; minor areas elsewhere.
Habitat: Landforms: upland valley plains. Soils: alluvial, etc. Altitude: 250 to 750 m approx. Temperature: very hot summers, very warm winters. Precipitation: up to 300 mm with a summer maximum.
Upper stratum: dominated by various *Acacias* principally mulga. Other species include *A. pruino-carpa* and snakewood.

Substrata: represented by spinifex, typically *Triodia basedowii*. In some places emu bushes and *Cassias* may be present.

Transformations: some areas have been subjected to grazing by beef cattle and sheep.

ACACIA AND *CASUARINA* TALL SHRUBLANDS

See Chapter 9, *Acacia* and *Casuarina* open scrubs.

Southern and central Acacia *grassy tall shrubland: understorey exhibiting a wealth of ephemeral everlastings, etc., of such density that there are virtually no grasses. (nr Enngonia, Upper Darling, NSW)*

Other Tall Shrubland Types

BANKSIA TALL SHRUBLANDS — scrub heaths

See Chapter 9, *Banksia* open scrubs.

EREMOPHILA TALL SHRUBLANDS — emu bush shrublands

Location: within the eastern arid areas of Australia; minor areas elsewhere.

Habitat: Landforms: interdunal corridors, footslopes of sand-dunes. Soils: sandy. Altitude: generally below 400 m. Temperatures: summers are hot to very hot, winters mild to warm. Precipitation: generally below 250 mm.

Acacia *hummock grass tall shrubland: dominated by mulga over 4 m tall with a ground cover of hummock grasses in seed. (nr Hamersley Ranges, Pilbara, WA)*

Upper stratum: dominated by a variety of emu bushes generally between 2 and 4 m high. In some places other species may be present though not necessarily co-dominant; these include mulga, needlewood, whitewood and beefwood. Formation commonly grades into an *Eremophila* tall open shrubland.

Substrata: the ground is often bare near the bushes due to the density of the branches. Between the shrubs there may be some ephemeral grasses and herbs.

Transformations: some areas are extensively grazed by beef cattle; most areas probably affected by rabbits to some degree.

MIXED TALL SHRUBLANDS-1

Location: restricted areas within the semi-arid and arid regions of temperate Australia; North-West and Pilbara regions of WA.

Habitat: Landforms: on rocky hillsides, at the foot of rocky slopes, within rocky crevasses and along drainage lines. Soils: sandy. Altitude: generally below 500 m. Temperatures: summers are hot to very hot, winters are mild. Precipitation: generally below 350 mm; but these habitats are often sheltered or receive runoff from adjacent slopes.

Upper stratum: dominated by a variety of shrubs from 2 to 4 m high. Genera and species include *Acacias* (various wattles), *Cassias*, *Dodonaeas* (various hopbushes) and *Eremophilas* (emu bushes, tar bush, turpentine bush), etc. The *Cassia* and *Eremophila* species form dense bushy shrubs with branches at ground level. In parts of the North-West and Pilbara regions of WA *Cassia* and *Eremophila* species form a low shrubland on rocky hillslopes. In some places this formation may grade into a mixed tall open shrubland.

Substrata: the ground is often bare near the bushes due to the density of the branches. Perennial tussock grasses and ephemeral grasses may be present. In more rugged country areas of bare rock may be common.

Transformations: some formations may be unaltered due to the rocky nature of the environment but generally these habitats are incorporated into those areas subjected to extensive sheep and cattle grazing.

Acacia *low shrubland: exhibiting* banmung, *which rarely rises above the spinifex understorey; a Sturts desert pea is seen on the right; the white-flowered plant is possibly* Aerva jauanica? *(Burrup Peninsula, Pilbara, WA)*

MIXED TALL SHRUBLANDS-2

Location: scattered throughout the semi-arid northern and semi-arid/subhumid inland of eastern Australia, extending into northern NSW.

Habitat: Landforms: downs, plains and sandplains. Soils: various, often sandy. Altitude: generally below 500 m. Temperatures: summers are hot to very hot, winters are mild to hot. Precipitation: generally 300 to 600 mm with a summer maximum.

Acacia *low shrubland: dominated by* A. pyrifolia *with* A. ancistrocarpa, *visible in middle background, and soft spinifex forming the understorey; the dominants are about 1.5 m tall; the mounds are anthills. (Onslow Coastal Plain, North-West, WA)*

Mixed *tall shrubland −3: dominated by unidentified species of cypress pines, wattles and grevillea (not visible); the understorey here is shrubby with few grasses. (nr Newdegate, Wheatbelt, WA)*

Upper stratum: dominated by a variety of species in various combinations. Typical genera and species include ironwood and witchetty bush (*Acacia* sp.), whitewood (*Atalaya* sp.), corkwood (*Hakea* sp.) and inland rosewood (*Heterodendrum* sp.). In some instances these species appear as small stunted trees. The formation may grade into mixed tall open shrubland.

Substrata: varies. Typical understorey species include spinifex, perennial tussock grasses or low shrubs.

Transformations: some areas are unaltered, other areas are subjected to extensive grazing by beef cattle in the north and sheep grazing in the south.

MIXED TALL SHRUBLANDS-3 — includes Kwongan

Location: within the temperate subhumid/semi-arid regions of southern WA.

Habitat: Landforms: sandplains. Soils: sandy types. Altitude: up to 400 m. Temperatures: hot summers and mild winters. Precipitation: 250 to 500 mm with a definite winter maximum.

Upper stratum: this formation is also referred to as a scrub heath. The characteristic structure of the formation is complex due to the fact that the vegetation is regularly burnt, usually by natural causes. Regeneration is by seedling growth and coppicing which results in a structural change depending on the period since the last fire. The formation is initially open and low but as plants develop it becomes taller and more closed. Eventually an emergent layer develops which may reach over 4 m in height. Different plants will dominate depending on locality, e.g. flame grevillea in the Boorabin district, toothbrush grevillea in the Hyden district, *Casuarina corniculata* in the Karroun district and *Hakea obliqua* in the Badgingarra district. Other upperstorey plants include various *Acacia* and *Casuarina* broombushes or shrubs belonging to the PROTEACEAE family. (See also Chapter 9, *Acacia* and *Casuarina* open scrubs.)

Substrata: represented by a variety of low shrubs, heaths and sedges or there may be a herbaceous ground layer.

Transformations: many areas remain unaltered although in the more humid regions formations have been cleared for the cropping of wheat.

ATRIPLEX TALL SHRUBLANDS

See *Atriplex*, *Chenopodium* and *Maireana* low shrublands.

Atriplex, *Chenopodium* and *Maireana* *low shrubland: almost totally converted to a barley grass grassland by continual grazing; only a few remnant dominants remain. (nr Mossgeil, Riverina, NSW)*

Low Shrubland Types

ACACIA LOW SHRUBLANDS — includes banmung shrublands

Location: tropical monsoonal semi-arid coastal regions (Gulf of Carpentaria, Qld and WA); minor areas in Great Sandy Desert, WA.

Habitat: Landforms: adjacent to mudflats, sandplains, coastal plains. Soils: sandy. Altitude: low. Temperatures: hot to very hot summers, warm to hot winters. Precipitation: 300 to 370 mm with a summer maximum.

Upper stratum: dominated by banmung (*Acacia* sp.) which grows from 0.5 to 1.5 m tall. Occasional emergents on elevated sandpatches include *Acacia bivenosa* and *A. monticola*. Other species include short varieties of *A. pyrifolia* and *A. ancistrocarpa*.

Substrata: the understorey is bare in coastal areas, while the spinifex (*Plectrachne schinzii*) may be found in inland areas.

Transformations: most areas are unaltered.

ATRIPLEX, CHENOPODIUM AND *MAIREANA* LOW SHRUBLANDS — saltbush-bluebush shrub steppes

Location: widespread throughout arid and semi-arid temperate Australia, especially western NSW, northern SA and south-eastern WA.

Habitat: Landforms: mainly flat to slightly undulating plains and downs, lower hillslopes of ranges; also along drainage lines and riverflats. Soils: grey-brown and red calcareous soils, desert loams, etc. Altitude: generally below 300 m. Temperatures: summers are hot to very hot, winters are cool to mild. Precipitation: generally below 250 mm; up to 350 mm in parts of NSW.

Upper stratum: dominated by chenopod shrubs up to 1 m high. Normally these shrubs occur in stands of one species (monospecific stands) or as mixed stands of two or more species. Dominated by the genera *Atriplex* and *Maireana* (previously *Kochia*), species include bladder saltbush, pearl bluebush, black bluebush, southern bluebush, old-by beef cattle and sheep; many areas are severely affected by overgrazing. Formations in the wetter parts of NSW have virtually disappeared, being replaced by the exotic barley grass. Rabbits too have affected parts of this formation.

man saltbush, cotton bush (on clay soils) among others. Old-man saltbush may grow to 3 m in height thus forming *Atriplex* tall shrublands. In many places saltbush and bluebush form the understorey of adjacent low woodlands, low open woodlands, tall shrublands and tall open shrublands dominated by species of *Eucalyptus, Acacia, Casuarina* or *Myoporum*. In addition other chenopod shrubs of the genera *Chenopodium* create low shrubland formations on drainage lines and river-flats. Typical species include nitre goosefoot and golden goosefoot. In the Whyalla-Port Augusta district *Ixiolaena leptolepis* forms an alliance with *Atriplex vesicaria*. Though most of these formations are shrublands there are areas where the protective foliage cover may exceed 30 per cent thus forming a low open scrub, or be less than 10 per cent thus forming a low open shrubland. A few references have mentioned bluebush (*Chenopodium* sp.) growing around the 'dry bogs' of the Barkly Tablelands in the tropical regions of the NT. Among the bluebushes are found reeds. See also *Nitraria* low shrublands.

Substrata: the spaces between shrubs is often bare though forbs and grasses are common after winter and summer rains respectively. *Bassia* species (bindii) are generally present.

Transformations: subjected to extensive grazing

Atriplex, Chenopodium and Maireana *low shrubland: dominated by saltbush which covers an ever so slight depression; the horizon is clothed in eucalypts. (nr Caiguna, Nullarbor Plain, WA)*

NITRARIA LOW SHRUBLANDS — Nitre bush shrublands

Location: restricted locations adjacent to saltbush-bluebush formations, and drainage systems in temperate semi-arid and arid Australia; adjacent to some salt marshes.

Habitat: Landforms: often located between salt-bush-bluebush formations and samphire formations; riverflats and some floodplains, landward side of salt marshes. Soils: grey-brown and red calcareous soils with a moderate salt content; solonchaks with a reduced salt content. Altitude: generally below 300 m. Temperatures: summers are hot to very hot, winters are mild to very warm. Precipitation: generally below 250 mm.

Upper stratum: dominated by nitre bush, often in alliance with black bluebush (*Maireana* sp.), and marsh saltbush (*Atriplex* sp.) in salt marsh environments. May also be found in the understorey of some mallee scrubs (dominated by red mallee/gilja), black box woodlands and, rarely, belah low woodlands. In places this formation may be dense enough to constitute a *Nitraria* low open scrub. In addition nitre goosefoot (*Chenopodium* sp.) may be

Atriplex, Chenopodium and Maireana low shrubland: plain covered in southern blue bush; the ploughed effect is probably due to adjacent roadworks. (Mundi-Mundi Plain, the North-East, SA)

present on the alluvial country associated with the major rivers. See also Samphire low shrublands.

Substrata: in salt marsh environments the understorey may exhibit salt grass, round-leaved pig-face, etc. On alluvial formations love grass, spike rushes and nardoo may be present.

Transformations: may be subjected to extensive grazing by sheep.

SAMPHIRE LOW SHRUBLANDS —
samphire shrublands

Location: within arid and semi-arid regions adjacent to saltlakes; along some low-lying coasts and estuaries. See also Chapter 16, Salt marsh formations.

Habitat: Landforms: adjacent to, and sometimes covering, saltlakes; adjacent to low-lying coasts and estuaries, salt marshes. Soils: solonchaks, etc. Altitude: inland types generally below 500 m. Temperatures: summers are hot to very hot, winters are mild to warm. Precipitation: low in arid areas; may be relatively high elsewhere.

Upper stratum: dominated by low shrubs generally less than 1 m high. Typical genera include *Arthrocnemum, Pachycornia, Frankenia* and *Salicornia*, commonly referred to as samphires and glassworts. These formations may extend into less saline and non-saline situations in alliance with nitre

Samphire low shrubland: species unknown but in flower, covering a coastal mudflat. (Port Germain, Upper North, SA)

Samphire low shrubland: colonising the edge of an inland salt lake; the density of the dominant plants varies according to the distance from the shoreline. (Lake Goongarrie, Eastern Goldfields, WA)

bush, saltbushes, burrs, etc. In addition samphire formations grade into mangrove formations in coastal areas. The formations may also exhibit areas of dense growth (samphire low open scrubs), and light growth (samphire low open shrublands). The *Frankenia* genus is often represented in the latter shrublands, for the species colonise saltpans forming small hummocks as they do so.

Substrata: often exhibits areas of bare salty soil. Some other low shrubs and grasses may be present.

Transformations: many areas are unaltered though some coastal areas may be affected by alterations to adjacent coastal environments. Some inland areas may be extensively grazed by sheep when samphires are associated with saltbushes. Samphire low shrublands are becoming increasingly common around drainage sumps in salt-affected irrigation areas.

Dodonea *low shrubland: occupying a gentle rocky slope of a low inland range; such hopbush shrublands are uncommon. (Fraser Range, Eastern Goldfields, WA)*

Unknown low shrubland: possibly Acacia, *covering a low rocky rise; these shrubs were very low, about 60 cm; they almost formed an open scrub in some places. (south of Kingoonya, Gairdner Plain, SA)*

CASSIA AND EREMOPHILA LOW SHRUBLANDS

See Mixed tall shrublands-1.

OTHER LOW SHRUBLANDS

Other low shrublands exist in restricted environments, e.g. on and adjacent to sea cliffs, etc. In this situation salt tolerant shrubs predominate, generally in association with various grasses and herbs. Often this formation grades into, or could even be referred to as an open heath or heathland. Typical species in southern areas include the coastal saltbush, crimson berry, coastal cyathodes, shrubby glasswort, plus dwarf forms of native plum, silver banksia, manuka tea-tree, etc. On harshly exposed coastal sites the sea box, which grows to 2.5 m, is common in southern Australia.

Heathland Types

DWARF HEATHLANDS AND OPEN HEATHLANDS — feldmark

Location: See Chapter 9, Alpine and subalpine open heaths.

Habitat: See Alpine and subalpine open heaths. Feldmark habitats are limited to exposed rocky wind-blasted ridges at high altitudes and to sheltered areas covered by snow patches for most of the year. These habitats represent the limits of plant growth in alpine situations. Some very small alpine areas are devoid of vegetation due to the harshness of the climate. These areas consist of frost-shattered rocks and are referred to as 'potato fields' in parts of Tasmania. Some feldmark formations are so open they are referred to as dwarf open heathlands.

Stratum: dominated by a variety of low shrubs and herbs including rock heaths, alpine speedwell, Australian edelweiss, snow buttercups. and spreading comprosma.

Transformations: these fragile formations are prone to trampling by hikers.

Dwarf open heathland: this is a windswept feldmark; tiny plants can be seen among the frost-shattered rocks in the foreground; this locality represents the limit of plant growth due to cold. (nr Mt Lee, Snowy Mountains NSW)

Chapter Eleven

OPEN SHRUBLANDS

Introduction
Eucalyptus Types
Shrubby or heathy tall open shrublands — mallee heath-1, Shrubby or heathy
low open shrublands — mallee heath-2, Hummock grass tall open shrublands — arid
mallee-2, *Eucalyptus* and *Acacia* mixed tall open shrublands

Acacia Types
Acacia shrubby tall open shrublands-1 — mulga shrublands-4, *Acacia* shrubby tall open
shrublands-2, *Acacia* low shrubby tall open shrublands, North-eastern *Acacia* shrubby and
grassy tall open shrublands, *Acacia* grassy tall open shrublands — mulga
shrublands-5, etc., Northern *Acacia* grassy tall open shrublands, *Acacia* hummock grass
tall open shrublands, *Acacia* hummock grass low open shrublands, *Acacia* grassy and
hummock grass tall open shrublands, *Acacia* shrubby low open shrublands, *Acacia* and
Casuarina tall open shrublands

Other Types
Mixed tall open shrublands-1, Mixed tall open shrublands-2, *Eremophila* tall open
shrublands, *Atriplex* and *Bassia* very open low shrublands, *Hakea* hummock grass tall open
shrublands, *Atriplex, Chenopodium* and *Maireana* low open shrublands, Samphire low open
shrublands, Dwarf open heathlands, Other low open shrublands

Introduction

The open shrublands may be considered an extension of the shrubland formations. They are
dominated by a sparse covering of shrubs, often so sparse that these formations could readily be
described by the prevailing understorey or ground cover and the shrubs as emergents. Like the
shrublands they are further subdivided into tall (over 2 m) or low (less than 2 m). The existence of low open shrublands is rare and mainly limited to those communities existing on the
edge of saltlakes, salt marshes, etc. or in severely degraded shrub steppes.

Open shrublands are dominated by a variety of genera which include *Eucalyptus, Acacia,
Atriplex* and *Bassia*. Most open shrublands are found in the most arid and harsh regions of
Australia, hence they must withstand low and erratic rainfall, very long droughts (it is after all
the normal condition) and extremely high summer temperatures. These harsh conditions are
further enhanced by thin or rocky soils or soils with a high salt content.

Not all these shrublands are in the arid regions. The Mallee heaths are found in the subhumid regions of southern Australia. This formation is typically a heath (see the introduction
to Chapter 9 Open Scrubs and Heaths) with a scattering of mallee eucalypts. Though
conditions are less severe than in the arid areas soils are such that they are only marginally
capable of supporting a tall shrubby growth.

Due to the variations in figures quoted as regards these shrublands it is difficult to estimate
the area they occupy. A figure for both tall and low open shrublands would possibly be about
15 per cent of the land area and would include about 40 major alliances.

Shrubby tall open shrubland: exhibiting the unusual mallee tallerack, whose whipsticks can be seen rising above a very dense heath understorey; dominants' heights are about 2 m. (north-west of Esperance, Southern Coastal region, WA)

Eucalyptus Types

SHRUBBY OR HEATHY TALL OPEN SHRUBLANDS — mallee heath-1

Location: in restricted subhumid areas of Vic., SA and WA; southern semi-arid coastal regions of SA, WA.

Habitat: Landforms: slightly undulating sandplains, minor dunes. Soils: calcareous sands, podzols, i.e. sandy soils. Altitude: generally below 150 m. Temperatures: summers are very warm to hot, winters are cool to mild. Precipitation: up to 600 mm with a definite winter maximum.

Upper stratum: dominated by a variety of eucalypt species up to 3 m tall. In some places the dominant species are less than 2 m; thus the formation could be described as a shrubby or heathy low open shrubland. Typical species, which exhibit a mallee habit, include the yellow mallee in the eastern States and tallerack (replaced by the ridge-fruited mallee east of Esperance) in WA.

Substrata: many species are represented in the understorey. Typical genera include *Dryandra, Hakea* and *Verticordia* in WA and various heaths, such as *Banksias, Acacias* and *Casuarinas* in the east. Other species include *Melaleucas*, quandongs, etc. In eastern regions this formation represents a transition between mallee-broombush and dry temperate heaths. In the shrubby or heathy low open shrublands saltbush species may also be present.

Transformations: many areas are unaltered; other areas have been cleared and sown with exotic pastures such as subterranean clover.

SHRUBBY OR HEATHY LOW OPEN SHRUBLANDS — mallee heath-2

See Shrubby or heathy tall open shrublands.

Shrubby low open shrubland: dominated by low clumps of red mallee (?) seen at the centre right; the understorey, nearly as high as the dominants, includes heaths and saltbushes; dominants' heights are barely 1 m; these formations occupy slight rises or occur near coastal cliffs. (west of Nullarbor Roadhouse, Nullarbor Plain, SA)

HUMMOCK GRASS TALL OPEN SHRUBLANDS — arid mallee-2

Location: the southern arid areas of WA with extensions into SA; primarily in the northern and western portions of the Great Victoria Desert.

Habitat: Landforms: sandplains and some interdunal areas. Soils: siliceous sands, etc. Altitude: generally below 500 m. Temperatures: summers are very hot, winters are mild to very warm. Precipitation: generally below 200 mm.

Upper stratum: dominated by short mallee eucalypts, typically Kingsmill mallee. See also Chapter 10, *Eucalyptus* and *Acacia* mixed tall shrublands.

Substrata: the understorey is represented by hard spinifex.

Transformations: generally unaltered.

EUCALYPTUS AND *ACACIA* MIXED TALL OPEN SHRUBLANDS

Location: tropical arid areas of NT, e.g. Tanami Desert.

Habitat: Landforms: sandplains and sand-dune country. Soil: siliceous sands, etc. Altitude: generally below 300 m. Temperatures: summers are very hot, winters are very warm. Precipitation: below 300 mm with a definite summer maximum.

Upper stratum: dominated by a sparse, widely scattered shrub layer composed of *Acacia maitlandii*, *A. kempeana*, *A. dictyophleba*, *A. coriacea*, *A. tenuissima* and Murrays wattle; and the eucalypts blue mallee and red-bud mallee.

Substrata: shrubs include *Cassias*, *Grevilleas*, *Hakeas* and emu bushes. The ground layer is re-

Acacia *low shrubby tall open shrubland: exhibiting shrubby forms of western myall and an understorey of saltbush. (Roe Plain, Nullarbor Plain, WA)*

Acacia *grassy tall open shrubland: runs across the centre towards the right in this view; a shrubland is seen on the left; the dominant is mulga although some cypress pines can be seen in the foreground; the area receives runoff from the adjacent grassy hillslopes. (Byguano Range, Far West, NSW)*

presented by soft spinifex in the north and hard spinifex in the south. Other grasses and forbs may be present.

Transformations: virtually unaltered.

Acacia Types

ACACIA SHRUBBY TALL OPEN SHRUBLANDS — mulga shrublands-4

Location: primarily within the eastern arid regions of inland Australia.

Habitat: Landforms: sand-dune country. Soils: siliceous sands. Altitude: 100 to 450 m approx. Temperatures: summers are very hot, winters are warm. Precipitation: less than 250 mm.

Upper stratum: dominated by mulga, generally in alliance with whitewood (*Atalaya* sp.). Other allies include needlewood (*Hakea* sp.), dead finish (*Acacia* sp.) and *Grevillea juncifolia*. In addition the Murrays wattle and the dune wattle grow on the edges of dunes while *Acacia calcicola* grows on low eroded dunes.

Substrata: this includes a scattering of *Cassias* hopbushes and emu bushes. Grasses that may be found include species of kerosene, nine-awn, love and wanderrie grasses.

Transformations: virtually unaltered.

ACACIA SHRUBBY TALL OPEN SHRUBLANDS-2

Location: throughout the arid regions of SA, WA, and some minor areas in Qld; also includes some semi-arid areas in WA.

Habitat: Landforms: undulating plains, sand-dune country, alluvial plains. Soils: red earths, siliceous sands, alluvial soils. Altitude: generally below 500 m. Temperatures: summers are hot to very hot, winters are warm. Precipitation: generally below 250 mm.

Upper stratum: dominated by a variety of *Acacias*. Close to where mulga is present there may be areas dominated by turpentine mulga; in the sand-dune country of SA sandhill mulgas predominate, often in alliance with belah (*Casuarina* sp.) in the south and cypress pine (*Callitris* sp.) in the north. In WA the sandhill mulgas ally with other *Acacias* including Murrays wattle, sandhill wattle, jam tree and *Acacia sclerosperma*. Other tall shrubs include emu bushes, *Grevilleas* and broombush, and the eucalypts Oldfields mallee and Tammin mallee. Within the Ashburton River basin of WA snakewood dominates on alluvial and clayey soils and allies itself with bramble wattle, dead finish and *Acacia sclerosperma* in the south of the region. In some small areas dead finish and bramble wattle may be locally dominant.

Substrata: all these *Acacia* communities have a shrubby understorey. *Cassias* are common in most areas. Other shrubs include bastard mulga, hopbushes, emu bushes, etc. Generally the ground layer exhibits a sparse covering of kerosene, love and nine-awn grasses. In some places there may be an ephemeral ground layer which includes members of the ASTERACEAE family.

Transformations: some areas are subjected to extensive grazing by beef cattle and sheep. Many areas are unaltered.

ACACIA LOW SHRUBBY TALL OPEN SHRUBLANDS

See Chapter 10, *Acacia* low shrubby tall shrublands.

NORTH-EASTERN ACACIA SHRUBBY AND GRASSY TALL OPEN SHRUBLANDS

An arid version of these woodlands and open woodlands dominated by the *Acacias* boree and lancewood but exhibiting a shrubby form. See Chapter 6, North-eastern *Acacia* woodlands and low woodlands.

ACACIA GRASSY TALL OPEN SHRUBLANDS — mulga shrublands-5, etc.

Location: throughout the arid interior.
Habitat: Landforms: plains, downs and lowlands; interdunal areas. Soils: earthy sands, siliceous sands, calcareous soils. Altitude: generally below 500 m.

Temperatures: summers are very hot, winters are mild to very warm. Precipitation: generally below 200 mm.

Upper stratum: dominated by mulga in areas close to mulga low woodlands and tall shrublands; dominated by the gidgee on the clayey interdunal soils of the south-eastern parts of the Simpson Desert. Gidgee may also form tall shrubs and trees as an understorey to woodlands in more favourable areas. The witchetty bush, a shrub which grows to 2 or 3 m, may be found on calcareous soils.

Substrata: represented by a variety of perennial grasses, e.g. love grasses, and annual forbs. Ephemeral forbs may be present after rain.

Transformations: mulga areas may be extensively grazed by beef cattle and sheep.

Acacia *hummock grass tall open shrubland: exhibiting dune wattles; on the dune the understorey is sparse although hummock grasses can be seen on the right. (Amphi Sandhills, Upper Darling, NSW)*

NORTHERN ACACIA GRASSY TALL OPEN SHRUBLANDS

See Chapter 10, Northern *Acacia* grassy tall shrublands.

ACACIA HUMMOCK GRASS TALL OPEN SHRUBLANDS

Location: tropical arid and temperate semi-arid and arid regions of WA and NT.
Habitat: Landforms: sandplains, interdunal areas, undulating plains, low rises. Soils: siliceous sands, earthy sands, etc. Altitude: generally below 600 m. Temperatures: summers are very hot, winters are very warm. Precipitation: 150 to 300 mm with a summer maximum.

Upper stratum: dominated by species of *Acacias*, often very widely spaced. Typical species include mulga at the southern and westernmost fringes and wirewood in the western deserts. Other species include kanji, occasionally in alliance with dead finish and Pindan wattle, on the plains and low rises of the Pilbara region, WA; Pindan wattle, occasionally in alliance with *Acacia monticola*, at the western edge of the Great Sandy Desert and along dune corridors of the Great Victoria Desert. In some other areas *A. coriacea* allies with corkwood (*Hakea* sp.). In some localities corkwood and *Grevillea pyramidalis* may co-dominate with wirewood, etc. For further information on the northern desert areas see *Eucalyptus* and *Acacia* mixed tall open shrublands.

Substrata: represented by hummock grasses, typically soft spinifex in the north and hard spinifex in the south. *Plectrachne schinzii* in also found on deep and coarse soils. In the kanji communities there may be a *Cassia* and *Acacia* shrubby understorey.

Transformations: most of these shrublands are unaltered though small areas that border on better country may be grazed by beef cattle.

ACACIA HUMMOCK GRASS LOW OPEN SHRUBLANDS

Location: within the tropical semi-arid regions of WA, i.e. North-West and Pilbara regions.
Habitat: Landforms: coastal plains, alluvial plains, upland plains. Soils: alkaline red soils. Altitude: up to 400 m. Temperatures: hot to very hot summers, very warm winters. Precipitation: 250 to 300 mm with a summer maximum.
Upper stratum: dominated by low spindly shrubs of *Acacia pyrifolia* less than 2 m tall. Corkwood (*Hakea* sp.) and blister bush (*Grevillea* sp.) may also be present.
Substrata: there is a ground cover of spinifex, typically *Triodia basedowii*.
Transformations: some areas subjected to grazing by beef cattle and sheep.

ACACIA GRASSY AND HUMMOCK GRASS TALL OPEN SHRUBLANDS

Primarily a shrubland version of *Acacia* grassy low open woodlands. Dominant species include Georgina gidgee, mimosa and boree. The understorey may also include hummock grasses. See Chapter 7, *Acacia* grassy low open woodlands and *Acacia* hummock grass low open woodlands.

Acacia *hummock grass low open shrubland: dominated by* A. pyrifolia, *examples of which can be seen on the foreground slope rising slightly above the soft spinifex understorey; dominant's heights are about 1 m; such a formation could also be called a* Trioda *and* Plechtrachne *open hummock grassland with* A. pyrifolia *emergents. (Chichester Range, Pilbara, WA)*

ACACIA SHRUBBY LOW OPEN SHRUBLANDS

Location: within the temperate semi-arid and arid regions of Australia.
Habitat: Landforms: dissected plains, low hills, sand-dunes, etc. Soils: red earths, lithosols, etc. Altitude: generally below 500 m. Temperatures: summers are hot to very hot, winters are mild to warm. Precipitation: below 300 mm.
Upper stratum: dominated by bastard mulga, and, in some instances, turpentine mulga, some 1 to 2 m tall. Both species may co-dominate with mulga. In some bastard mulga formations Queensland peppermint (*Eucalyptus* sp.) may be present.
Substrata: represented by a usually well-developed low shrub layer which includes hopbushes, emu bushes, *Cassias* and *Cathium* species. Generally there is a sparse ground layer composed of kerosene, love and wanderrie grasses, the latter being in bastard mulga formations.
Transformations: some areas may be extensively grazed by sheep and beef cattle.

ACACIA AND CASUARINA TALL OPEN SHRUBLANDS

See Chapter 9, *Acacia* and *Casuarina* open scrubs.

Other Types

MIXED TALL OPEN SHRUBLANDS-1

See Chapter 10, Mixed tall shrublands-1.

MIXED TALL OPEN SHRUBLANDS-2

See Chapter 10, Mixed tall shrublands-2.

EREMOPHILA TALL OPEN SHRUBLANDS — Emu bush open shrublands

See Chapter 10, *Eremophila* tall shrublands.

ATRIPLEX AND *BASSIA* VERY OPEN LOW SHRUBLANDS

Location: within the more arid regions of the Lake Eyre basin, especially in the north-east of SA; also in the arid regions to the west of the Flinders Ranges, SA.

Habitat: Landforms: gibber plains and downs. Soils: those exhibiting gilgai formations (desert tableland soils). Altitude: generally below 200 m. Temperatures: summers are very hot, winters are warm. Precipitation: below 200 mm.

Stratum: dominated by species of *Atriplex*, particularly pop saltbush, bladder saltbush (in moister areas) and silver saltbush (in drier areas). These low shrubs occur in gilgai depressions generally in alliance with *Ixiolaena leptolepis* and the grasses love grass, panic grass and barley Mitchell grass. Although the *Atriplex* species are really dwarf shrubs they have been considered to function as annuals in this environment. Adjacent to the gilgai depressions are the shelf areas. Any rain falling on these shelves quickly runs off into the depressions, hence the relatively prominent vegetation there. The shelves themselves are very arid and only support a sparse growth of samphires (*Arthrocne-*

mum and *Pachycornia* spp) and burrs (*Bassia* spp). Though the ground cover is very sparse ephemeral plants may appear after rain. Along drainage lines mulga and red mulga may be seen.

Transformations: may be subjected to extensive grazing by beef cattle.

HAKEA HUMMOCK GRASS TALL OPEN SHRUBLANDS

See *Acacia* hummock grass tall open shrublands. In some instances *Hakea* tall open shrublands may exhibit a grassy understorey.

ATRIPLEX, CHENOPODIUM AND *MAIREANA* LOW OPEN SHRUBLANDS

See Chapter 10, *Atriplex, Chenopodium* and *Maireana* low shrublands.

Atriplex *and* Maireana *low open shrubland: here a species of blue bush has colonised the upper surface of a lunette (a type of sand-dune). A few ephemerals can be seen. (Cawndilla Lake, Upper Darling, NSW)*

SAMPHIRE LOW OPEN SHRUBLANDS

See Chapter 10, Samphire low shrublands.

DWARF OPEN HEATHLANDS

See Chapter 10, Dwarf heathlands.

OTHER LOW OPEN SHRUBLANDS

These formations, which could include mallee heaths and some *Acacia* open shrublands are of restricted extent and may be located within those formations previously described.

Atriplex *and* Bassia *very open low shrubland occupying stony downs: low open woodlands of red mulga line the drainage channels. (north of Innamincka, Sturts Stony Desert, SA)*

Chapter Twelve

CLOSED HERBLANDS AND GRASSLANDS

Introduction
Grassland Types

Poa and/or *Danthonia* closed tussock grasslands — includes wet tussock grasslands, *Eragrostis* and other closed grasslands — cane grass swamps, *Sporobolus* and other closed grasslands — salt-water meadows, *Dichanthium* and other grasslands — includes blue grass grasslands, *Phragmites* closed grasslands — reed beds, *Chionachne* closed grasslands — coastal cane grass grasslands, *Paspalum* closed grasslands — swamp grasslands, Other closed grasslands — includes *Diplachne* and *Cynodon* closed grasslands

Herbland Types

Seagrass formations — marine meadows, Tall alpine herbfields — alpine meadows, Short alpine herbfields — high moors, Alpine and subalpine bogs, Alpine and subalpine fens, *Oryza* and *Eleocharis* closed herblands — wild rice–water chestnut herblands, *Eleocharis* closed herblands — spike-rush herblands, *Baumea* closed herblands — jointed twig-rush herblands, *Typha* closed herblands — bulrush herblands, *Pseudorophis* closed herblands — spiny mudgrass herblands, *Restio* closed herblands — wiry-rush herblands, Other closed herblands

Other Types

Closed fernlands

Eragrostis and other closed grasslands: this formation is a cane grass swamp, a closed formation but with open patches; a lignum bush lies to the right. (nr Lake Bindegolly, Bulloo, Qld)

Introduction

The closed herblands and grasslands are dominated by non-woody plants or herbs. They are of such density that little or no ground cover can be seen. These herblands are composed of a variety of plants, typically grasses, sedges, rushes and other forbs or a mixture of these. They are found in many areas, especially within the humid, monsoonal, alpine and littoral regions. They occupy the heavy clay soils of floodplains, the treeless alpine and subalpine areas of high mountains, various other soils subjected to seasonal or continual inundation or wetting, still backwaters and lagoons of the major coastal rivers and the swales of some coastal dunes. The formations are generally very small, often only a fraction of a hectare in area, although they may be locally extensive in some places.

In many cases, especially those herblands dominated by grasses, the leaves of the dominant plants intertwine to form a low, dense canopy between 0.25 and 2 m high. Consequently the canopy is often continuous and 'mat-like'. In other closed herblands the dominants stand so close that they form a 'wall' of erect stems, branches, leaves and flowers, etc. As a result the understorey of these formations is sparse or non-existent except where the canopy is relatively sparse or broken.

For information on the approximate areas covered by these formations and the number of alliances see the introduction to Chapter 13 Herblands, Sedgelands and Grasslands.

Poa *and* Danthonia *closed tussock grassland: exhibiting tussocks of some* Poa *species; the other species were unidentified; the tree, being solitary, is considered an emergent; behind lies a bog heath. (nr Polblue Swamp, Northern Tablelands, NSW)*

Grassland Types

POA AND/OR DANTHONIA CLOSED TUSSOCK GRASSLANDS — includes wet tussock grasslands

Location: throughout the humid and subhumid areas of western Vic., also in restricted montane and tableland areas of south-eastern NSW and eastern Vic. as well as exposed situations in southern Tas. **Habitat:** Landforms: slightly undulating basalt plains (western Vic.); exposed headlands and islands (Tas.); tableland and montane valleys elsewhere. Soils: various, especially those derived from basalt or with a significant clay content. Altitude: up to 1200 m or so. Temperatures: summers are mild to very warm, winters are very cold to cool.

Precipitation: generally over 750 mm often with a winter-spring maximum.

Stratum: dominated by species of *Poa* tussock grasses and wallaby grasses (*Danthonia* spp). These grasses are tussocky with interlacing leaf canopies. Smaller herbs are also present. In montane and tableland areas *Poa* grasses form alliances with kangaroo grasses (*Themeda* spp) among others, as well as some sedges, e.g. *Carex* spp, to form what is commonly known as wet tussock grasslands. In southern Tas. and on some offshore islands blue tussock grass (*Poa* sp.) commonly dominates exposed headlands.

Transformations: virtually all of these grasslands have been altered since the introduction of sheep. Where grazing is intensive exotic sown pastures of subterranean clover and perennial rye grass may be found. It's probable that in most localities this formation was originally a *Poa-Themeda-Stipa* alliance.

ERAGROSTIS AND OTHER CLOSED GRASSLANDS — cane grass swamps

Location: on some floodplains and within shallow depressions (stream floodouts) throughout semi-arid and arid Australia.

Habitat: Landforms: floodplains, stream floodouts, shallow depressions. Soils: clay and/or silty soils often with a high soluble salt content. Altitude: generally below 500 m. Temperatures: summers are hot to very hot, winters are mild to warm. Precipitation: varies, generally below 300 mm; areas subjected to occasional inundation.

Stratum: dominated by cane grass (*Eragrostis* sp.), a tall perennial grass that occupies depressions which are subjected to occasional floods. In some localities cane grass grows in an alliance with umbrella cane grass (*Leptochloa* sp.). Within the centre of large depressions a variety of grasses and forbs may occupy any small sandy islands contained therein. Dominants grow up to 3 m high. In many places cane grass formations are surrounded by other distinctive formations dominated by other plants. Some cane grass swamps are surrounded by goosefoot (*Chenopodium* sp.) in an alliance with other *Eragrostis* species, i.e. the love grasses. Yet again other swamps exhibit a distinctive zoning around the central cane grass formation. These zones, which relate to a decreasing salt content within the soil, include a monospecific formation dominated by *Cressa cretica*; a love grass (*Eragrostis* spp) zone which occurs on exposed mud, here the fern species nardoo (*Marsilea* sp.) may be present; and an outer zone dominated by the pop saltbush (*Atriplex* sp.) where nardoo again may be present.

Although these formations are commonly swamps they are dry over 90 per cent of the time.

Transformations: formations may be subjected to grazing, especially after periods of flooding.

SPOROBOLUS AND OTHER CLOSED GRASSLANDS — salt-water meadows

Location: widely distributed in coastal saline areas, especially within tropical regions.

Habitat: Landforms: low coastal plains with salt marshes subjected to occasional flooding by especially high tides, etc. Soils: saline. Altitude: virtually at sea-level. Temperatures: vary. Precipitation: varies.

Stratum: dominated by a variety of rhizomatous and tussocky grasses including the salt-water couch (*Sporobolus* sp.). Also found within the formation are species of rushes (*Juncus* spp) and sedges (*Cyperus* spp) in some areas. Salt grass (*Distichlis* sp.) may be found on adjacent, flood-free higher ground. Other grasslands within this geographical and habitat area include those dominated by *Xerochloa* species. These are found on the landward side of salt-water couch or mangrove formations.

Transformations: some areas are occasionally grazed by beef cattle; other areas adjacent to intensive urbanisation may be degraded.

DICHANTHIUM AND OTHER GRASSLANDS — blue grass grasslands

Location: throughout the monsoonal and tropical semi-arid regions of northern and north-eastern Australia, especially in coastal and subcoastal situations.

Habitat: Landforms: coastal plains, etc. Soils: grey crackling clays, red and yellow earths. Altitude: generally low. Temperatures: very warm to very hot throughout the year; milder in more southern regions during winter. Precipitation: generally over 400 mm, usually over 600 mm, with a definite summer maximum.

Stratum: dominated by blue grass which grows to 1.2 m tall during the wet season. Blue grass often forms alliances with brown-top grasses (*Eulalia* spp), kerosene grasses (*Aristida* spp), panic grasses (*Panicum* spp), Mitchell grasses (*Astrebla* spp) and the *Bothriochloa* spp of blue grasses. Generally the panic grasses are found in the wettest areas. In some places these allied species may form small grasslands in their own right.

Transformations: most areas are extensively grazed by beef cattle. Should grazing be too heavy then the presence of the dominants will decrease.

PHRAGMITES CLOSED GRASSLANDS —
reed beds

Location: widespread throughout NSW, Vic., south-east Qld, southern SA, Tas. and northern tropical Australia.
Habitat: Landforms: edges of streams, lakes, swamps, drains and brackish coastal estuaries (not in salty water). Soils: saturated muds, etc. Altitude: generally below 900 m. Temperatures: vary. Precipitation: varies, plants subjected to flooding, water depth up to 120 cm.
Stratum: dominated by two species of *Phragmites*, the common reed found in temperate Australia and *P. karka* in tropical Australia. Plants grow to 3 m and form either small clumps on the edge of water bodies or extensive reed beds in estuarine waters.
Transformations: many reed beds are still intact although some have been destroyed by stream engineering works, urbanisation, etc.

CHIONACHNE CLOSED GRASSLANDS —
coastal cane grass grasslands

Location: within *Dichanthium* and other grasslands; see appropriate heading.
Habitat: Landforms: shallow depressions, banks of tropical rivers. Other features: see *Dichanthium* and other grasslands.
Stratum: dominated by coastal cane grass which produces dense, reed-like culms during the wet season. Heights reach 3 to 4 m. During the dry season the grasses dry out. Other species include various sedges, spike-rushes and spiny mudgrass.
Transformations: see *Dichanthium* and other grasslands.

PASPALUM CLOSED GRASSLANDS —
swamp grasslands

Location: found mainly throughout monsoonal northern Australia; minor areas in temperate humid regions.
Habitat: Landforms: seasonally flooded floodplains. Soils: alluvial. Altitude: virtually at sea-level. Temperatures: summers are hot to very hot and humid, winters are warm. Precipitation: generally over 1000 mm with a definite summer maximum.
Stratum: dominated by a variety of paspalum grasses, typically water couch in association with numerous other species of grasses and sedges. Although most paspalum is introduced there are 5 Australian species.
Transformations: may be subjected to grazing by livestock.

OTHER CLOSED GRASSLANDS

Within the northern part of the continent in some wet habitats is found beetle grass (*Diplachne* sp.), a perennial tussock grass which grows to 1 m high. It is found along some rivers, around swamps and on coastal muds. It commonly forms alliances with the pale spike-rush (*Eleocharis* sp.).

Couch grass (*Cynodon* sp.) is very common in lawns but may also be found from coastal areas to the interior, especially near watercourses and on riverflats, etc.

Brown-top (*Eulalia* spp), kerosene grass (*Aristida* spp), panic grass (*Panicum* sp.) and the *Bothriochloa* species of blue grass may form small grasslands. For further information see *Dichanthium* and other grasslands.

Tall alpine herbfield; presenting a lush display of alpine vegetation; in the centre is mountain celery, on the right pineapple grass. (nr Rawson Pass, Snowy Mountains, NSW)

Tall alpine herbfield exhibiting a field of daisies. (nr Mt Kosciusko, Snowy Mountains, NSW)

Eleocharis closed herbland: *although only a small clump, these tall spike-rushes will eventually produce a closed formation. (Flat Rock Creek, South Coast, NSW)*

Herbland Types

SEAGRASS FORMATIONS — marine meadows

Location: widely distributed throughout Australian coastal and embayment waters in areas of reduced oceanic activity.

Habitat: Landforms: gulfs, bays, estuaries on sandbars, mudbanks, etc. Other features: formation occurs on silts and muds in oceanic waters up to a depth of 30 m.

Stratum: dominated by a variety of seagrasses; up to 25 species have been described. Zonation of species is distinctive. For instance eel grass (*Zostera* sp.) is commonly exposed at low tide on sheltered sandbars and mudbanks. This plant extends downwards to a depth of 2 to 3 m. The *Pisidonia australis* grows from 30 cm to 12 m below the low-tide level and only at a very low tide will the leaves of the shallowest plants project above the water. Other plants such as the sea nymph (*Amphibolus* sp.) may be colonised by algae. Seagrasses are often washed up on some sandy shores by storms.

Transformations: the changing of intensity and quality of undersea sunlight by increased turbidity, effluents, suspended sediments, etc., will reduce the distribution of seagrasses.

TALL ALPINE HERBFIELDS — alpine meadows

Location: within the alpine areas of south-eastern Australia; restricted alpine areas in Tas.

Habitat: Landforms: generally among, and protected by, rocky outcrops on upland plateaux and hillsides. Soils: alpine humus soils, lithosols, etc. Altitude: generally above 1800 m in NSW,

1600 m in Vic. and 1200 m in Tas. Temperatures: summers are cool, winters are very cold to cold. Precipitation: up to 2500 mm with a winter-spring maximum, continuous snow cover for up to 6 months of the year.

Stratum: on the mainland tall alpine herbfields are dominated by a variety of herbaceous plants up to 60 cm tall. A widespread alliance, particularly on the Kosciusko Plateau, NSW, is the silver snow daisy-snowgrass one. Other typical species include wallaby grass, everlasting daisies, white buttercups, white and purple eyebrights and the prostrate alpine lily. In addition there is a variety of sedges, rushes and alpine ferns. In Tas. the wiry-rush grows with snowgrasses and a variety of other plants including the native gentian, *Carpha alpina* and *Rubus gunnianus* among others.

Transformations: some areas in Vic. are subjected to grazing and trampling by beef cattle during the summer months. Erosion and trampling by hikers is also a localised problem.

Short alpine herbfield: the plants here are very prostrate with only the leaves of grasses rising above the general level; patches of rock can be clearly seen. (nr Blue Lake, Snowy Mountains, NSW)

113

SHORT ALPINE HERBFIELDS — high moors

Location: see Tall alpine herbfields.

Habitat: see Tall alpine herbfields. Short alpine herbfields are less protected and may be covered with snow for up to 8 months of the year.

Stratum: these herbfields are dominated by prostrate, almost carpet-like, plants and are limited to the higher and more exposed peaks and tops. They are commonly fed by melt-water streams and cover gravelly patches of ground. Common plants include a variety of daisies, gentians, several heaths and various mat-forming plants. In Tas. cushion plants of various species are common; on the margins of pools and watercourses a member of the lily family, pineapple grass, forms dense, raised clumps on boggy ground.

Transformations: see Tall alpine herbfields.

ALPINE AND SUBALPINE BOGS

Location: within the alpine and subalpine areas of south-eastern Australia and Tas.

Habitat: Landforms: constantly wet and irregular slopes. Soils: peats. Altitude: generally above 1400 m in NSW, 1200 m in Vic. and 900 m in Tas. Temperatures: summers are cool, winters are very cold to cold. Precipitation: up to 2500 mm; bogs are permanently inundated.

Stratum: this formation is one of the richest alpine habitats. Sphagnum moss is a common feature of bogs; (see also Chapter 15, *Sphagnum* mosslands). In Tas. the fern *Gleichenia dicarpa* may completely dominate a bog. Other species in Tas. bogs include boronias, rocket plants, native dogrose, shrubby pines, swamp heaths and species of *Richea* among many others. Mainland bogs exhibit yellow alpine bottlebrush, tea-tree, ground orchids, buttercups and species of *Epacris* among others. Common to both areas are trigger plants and numerous daisies.

Transformations: see Tall alpine herbfields.

ALPINE AND SUBALPINE FENS

Location: see Alpine and subalpine bogs.

Habitat: Landforms: found on wet level or slightly sloping ground which is subjected to inundation for much of the year; fens are occasionally found adjacent to watercourses. Other features: see Alpine and subalpine bogs.

Stratum: composed of a mixture of sedges, grasses and reeds as well as forbs such as mountain purslane, ground orchids, Australian edelweiss, buttercups, etc. The formation is often difficult to distinguish from surrounding formations.

Transformations: see Tall alpine herbfields.

Alpine fen: composed of various grasses, mosses and other herbs; the soil here is constantly wet. (Bogong High Plains, Victorian Alps, Vic.)

ORYZA AND *ELEOCHARIS* CLOSED HERBLANDS — wild rice–water chestnut herblands

Location: coastal monsoonal regions of NT; minor areas in northern Qld.

Habitat: Landforms: estuarine plains subjected to seasonal inundation. Soils: black earths, etc. Altitude: virtually at sea-level. Temperatures: very warm to very hot throughout the year. Precipitation: generally over 1500 mm with a definite summer maximum.

Stratum: this formation is composed of a variety of tussocky and rhizomatous herbs, the most notable being wild rice (*Oryza* sp.) and the water chestnut (*Eleocharis* sp.). This formation lies under water for up to 4 months.

Transformations: some areas are subjected to light grazing by beef cattle; other areas are browsed and trampled by buffaloes.

ELEOCHARIS CLOSED HERBLANDS — spike-rush herblands

Location: throughout the humid and subhumid regions of northern and eastern Australia (with minor extensions into the semi-arid regions of the Murray-Darling river basin).

Habitat: Landforms: floodplains subjected to seasonal flooding, edges of open bodies of water. Soils: various. Altitude: generally low except along the tablelands of NSW. Temperatures: vary. Precipitation: varies; habitat seasonally flooded.

Stratum: dominated by a variety of herbs of the *Eleocharis* genus. Typical species include the tall spike-rush, common throughout the northern monsoonal and eastern and southern humid regions, and the water chestnut which allies itself with wild rice in the monsoonal regions (see *Oryza* and *Eleocharis* closed herblands). Other species include sag which allies itself with emerged and submerged aquatics in northern NSW and pale spike-rush which forms alliances with the common spike-rush on the edge of ephemerally flooded depressions and on the floodplains of the Murray-Darling river systems; other allies include lignum and other grasses and sedges.

Transformations: most formations are probably still unaltered except where affected by drainage works, flood mitigation programmes, etc.

Eleocharis *closed herbland: here the tall spike-rushes have completely colonised a small riverflat swamp. (Calymea Creek, South Coast, NSW)*

BAUMEA CLOSED HERBLANDS — jointed twig-rush herblands

Location: throughout the humid coastal regions of Australia.

Habitat: Landforms: dune swales, edges of standing water, coastal lagoons. Soils: sandy, etc. Altitude: virtually at sea-level. Temperatures: vary. Precipitation: varies.

Stratum: dominated by herbs of the *Baumea* genus. Species vary depending on latitude, depth and permanence of water. Allies include species of club-rushes (*Scirpus* spp), cutting and thatching grasses (*Gahina* spp), wiry-rushes (*Restio* spp), *Lepidosperma*, etc. In some places this formation may be fairly open.

Transformations: some formations still intact; others affected by sand mining operations, etc.

Thypa *closed herbland occupying the edge of a billabong: the dominant plant is the bulrush; the trees in the background are cadjeputs. (Miaree Pool, Pilbara, WA)*

TYPHA CLOSED HERBLANDS — bulrush herblands

Location: temperate coastal and south-east inland Australia; south-west WA.

Habitat: Landforms: dune swales and other depressions, irrigation ditches. Soils: various. Other features: vary; generally depressions are either permanently or seasonally waterlogged.

Stratum: dominated by bulrushes or narrow-leaved cumbungi. In the eastern coastal regions the dominant plant is the broad-leaved cumbungi.

Transformations: most formations probably still intact; other areas affected by drainage works, flood mitigation programmes and sand mining.

PSEUDOROPHIS CLOSED HERBLANDS — spiny mudgrass herblands

Location: coastal areas of eastern Australia north of the central NSW coast.

Habitat: Landforms: edges of still watercourses, lagoons, etc. Soils: muds, etc. Altitude: virtually at sea-level. Temperatures: summers are warm to hot and humid, winters are warm. Precipitation: generally over 800 mm with a summer maximum.

Stratum: dominated by tangled masses of spiny mudgrass on the edges of still waters; commonly in the same place as rushes (*Juncus* spp). In some places it may form alliances with coastal cane grass (*Chionachne* sp.).

Transformations: intact except where disturbed by changes to water quality, land fills, etc.

115

RESTIO **CLOSED HERBLANDS** — wiry-rush herblands

See Chapter 13, *Restio* herblands.

OTHER CLOSED HERBLANDS

See Chapter 13, Other herblands.

Other Types

CLOSED FERNLANDS

See Chapter 13, *Cyanthea* and *Dicksonia* fernlands among others; *Pteridium* fernlands and Other fernlands.

Other closed herbland: the species here were unidentified but were probably annuals; the habitat is the mouth of a limestone cavern, which remains relatively cool and humid. (Abercrombie Caves, Central Tablelands, NSW)

Chapter Thirteen

HERBLANDS, SEDGELANDS AND GRASSLANDS

Introduction
Grassland Types
Astrebla tussock grasslands — Mitchell grass plains,
Themeda and/or *Danthonia* tussock grasslands— kangaroo and/or walllaby grass
grasslands, *Eriachne* and *Themeda* grasslands, *Stipa* grasslands — spear grass grasslands,
Alpine and subalpine tussock grasslands — sod tussock grasslands, *Dichanthium* tussock
grasslands — blue grass grasslands,
Eragrostis and other grasslands — cane grass swamps,
Other grasslands — includes *Enneapogon, Triraphis* and *Tripogon* grasslands

Sedgeland Types
Gymnoschoenus tussocky sedgelands — button grass plains,
Gahnia tussocky sedgelands, *Carex* sedgelands,
Other sedgelands — includes *Calorophus* and *Leptocarpus, Leptocarpus, Evandra,*
Anarthria and *Lyginia* and *Lepyrodia* among others

Herbland Types
Lomandra tussock herblands — iron grass herblands, *Restio* herblands — wiry-rush
herblands, Other herblands — includes *Carpobrotus, Senecio, Juncus* among others

Fernland Types
Cyanthea and *Dicksonia* fernlands among others — tree fern gullies, *Pteridium*
fernlands — bracken fernlands, Other fernlands — includes *Marsilea, Gleichenia* and
Azolla family fernlands, etc.

Alpine and subalpine tussock grassland: exhibiting the moderately tall and thick tussocks of snowgrass; the valley is treeless due to cold air drainage. (nr Coolamon Stn, Snowy Mountains, NSW)

Introduction

Like the closed herblands and grasslands, the herblands, sedgelands and grasslands are dominated by non-woody or herbal plants such as grasses, sedges, rushes, ferns or a mixture of these. Unlike the closed herblands they have an open canopy through which some type of ground cover can be seen. This may be a closed understorey of mat-like plants, smaller scattered species, ephemeral plants or patches of bare ground. The open canopy is due to the spacing of the plants and their growth form, which in most cases is tussocky. The nature of tussocky growth is such that a closed mat-like canopy is unlikely to develop if the spacing of plants is too great. The obvious exception to this form are the tree ferns whose growth behaviour is more typical of the single-stemmed woody plants.

Herblands are found in all climatic zones and the most widespread of these, the grasslands, generally occupy those regions which receive only a moderate amount of precipitation. Consequently many herblands must survive either high summer temperatures and periods of extended drought or, in upland and southern regions, freezing winter temperatures and cold winds. Most of the sedgelands are located in more humid environments, typically coastal situations, coastal river floodplains and montane and alpine areas. Most fernlands are located in the humid regions.

Grasslands typically occupy heavy clay soils. The most expansive grasslands are those dominated by Mitchell grass. They are located throughout the tropical and northern temperate semi-arid regions of northern and north-eastern Australia. The Mitchell grass communities are summer growing in response to the precipitation received at that time of the year. Subtle variations occur in these grasslands, different species dominating different areas depending on the effective rainfall received, the degree and intensity of grazing and whether they occupy minor depressions, where the soil is badly drained, or the adjacent rises, where the soil is better drained.

The sedgelands, like those described in Chapter 12 Closed Herblands and Grasslands, are found on soils that are permanently, seasonally or periodically inundated or remain wet due to waterlogging, poor drainage, etc. The most widespread of these sedgelands are the button grass plains of south-west Tasmania. Their environment is a flat, boggy lowland of waterlogged, peaty soils which is located in a very high precipitation belt. This belt also experiences cool temperatures and gale force winds throughout the year.

Fernlands are found in all climatic zones although the major fern formations occupy humid, moist environments sheltered from fires and scorching summer temperatures. Though typically found in understoreys tree fern formations, the most extensive types, occupy sheltered gullies where the correct environmental conditions can be maintained.

Herblands are occasionally subjected to fires, especially the grasslands. Fires are likely to be more common and intense after a long dry period which has followed a wet period. During a wet period considerable growth may take place, growth which converts to fuel during a dry phase. Although herblands will be destroyed by a major fire, a low intensity burn helps to regenerate new growth and reduce the likelihood of shrub regrowth.

Most herblands, especially sedgelands and fernlands, are relatively small formations and, along with the closed and open herblands (except spinifex grasslands) are estimated to occupy some 7.8 per cent of Australia's land area and account for some 120+ major alliances. Most of this land area is accounted for by the Mitchell grass formations. The closed grasslands and grasslands support 87 species of birds and 10 species of mammals.

Grassland Types

ASTREBLA TUSSOCK GRASSLANDS — Mitchell grass plains

Location: widespread throughout semi-arid Qld and NT; minor areas in semi-arid NSW and WA; minor areas in subhumid central Qld.

Habitat: Landforms: rolling plains and downs. Soils: grey, brown and red clays. Altitude: generally below 450 m. Temperatures: summers are hot to very hot, winters are mild to very warm. Precipitation: generally below 600 mm with a definite summer maximum.

Stratum: dominated by the tussocky Mitchell grass, primarily curly Mitchell grass in the wetter areas and barley Mitchell grass in drier and northern areas. Other *Astrebla* species may also be present. The tussocks are generally 0.5 to 1 m high and 6 to 12 m apart. Except in drought years the spaces between the tussocks are occupied by other grasses and herbs. These other grasses include blue grasses (*Dichanthium* spp), panic grasses (*Panicum* spp), kerosene grasses (*Aristida* spp) and love grasses (*Eragrostis* spp). The blue grasses and panic grasses are common allies in higher rainfall areas while the love grasses are common in drier areas. In some areas these *Astrebla* grasslands form the understorey of *Acacia* shrublands and open shrublands dominated by gidgee, boree and mimosa. *Acacia* low open forests and woodlands also occur in restricted areas.

Transformations: most areas are extensively grazed by sheep and/or beef cattle with considerable reduction of the dominants occurring in some localities. A few small areas have been replaced by agricultural crops. In some areas pastoralists promote the growth of love grass over Mitchell grasses as it is more palatable to stock.

THEMEDA AND/OR DANTHONIA TUSSOCK GRASSLANDS — kangaroo and/or wallaby grass grasslands

Location: mainly subhumid areas of western Vic., minor areas elsewhere.

Habitat: Landforms: slightly undulating basalt plains, headlands. Soils: clay soils derived from basalt. Altitude: generally below 200 m. Temperatures: summers are mild to hot, winters are cool. Precipitation: up to 800 mm with a winter-spring maximum.

Astrebla *tussock grassland: dominated by Mitchell grass, here closely cropped so that the tussocks appear small and stunted; after seasonal rains the fully developed plants would cover more ground surface. (Min Min Creek, Channel Country, Qld)*

Stratum: dominated by the tussocky kangaroo grass which occasionally forms alliances with wallaby grass (*Danthonia* spp). Generally *Themeda* tussocks are up to 30 cm high and 10 to 15 cm across at the base. Some headlands along the NSW coast exhibit treeless areas dominated by kangaroo grasses.

Transformations: most of these formations have been cleared for farming.

ERIACHNE AND THEMEDA GRASSLANDS

Location: monsoonal northern Australia, especially Arnhem Land, Top End, NT.

Habitat: Landforms: estuarine floodplains subjected to inundation for 3 to 4 months of the year. Soils: podzols. Altitude: virtually at sea-level. Temperatures: hot to very hot throughout the year. Precipitation: generally over 1250 mm with a definite summer maximum.

Stratum: dominated by the perennial grasses *Eriachne burkittii* and *Themeda australis*. Normally *E. burkittii* is subjected to longer inundation due to its slightly lower situation.

Transformations: may be lightly grazed during the dry season.

STIPA GRASSLANDS — spear grass grasslands

Location: temperate, subhumid southern and eastern Australia; southern temperate semi-arid SA and WA.

Habitat: varies.

Stratum: dominated by spear grass in alliance with the kangaroo grass (*Themeda* spp) and the *Poa* species of tussock grasses. Natural *Stipa* grasslands are of small size and limited distribution though the species is common in the understorey of various grassy woodlands. The original pre-grazing height of *Stipa* formations was 1 to 2 m. *Stipa* grasslands are locally common in the southern Nullarbor Plain region.

Transformations: the formation is subjected to grazing by sheep and beef cattle. In some areas, grazing has effectively replaced spear grass with wallaby grass (*Danthonia* spp). In addition exotic pastures have replaced the original formation in most places. In areas that have never been grazed, e.g. some offshore islands, some small spear grass communities remain.

ALPINE AND SUBALPINE TUSSOCK GRASSLANDS — sod tussock grasslands

Location: restricted to the alpine and subalpine areas of NSW, Vic., Tas. and the ACT.
Habitat: Landforms: alpine valleys; cold-air drainage basins (frost hollows) in subalpine areas. Soils: acid, humic soils. Altitude: generally above 1200 m on the mainland; 900 m in Tas. Temperatures: cool to mild summers, very cold to cold winters, locally severe frosts below the winter snowline. Precipitation: 700 to 2500 mm with a winter maximum.

Stipa *grassland: this tussocky grassland dominated by spear grass covers a slight depression; the bare earth can be seen among the tussocks in the foreground. (nr Caiguna, Nullarbor Plain, WA)*

Carex *sedgeland: occupying a small alluvial fan at the base of a steep slope; here moisture collects, keeping the soil damp; the plant appears to be a tussock sedge. (Bamarang, South Coast, NSW)*

Stratum: dominated by sod tussock grasses including snowgrass (*Poa* sp.), wallaby grass (*Danthonia* spp), kangaroo grass (*Themeda* spp) and *Calorophus lateriflorus*.
Transformations: lower altitude grasslands are subjected to sheep grazing. Higher altitude grasslands are subjected to beef cattle grazing during summer in Victoria. Illegal grazing occasionally occurs in national parks and reserves.

DICHANTHIUM TUSSOCK GRASSLANDS — blue grass grasslands

See Chapter 12, *Dichanthium* and other grasslands.

ERAGROSTIS AND OTHER GRASSLANDS — cane grass swamps

See Chapter 12, *Eragrostis* and other closed grasslands.

OTHER GRASSLANDS

Other minor grasslands are found in the semi-arid and arid regions of Australia. Within degenerated areas of *Atriplex*, *Chenopodium* and *Maireana* low shrublands a type of nine-awn grass (*Enneapogon avenaceus*) may form monospecific grasslands which grow to a height of 20 cm. On worn sand patches and on lunettes (light-coloured dunes adjacent to some inland lakes) grows purple needlegrass (*Triraphis mollis*) after summer or autumn rains. This grass, which grows to 40 cm allies itself with various forbs. Within eastern semi-arid low woodlands five-minute grass (*Tripogon lolliformis*) may be locally dominant on bare areas after late summer rains. Five-minute grass forms alliances with *Bassia* spp and *Sporobolus* spp.

Alpine and subalpine tussock grasslands: relatively common in the high upland valleys of south-east Australia; the dominant grass is generally snowgrass. (upper reaches of Snowy River, Snowy Mountains, NSW)

Sedgeland Types

GYMNOSCHOENUS TUSSOCKY SEDGELANDS — button grass plains

Location: restricted to the humid western and mountainous districts of Tas.

Habitat: Landforms: wet, boggy country. Soils: peaty podzols. Altitude: generally low. Temperatures: summers are cool to mild, winters are cold to cool. Precipitation: generally over 1200 mm.

Stratum: dominated by button grass which may occur in pure stands or with smaller heaths of the EPACRIDACEOUS family. A variety of grasses, sedges, ferns and mosses may also be present.

Transformations: most areas are generally unaltered though grazing leases have recently been granted in some marginal districts. Hydro-electricity works have flooded some areas.

GAHNIA TUSSOCKY SEDGELANDS

Location: restricted distribution in the subhumid regions of SA especially the Lower South-East and the western coast of the Eyre Peninsula.

Habitat: Landforms: seasonally flooded lowlands. Soils: rendzinas. Altitude: low. Temperatures: summers are very warm to hot, winters are cool. Precipitation: generally between 600 and 800 mm with a definite winter maximum.

Stratum: dominated by large, tussocky sedges of the *Gahnia* genus. Dominant species include cutting grass and thatching grass. In some localities white tussock grass (*Poa* sp.) may dominate. Between the tussocks is a variety of wet habitat species including various rushes. The salt grass (*Distichlis* spp) may occur in some areas.

Transformations: most, if not all, areas have been drained, cleared and sown with exotic pastures.

Lomandra tussock herbland: dominated by iron grass; these small tussocks actually belong to the lily family; there is a ground layer of ephemerals. (nr Orroroo, Upper North, SA)

Other fernland; this depression is actually a streambed which has been temporarily colonised by the unfern-like nardoo; the nardoo has here formed a closed fernland. (nr Roebourne, Pilbara, WA)

CAREX SEDGELANDS

Location: montane, subalpine and alpine areas of NSW, Vic., Tas. and ACT; humid lowland country elsewhere.

Habitat: Landforms: permanently waterlogged and occasionally flooded depressions; damp areas. Soils: various. Altitude: 600 to 2000 m; below 600 m elsewhere. Temperatures: summers are cool to very warm, winters are very cold to cool; mild to warm elsewhere. Precipitation: varies; habitat occasionally flooded.

Stratum: dominated by the sedge *Carex gaudichaudiana* generally in alliance with the common spike-rush and other grasses and forbs (this produces a fen) or with sphagnum moss and other grasses and forbs (so producing a bog). Often *Carex* sedgelands are surrounded by sod tussock grasslands in subalpine and alpine areas or wet tussock grasslands in montane areas. See also Chapter 12, Alpine and subalpine bogs and fens. In other areas the tussock sedge may dominate.

Transformations: most formations probably still intact.

OTHER SEDGELANDS

In some places different species to those already described form minor sedgelands. These include the *Calorophus* and *Leptocarpus* sedgelands found in the eastern States. The dominants may be allied with the following species; grasstrees (*Xanthorrhoea* spp), wiry-rushes (*Restio* spp) or thatching grasses (*Gahnia* spp). On the Coastal Plain, WA are found *Leptocarpus* sedgelands within the *Banksia* woodlands and low woodlands. They are located on the flat, sandy areas between dunes which are waterlogged in winter. The dominant sedge is the *Leptocarpus aristatus*. During spring and summer ephemeral plants occur in the formation. In addition there may be the occasional emergent shrub. *Evandra, Anarthria* and *Lyginia* sedgelands are found in the wettest areas of the South-West, WA behind coastal dunes and on some riverflats, etc. They occupy small areas. The ground layer may exhibit insectivorous plants. On some sandstone outcrops, for example the Budawang Ranges (South Coast-Southern Tablelands, NSW) are sedgelands and open sedgelands dominated by the tussocky sedge *Lepyrodia scariosa* which grows to a height of 70 cm. Some other minor sedges include *Ptilanthelium deustem, Lepidosperma limicola* and *Xyris operculata*.

Herbland Types

LOMANDRA TUSSOCK HERBLANDS — iron grass herblands

Location: restricted to the subhumid areas of the northern Mt Lofty Ranges and southern Flinders Ranges of SA.

Habitat: Landforms: upland plains and downs. Soils: red-brown earths, etc. Altitude: generally between 300 and 600 m. Temperatures: summers are hot to very hot, winters are cool. Precipitation: generally around 450 to 600 mm with a winter maximum.

Stratum: dominated by the tussocky iron grass with varieties of wallaby grass present. The tussocks are small, generally less than 30 cm high. Numerous other herbs develop between the tussocks.

Transformations: most of the formation is grazed by sheep or has been cleared for agricultural crops. Natural stands of this grassland are probably absent due to the introduction of exotic herbs and grasses.

RESTIO HERBLANDS — wiry-rush herblands

Location: see *Gymnoschoenus* tussocky sedgelands.

Habitat: see *Gymnoschoenus* tussocky sedgelands.

Stratum: dominated by species of the *Restio* genus. Typical species include the wiry-rush (*R. australis*) allied with *Hypolaena fastigiata; Restio oligocephalus* allied with *R. complanatus* or *Lepidosperma filiforme; Restio tetraphyllus* and *Leptocarpus tenax* allied with *Xyris operculata*. All of these plants are found in waterlogged sites, and may produce *Restio* closed herblands.

Transformations: virtually unaltered except where affected by hydro-electricity works.

OTHER HERBLANDS

There are many other herbs which form small formations in restricted areas such as in exposed coastal situations, on headlands, cliff-faces, beachfronts, etc. These include formations dominated by pig-face (*Carpobrotus* sp.), variable groundsel (*Senecio* sp.), *Senecio spathulatus,* stinging nettles, dune thistles, sea parsley, coast everlasting, etc. These plants, among others, may also form closed or open herblands depending on their ground cover.

The common rush (*Juncus* sp.) is often found in moist areas adjacent to swamps, pools, watercourses and at the foot of slopes where groundwater reaches the surface. In some places it produces formations in its own right, e.g. meadow swamps.

Fernland Types

CYANTHEA AND DICKSONIA

FERNLANDS among others — tree fern gullies

Location: throughout the humid eastern and south-eastern regions of the mainland and Tas.; also within some humid environments in drier areas.

Substrata: generally there is a ground layer of numerous other ferns and mosses. These smaller ferns will cover slow flowing streams with a deep, mat-like formation. For instance the fishbone water fern forms extensive colonies along creek banks in the mountainous country of Vic. In many places tree ferns form a part of the understorey of shrubby tall open forests and some closed forests.

Cyanthea *and* Dicksonia *fernland: occupying the fringes of a stream, a habitat that is rarely, if ever, dry; the ground cover is sparse due to shading by the rough tree fern dominants. (nr Glenelg River, Western Districts, Vic)*

Transformations: generally unaltered in protected environments, otherwise they are subjected to land clearing and forestry programmes in conjunction with the clearing of other formations.

Habitat: Landforms: generally adjacent to watercourses and on marshy ground, particularly within sheltered gullies. Soils: various. Altitude: varies. Temperatures: vary; the environment in gullies is generally cooler in summer and warmer in winter than in surrounding areas. Precipitation: varies; generally above 1200 mm, gully environments are generally more humid than surrounding areas.

Upper stratum: dominated by a variety of tree ferns including the rough tree fern (*Cyanthea* sp.) and the soft tree fern (*Dicksonia* sp.). Other tree ferns include the prickly tree fern which often forms pure stands, the skirted tree fern and the slender tree fern. The king fern (*Todea* sp.) may also be present in some areas. In north-east Qld, on the Evelyn Tableland, there is a grassy fernland dominated by the *Cyanthea celebica*. This fern grows to a height of 6 m.

PTERIDIUM FERNLANDS — bracken
fernlands

Location: throughout the 'wet' forests of eastern Australia and Tas. and the high rainfall areas of WA, also offshore Tas. islands.
Habitat: see Chapter 5, Shrubby tall open forests.
Stratum: dominated by the *Pteridium* species Austral bracken and other *Pteridium* types. (Some biologists argue that there is only one species of bracken.) Though more commonly observed within the understorey of tall open forests bracken may dominate in clearings and other disturbed areas. Bracken is also common on many offshore islands of Tas. where it may occur with the common nettle (*Urtica* sp.).
Transformations: bracken generally occupies unused land that has been cleared for farming within tall open forest formations.

OTHER FERNLANDS

As ferns are found in a variety of habitats, including arid areas, it is likely that different species may temporarily occupy small corners of the landscape and so form distinctive formations. For instance a species of *Marsilea,* the common nardoo, occupies depressed areas subjected to intermittent flooding. This fern is a creeping rhizome which looks like a four-leafed clover. It grows quickly after flooding only to eventually dry out leaving behind a muddy surface. Nardoo often grows in alliance with other plants (see Chapter 12, *Eragrostis* and other closed grasslands). In Tas. another fern, the *Gleichenia dicarpa,* may dominate an alpine bog formation. The AZOLLA family of ferns includes species of vigorous growers that completely cover the surface of pools and swamps. In rock crevices some ferns, which generally form monospecific communities include the rock fern, a common and widespread species as well as the bristly cloak fern, blanket fern, *Gymnogramma reynoldsii* and rock isotome. In many cases these fernlands may exist as closed formations.

Pteridium *fernland: dominated by bracken growing on disturbed land the bracken shown here has colonised a piece of moist ground near a small stream. (Bamarang, South Coast, NSW)*

Chapter Fourteen

OPEN AND VERY OPEN HERBLANDS AND GRASSLANDS

Introduction
Grassland Types
Trioda and *Plectrachne* open hummock grasslands — spinifex grasslands, *Trioda* and *Plectrachne* very open hummock grasslands, *Zygochloa* open hummock grasslands — sandhill cane grass, *Astrebla* open tussock grasslands — open Mitchell grass plains, *Eragrostis* open grasslands — love grass grasslands
Other Types
Atriplex and *Bassia* very open herblands, Other open and very open herblands, Open fernlands

Trioda *and* Plectrachne *open hummock grassland: this grassland is sparse, the dominant plant being feathertop spinifex, which is seeding; baby plants can be seen on the dune surface; the pink plant is* Verticordia forrestii*? (Yannarie Coastal Plain, North-West, WA)*

Introduction

The open and very open herblands and grasslands are dominated by non-woody plants. Their principal locations are within the semi-arid and arid regions of Australia. Generally they are located on heavy clay downs, sandplains, sand-dunes and rocky hillsides. Here they experience the very arid conditions of high summer temperatures, low precipitation, high evaporation and lengthy droughts (the normal condition in this environment).

Due to the density of the dominant's vegetative cover the ground is clearly seen, either as bare earth, sand or rock, occasionally with perennial and annual grasses and forbs, or covered with ephemeral plants after rain. Often the ground cover or understorey is composed of the desiccated stems of these ephemerals.

The most widespread herblands are those dominated by spinifex. Spinifex is common in the understorey of many formations, particularly in the northern semi-arid and arid regions, though in some places it is locally dominant. With a few exceptions the other herblands are of limited extent.

Open and very open herblands are not extensive in terms of total land cover. Although an estimated 15 to 20 per cent of the land area is covered with spinifex and other sparse herbs, the area dominated by these formations is considerably less. A number of species of birds and mammals are found in these habitats and some are virtually restricted to them.

Trioda *and* Plectrachne *open hummock grassland: dominated by* T. pungens; *this landscape is rocky and especially arid; no other plant life was seen. (Chichester Range, Pilbara, WA)*

Grassland Types

TRIODA AND PLECTRACHNE OPEN HUMMOCK GRASSLANDS — spinifex grasslands

Location: in various localities throughout semi-arid and arid Australia, especially in northern regions.

Habitat: Landforms: sandplains, sand-dune country, rocky hillslopes. Soils: siliceous sands, earthy sands, lithosols, etc. Altitude: up to 1000 m or so. Temperatures: summers are hot to very hot, winters are warm to hot. Precipitation: generally below 300 mm, usually with a summer maximum.

Stratum: dominated by species of *Trioda* and *Plectrachne*. Commonly called spinifex or porcupine grass these plants are hummock-forming evergreen perennials which appear as mounds up to 1 m high. In the middle of, and between, the mounds is normally bare soil or rock. Although hummock grasslands are common and widespread throughout northern and central Australia, areas of spinifex as the dominant species are limited in distribution. Usually spinifex forms the understorey to a variety of formations, especially *Acacia* shrublands and open shrublands, some *Eucalyptus* open scrubs and shrublands and a few other types. In some instances, if the ground cover is particularly sparse, a spinifex formation is referred to as a *Trioda* and *Plectrachne* very open hummock grassland. Such formations are rare. Typical species of spinifex include hard spinifex and soft spinifex among others. After a succession of good years or within a few years after fire other grasses may occupy the bare ground between the hummocks. Typical grasses include kerosene grass, love grass and parakeelya grass among many others. The taller and widely spaced shrub and tree species include beefwoods, corkwoods, native poplars, various eucalypts, mulga and desert oaks.

Transformations: most spinifex areas are virtually unused. Some marginal areas may be extensively grazed by beef cattle, especially during good seasons.

TRIODA AND PLECTRACHNE VERY OPEN HUMMOCK GRASSLANDS

See *Trioda* and *Plectrachne* open hummock grasslands.

ZYGOCHLOA OPEN HUMMOCK GRASSLANDS — sandhill cane grass

Location: throughout the eastern arid regions, i.e. Simpson Desert, Strzelecki Desert, Tirari Desert, etc.

Habitat: Landforms: on sand-dune slopes, some dune crests. Soils: siliceous sands. Altitude: generally below 250 m. Temperatures: summers are very hot, winters are warm to very warm. Precipitation: less than 250 mm.

Stratum: dominated by the sandhill cane grass, occasionally forming an alliance with hard spinifex (*Trioda* sp.). Dominant plant height is up to 1.2 m. After rains the ephemeral plants roly-poly, tangled mulla mulla and the green bird flower are common.

Transformations: virtually unaltered.

Zygochloa *open hummock grassland: here the sandhill cane grass is scattered across the crest of a dune, its presence stabilising the dune's upper surface. (north of Birdsville, Simpson Desert, Qld)*

ASTREBLA OPEN TUSSOCK GRASSLANDS — open Mitchell grass plains

Location: arid south-west Qld; arid north-east SA.

Habitat: Landforms: plains and downs. Soils: grey, brown and red clays. Altitude: generally below 200 m. Temperatures: summers are hot to very hot, winters are warm. Precipitation: below 250 mm.

Stratum: dominated by the tussocky barley Mitchell grass which provides a sparse ground cover. Other species include varieties of *Bassia* and love grass (*Eragrostis* sp.). Ephemeral species are common after rain. In drier regions love grass may be present without the barley Mitchell grass.

Transformations: subjected to extensive grazing by beef cattle.

ERAGROSTIS OPEN GRASSLANDS — love grass grasslands

See *Astrebla* open tussock grasslands.

Zygochloa *open hummock grassland: dominated by sandhill cane grass which occupies a dune crest; here the plants have formed a dense clump. (east of Twilight Bore, Strzelecki Desert, SA)*

Astrebla *open tussock grassland: covering a gently sloping plain; the dominant plant is barley Mitchell grass; ephemerals would be present after rain. (nr Warri Gate, Bulloo, Qld)*

Eragrostis *open grassland: covers a plain in patches; though the density of growth appears relatively thick in places, other areas are devoid of any but ephemeral growth; the grass is a type of love grass. (George River Valley, Pilbara, WA)*

Other Types

ATRIPLEX AND BASSIA VERY OPEN HERBLANDS

See Chapter 11, *Atriplex* and *Bassia* very open low shrublands.

OTHER OPEN AND VERY OPEN HERBLANDS

In a few restricted localities other types of very open herblands can be differentiated. A variety of plants grows in rocky environments, especially cliff-faces and rocky ledges. In humid environments species of *Doryanthes* (red lilies) and *Dendrobium* (rock orchids) are found. The giant red lily is found on east-facing escarpments in southern Qld. These plants often extend over 4 m outward and upward from the rock face. Rock orchids have a wide range from central Qld to east Gippsland in Vic. They form dense masses on granite and sandstone cliff-faces and ledges. Their 'height' is often over 30 cm when flowering. Between each mass or clump of plants is an 'understorey' of mosses, lichen and algal staining. Other rock faces, in all environments, will support some type of plants, given a suitable niche. See also Chapter 13, Other herblands.

OPEN FERNLANDS

See Chapter 13, *Cyanthea* and *Dicksonia* fernlands among others, *Pteridium* fernlands and Other fernlands.

Chapter Fifteen

NON-VASCULAR PLANTS

Introduction
Mossy Types
Closed mosslands, *Sphagnum* mosslands — sphagnum bogs, Other mosslands
and open mosslands
Algal Types
Rhodophyta based formations — red algae formations, *Cyanophyta* based formations —
blue-green algae formations, *Phaeophyta* based formations — brown algae formations,
Chlorophyta based formations — green algae formations
Other Types
Euglenoid based formations, Fungi-algae symbiotic formations — lichen formations

Introduction

The non-vascular plant formations are dominated by non-woody, non-herbal plants. These plants are distinguished by the fact that they do not possess conductive tissues for the transportation of nutrients, etc., as do the more commonly known vascular plants. As a result they must occupy moist or humid environments in order to get sufficient moisture to survive.

Virtually all non-vascular plant formations are found in oceanic or aquatic waters or in places where water is readily obtainable, i.e. adjacent to streams, sheltered rock faces in humid regions, etc. These formations are dominated by various mosses, lichens, waterblooms, seaweeds, etc.

Chlorophyta *based formation: dominated by sea lettuce on a limestone rock platform; this species of seaweed is common on southerly coasts during the winter. (Halls Head, Coastal Plain, WA)*

Because of their nature some of these formations are transitory, that is they occupy a place in the landscape but not necessarily for a lengthy period of time. This is true for the various algae or waterblooms that may occur when conditions are just right for their development. In other places they form permanent features in the landscape thereby producing distinctive plant formations. In such localities they are subjected to various environmental stresses just like their vascular cousins.

These formations are not considered to occupy extensive areas in terms of total land area nor are they locally extensive. As many of the plants, particularly the algae, are unnamed, unstudied or still remain to be discovered, little is known about their alliances or relationships within the environment.

Other mossland: this small mossland, species unknown, occupies the bed and banks of a small alpine stream which is supplied by snow melt. (Lake Cootapatamba, Snowy Muntains, NSW)

Mossy Types

CLOSED MOSSLANDS

See *Sphagnum* mosslands and Other mosslands and open mosslands.

SPHAGNUM MOSSLANDS — sphagnum bogs

Location: see Chapter 12, Alpine and subalpine bogs.
Habitat: see Alpine and Subalpine bogs.
Stratum: some alpine and subalpine bogs exhibit, and may even be dominated by, sphagnum moss. Due to its size and dense mass an extensive sphagnum bog may constitute a closed mossland formation. Other species, often heaths, may also be present; these constitute bog heaths.
Transformations: see Alpine and Subalpine bogs.

OTHER MOSSLANDS AND OPEN MOSSLANDS

Location: in suitably humid environments.
Habitat: Landforms: sheltered locations such as bare rock surfaces, cliff-faces, etc. Altitude: up to 2000 + m. Temperatures: vary. Precipitation: varies; generally found in humid environments.
Stratum: dominated by various species of mosses. Mosses, in alliance with lichens are found in feldmark and potato field formations on high alpine peaks, especially in Tas. (see Chapter 9, Alpine and subalpine open heaths). More extensive mossland formations may be found on some southerly aspected cliff-faces, e.g. Govetts Leap, Blue Mountains, NSW. Generally mosses are most obvious in various 'wet' forests such as cool temperate rainforests, etc., or in restricted humid environments such as moist gullies, riverbanks and so on. Mosses may be of such an extent and density to constitute a closed mossland or (rarely) an open mossland.
Transformations: generally unaltered as formations due to their restricted and often inaccessible habitats.

Algal Types

N.B. each of the following algal types may co-dominate or co-exist with any of the others.

RHODOPHYTA BASED FORMATIONS —
red algae formations

Location: various marine environments, especially southern Australia.
Habitat: Landforms: rock pools on intertidal platforms, deep offshore pools and chasms. Other features: mainly found in subtidal environments.
Stratum: dominated by a variety of seaweeds, many of which are only ever seen when washed ashore. This phyllum exhibits many forms; some appear as fine fern-like growths, others as encrustations on coral reefs, i.e. coralline algae. Some forms of red algae contain sufficient lime to appear as rocks while others are so gelatinous they appear on beaches as flotsam or jelly. Most seaweeds belong to this group of algae.
Transformations: generally unaltered.

CYANOPHYTA BASED FORMATIONS —
blue-green algae formations

Location: various aquatic environments throughout Australia.
Habitat: Landforms: mudflats, exposed reefs, intertidal rock platforms, inland pools. Other features: generally living on, under or near water.
Stratum: dominated by a variety of genera and species. Blue-green algae often forms a crust on mudflats, exposed rocky reefs, etc., that are protected from strong wave action. On rock platforms gelatinous colonies of *Rivularia firma* and brown, blotchy masses of *Symploca* species are found. In fresh water green, brown, orange or red sheets or masses of waterblooms are common on many pools during the warmer months.
Transformations: formations may vary from season to season.

PHAEOPHYTA BASED FORMATIONS —
brown algae formations

Location: various marine environments, especially temperate coasts.
Habitat: Landforms: lower intertidal and upper subtidal rocky shores. Other features: sometimes some species are found in rock pools.
Stratum: dominated by a variety of seaweeds, many of which are only ever seen when washed ashore. Like the red algae this group exhibits many

Phaeophyta *based formation: exhibiting Neptune's necklace occupying fissures in an intertidal rock platform. (Pebbly Beach, South Coast, NSW)*

forms and sizes. A common species includes bull kelp (*Durvillaea* sp.) which grows to 8 m in length and is sometimes seen at low tide on rocky shores exposed to heavy seas. Other common species include Neptunes necklace, a characteristic and often dominant plant of south-east Australian intertidal rock platforms; the leathery and sometimes dominant leather kelp, the sargassum weed and the giant kelp which can grow to a length of 60 m.
Transformations: generally unaltered.

CHLOROPHYTA BASED FORMATIONS —
green algae formations

Location: various aquatic environments throughout and around Australia.
Habitat: Landforms: rocky marine shores, estuaries, intertidal rock platform pools, freshwater pools, also on rocks, tree trunks, etc. Other features: also found in moist vegetative environments.
Stratum: this phyllum also exhibits a variety of shapes. Most of these algae are distinguished by their grass-green colour. Some are common on rocky shores; a typical marine species is the sea lettuce (*Ulva* sp.). Other forms of green algae are found in freshwater pools. In humid habitats forms of green algae may be seen as stains on rock surfaces.
Transformations: marine species of this phyllum are tolerant of pollution so are commonly seen in harbours, etc. Being rapid colonisers they are also common on recently fresh or clean surfaces, e.g. pylons, boat hulls, etc.

Chlorophyta *based formation: this seaweed (probably bubbleweed) has colonised a rock fissure which is subjected to vigorous wave action; each incoming wave completely submerges the plants. (nr Bermagui, South Coast, NSW)*

Other Types

EUGLENOID BASED FORMATIONS

A phyllum that appears to be both a plant and an animal. One genus, *Euglena*, appears as a mass of floating green material that is almost indescribable but is commonly seen in pools that contain decaying and rotting vegetable (and animal?) matter.

FUNGI-ALGAE SYMBIOTIC FORMATIONS — lichen formations

Lichens are not a single species of plant as such but a combination of either green or blue-green algae and some type of fungus. Together they function as one 'plant'. Lichens are found in virtually all environments and in some areas may produce a distinctive formation. Lichens will often form a thin crust on soil surfaces in semi-arid and arid regions. After a prolonged period of drought lichens may be the dominant 'plant' in areas otherwise occupied by ephemeral herblands. Also in very rocky environments, such as boulder streams or periglacial blockstreams, such as can be found in the alpine and subalpine regions of the mainland and Tas., lichens may again be the dominant 'plant'. Lichens are also commonly found within the understorey of other formations.

Chlorophyta *based formation: this green algae has colonised a rocky streambed on a shallow riffle between deeper pools; here the water flows fast and is oxygenated. (Clyde River, South Coast, NSW)*

Chapter Sixteen

FORMATIONS OF EXTREME, VARIED AND ALTERED HABITATS

Introduction
Ephemeral Types
Echinochloa and other closed grasslands — Channel sorghum grasslands, *Trigonella* and other closed herblands — Cooper clover herblands, Other ephemeral formations
Other Natural Types
Mangrove formations, Salt marsh formations, Freshwater wetland formations, Marine wetland formations, Coastal dune formations, Coastal cliff formations, Formations on 'bare' soil and rock surfaces, Alpine and subalpine formations or complexes, Desert formations or complexes, Areas devoid of vegetation
Man-Made Formations
Formations of urban areas, Formations of rural settlements, farms, etc., Agricultural formations

Introduction

The formations of extreme, varied and altered habitats include those types which do not readily fall into any preconceived classification. This includes complex formations such as mangrove wetlands and salt marshes which exhibit plant zonation along the edge of tidal estuaries, around water bodies, etc. Often each plant zone, which may be dominated by different genera and species, may be particularly small thus to separate them into individual formations would not enable the complete formation(s) to be appreciated. In other cases the formations may be transitory. This applies to the ephemeral formations which only exist for a short period of time after rains or floods. Then again some formations may be distinguished by occupying an altered habitat, one that could hardly be said to be natural. Examples of this would include the formations of urban areas, etc.

Each of these formations is subjected to one or more of the following environmental stresses; a high salt content in the soil or mud; inundation by tidal influences; extremes of wind and cold; periodic or seasonal inundation by streams, floods and rains; waterlogged soils; extensive areas of bitumen; concrete and roofing which drastically alter the runoff characteristics of precipitation and the availability of moisture to the soil; or the colonising of areas of bare rock, soil, overburden, coastal dunes, etc., with its attendant changes in ground temperature, oversurface runoff, winds and so on.

In many cases, particularly those formations hereunder described as wetlands, alpine and subalpine complexes and desert complexes, the individual formations that comprise the collective formation so described have been written up as individual formations in the preceding notes. Their inclusion here is to enable their relationship to each other to be more readily appreciated. This need stems from the fact that most of the individual formations are small and, in some cases, exhibit zones around or along some topographic feature.

The formations of extreme, varied and altered habitats have been subdivided as follows. The ephemeral types are dominated by herbs which occur after rain or floods. Generally they occupy small, but often locally extensive, areas in the semi-arid and arid regions of the country, typically on floodplains and other areas which receive runoff.

The second group includes other natural types not previously described or complexes of small, often minute, formations. The mangrove, salt marsh and marine wetland formations all occur on coastal plains and lowlands which form the coastline or along estuary and riverbanks further inland. In each case the formation must tolerate high levels of salt and tidal influences. Often these tidal influences vary, not only from place to place, but in total depth of high tides, and the duration from one, often extreme, high tide to the next. Conversely exposure at low tides varies from place to place and time to time. In some places a long exposure to the atmosphere means that the plant life found there must endure high temperatures and the desiccating influence of drying winds and long hours of sunshine.

Freshwater wetlands are found in areas subjected to continual, periodic or seasonal inundation by water. The vegetation of wetlands form aquatic and semi-aquatic alliances. Due to the depth and period of flooding and the consequent drying of plants no longer exposed to floodwaters there are often many distinguishable formations located over short distances. There are numerous physical, chemical and biotic factors which distinguish one wetland from the next. Those described hereunder are grouped in such a way that each broad type can be distinguished by the prevailing dominant plant type. Reference is made to the individual formations already described in the preceding chapters.

The coastal dune and cliff formations, partially described elsewhere, are subjected to stresses unique to their situation. In most places these topographic features are exposed to strong winds, salt spray and minor flooding in dune swales. The relative presence or absence of these stresses normally results in variations to the plant life present and consequently the formation to be found there.

The remaining natural formations are self-explanatory and their respective limiting factors are discussed under each heading.

The last group, the man-made formations, is an attempt to describe those plants present in terms of their structure. Although the plants must endure the common environmental stresses they also have to endure, depending on the degree of urbanisation, development and eradication of earlier natural species and formations, other stresses. These include changed runoff characteristics and soil moisture availability, the availability of nutrients, the presence of pollutants, weedicides and pesticides, and altered climatic conditions such as increased temperatures, reflectiveness of sunlight, protection from flooding rains and so on.

Due to their complexity, it is difficult to estimate the total land areas covered by each of these formations. The ephemeral formations would have to be included in the herblands; the coastal or littoral formations which would include mangroves, salt marshes, sand-dunes, etc., account for, or did account for, some 0.4 per cent of the total land area; the alpine complexes some 0.3 per cent; and the areas devoid of vegetation, best accounted for by the unvegetated saltlakes, some 0.6 per cent. In total the 'urban formations' represent nearly 1 per cent of the total land area. These formations support various bird and mammal species. The mangroves account for 35 bird species and 4 mammal species, the various wetlands 118 and 3 respectively and rocky habitats 6 and 12 respectively. In the wetlands some 68 species of birds are virtually restricted to that habitat for their survival.

Ephemeral Types

ECHINOCHLOA AND OTHER CLOSED GRASSLANDS — Channel sorghum grasslands

Location: arid south-west Qld and north-east SA.
Habitat: Landforms: broad floodplains subjected to occasional inundation. Soils: alluvial soils, etc. Altitude: up to 200 m. Temperatures: summers are hot to very hot, winters are mild to very warm. Precipitation: generally below 300 mm with a summer maximum.
Stratum: dominated by the *Echinochloa* species Channel sorghum as well as many other species. The various plants that dominate this formation only appear after inundation by summer (and autumn) floods. Within this area some watercourses and adjacent banks carry a low woodland formation while cane grass (*Eragrostis* sp.) occupies the moister depressions. The dense vegetation cover of Channel sorghum may last for several months.
Transformations: subjected to grazing by beef cattle before the vegetation cover thins out and dies.

TRIGONELLA AND OTHER CLOSED HERBLANDS — Cooper clover herblands

Location: see *Echinochloa* and other closed grasslands.
Habitat: see *Echinochloa* and other closed grasslands.
Stratum: dominated by a variety of forbs, especially the *Trigonella* species Cooper clover. This herbage is a result of winter flooding. The dense vegetation cover may last for several months.
Transformations: see *Echinochloa* and other closed grasslands.

Ephemeral herbland; on frontage country. Dominants unknown. Originally this was probably covered by Mitchell grass. (The post appears to be connected with an old road which passes by.) (nr Tuen, Warrego-Paroo, Qld)

Ephemeral herbland: colonising the edge of a lake bed that lies exposed; dominants unknown. (Cawndilla Lake, Upper Darling, NSW)

OTHER EPHEMERAL FORMATIONS

In semi-arid and arid areas floodplains, other plains and sand-dunes are often devoid of any vegetation except for the remains of dead plants such as stalks, stems, etc. After suitable rains these are transformed by the appearance and rapid growth of a variety of short-lived or ephemeral plants. These plants cover a wide range of species including ephemeral forms of spear grass, love grass, members of the ASTERACEAE family such as daisies, etc., as well as the Sturts desert pea, etc. Generally the maximum height of these plants is below 30 cm. In some places such ephemeral plants are found in the understorey of other formations. (See also Chapter 13, Other grasslands.)

After floods or heavy rains on the floodplains and frontage country of inland Australia there is often a prodigious growth of ephemeral plants such as verbena, wild sorghum, barley grass, etc.

Other Natural Types

MANGROVE FORMATIONS

Location: widespread, in suitable environments, throughout tropical, subtropical and northern temperate marine waters; rare in cooler marine waters, absent in Tas.

Mangrove open scrub: exhibiting grey mangroves colonising a tidal flat; note the breathing tubes common to these mangroves. (Corner Inlet, Gippsland, Vic.)

Habitat: Landforms: low-lying muddy (sometimes sandy) marine environments including gulfs, bays and estuaries free from strong wave action. Soils: marine muds, etc. Altitude: between mean sea-level and the extreme high water mark. Temperatures: vary; warmer areas support many more species. Precipitation: varies.

Stratum: mangrove formations form a diversity of formation types.

1. Mangrove closed forests: located between Daintree and Johnstone Rivers, north Qld; dominant heights reach 30 m, formation merges into tropical rainforest on landward side; typical species include grey mangrove, river mangrove, milky mangrove, large-leaved mangrove, white flowered black mangrove and some 23 other species. Formation threatened by land 'development' schemes in the area and pollution from nearby rivers.

2. Mangrove open forests: located along the north and north-west coasts; generally confined to creek banks and tidal inlets; dominant heights generally over 10 m, formation merges into salt flats, generally devoid of vegetation, on the landward side; typical species include those listed above and some 6 to 10 or more other species. Most formations are relatively intact.

3. Mangrove low open forests: located south of Townsville, Qld to central NSW coast; generally confined to tidal creeks and inlets; dominant heights generally below 10 m, formation often merges into salt marshes on landward side; typical species include those listed above in Qld waters (plus a few others in the north); in NSW waters the grey and river mangrove are common with the milky mangrove in the north. Most formations are, or could be, affected by increasing river pollution, flood mitigation works or land fill programmes.

4. Mangrove open scrubs and shrublands: located in southern NSW, Vic., SA and southern WA waters; generally confined to tidal creeks and inlets; dominant heights up to 3.5 m; formation is usually a narrow band adjacent to water line; only species is the grey mangrove. Formations may be affected by land fill programmes, etc.

5. Mangrove low open scrubs and low shrublands: located along the arid WA coast; generally confined to tidal inlets and sheltered coastlines; dominants often stunted; typical species include grey mangrove, river mangrove, milky mangrove and small stilted mangrove. Formations are relatively intact.

Other mangrove formations include fringing forests on sheltered coasts, riparian forests and immature forests, etc., on new mudflats.

Ephemeral herbland: close-up; the wealth of plant life is amazing for such an arid, stony area; a mulla mulla is on the right. (Grey Range, Bulloo, Qld)

Where mangrove species are numerous the formation exhibits a zonation. Moving away from the shore there is, in northern Qld, a landward zone forming fringing forests, the *Ceriops* zone which generally forms a thicket, the *Bruguiera* zone which forms a forest, the *Rhizophora* zone which also forms a forest and the seaward zone which is also a fringing forest or scrub. The names of the main zones refer to the dominant genus of the constituent species. Generally it is the middle zone that exhibits the tallest species.

Transformations: many formations remain unaltered in remote areas. In the more settled districts formations may be partially affected or totally removed by changing stream flows and resultant stream deposition, pollution, land filling and harbour and breakwater construction.

SALT MARSH FORMATIONS

Location: along low-lying coasts, primarily in temperate regions.

Habitat: Landforms: salt flats, estuaries. Soils: solonchaks, etc. Altitude: at sea-level. Temperatures: vary. Precipitation: varies.

Stratum: dominated by a variety of species. Main plants are the glassworts and samphires, species of which are found in all temperate regions (except *Salicornia* in SA). Other genera include *Sporobolus* in NSW, the saltbush (*Atriplex* spp) in SA and the salt grass (*Distichlis* spp). Among these dominant species are many others; see salt marsh zonation below. In the tropics salt marshes are dominated by *Arthrocnemum* and *Tecticornia* species. Salt marshes exhibit a zonation of species in response to degree and duration of water coverage, salt tolerance, etc.

Mangrove open scrub understorey: here the 'ground' is covered by the numerous breathing tubes of the grey mangrove. (Nickol Bay, Pilbara, WA)

In southern Australia these zones are (approximately) thus.

1. Seaward side: mangrove zone — *Avicenna* spp; *Spartina* zone — introduced plant, rare occurrence; *Salicornia* dominated zone — mainly in NSW, Vic., Tas.; *Arthrocnemum* dominated zone — mainly in Vic., SA, occasionally in WA, Tas.; *Suceda* zone (Vic.) or *Atriplex* zone (SA and other dry areas); *Puccinellia–Spartina*, etc., zone; *Juncus* zone — composed of rushes; *Stipa* complex — composed of spear grasses; *Schoens–Cotula* complex;

Mangrove low open scrub: on the edge of a colony; the flats behind are covered with a seagrass, probably Zostera muelleri, *which is exposed twice daily. (Corner Inlet, Gippsland, Vic.)*

Mangrove low shrubland: occupying a tidal estuary; possibly red mangrove. (mouth of the Gascoyne River, North-West, WA)

2. Landward side: Melaleuca or *Casuarina* zone.

Transformations: most areas are virtually unaltered except where affected by changes in stream flows, stream deposition, pollution or land filling.

FRESHWATER WETLAND FORMATIONS

Location: wetlands are found throughout Australia especially in the humid, subhumid and monsoonal regions. With a few exceptions they are nowhere particularly extensive. This classification does not include marine wetland environments.

Habitat: Landforms: generally low-lying areas, floodplains and depressions subjected to periodic, seasonal or irregular flooding; also adjacent to streams, pools, lakes and other bodies of open water. Soils: muds, silts, alluvial soils, etc. Other features: vary.

Wetlands produce a variety of formations depending on their location, their form and the dominant type of vegetation. Those formations described below have, more often than not, counterparts within those formation types listed previously. A feature of wetlands is the zonation of some vegetative types. The zonation is in response to the degree and duration of water coverage, the depth and permanence of water, the degree of stillness of water, etc. Space does not permit all these zones and their relationship to each other to be described. Bear in mind that where one species (sometimes more) dominates then it is assumed to be a distinctive formation irrespective of its dimensions.

The formations are as follows.

1. Swamp closed forests: see Palm-vine closed forests (Chapter 4).

2. Floodplain open forests and woodlands: located throughout Australia on floodplains subjected to seasonal periodic or irregular flooding. Inland dominants include the river red gum, black box, coolabah as well as, in northern Australia, the bean tree and screw palm. On the coastal floodplains the following species are typical: the southern mahogany and swamp mahogany, swamp she-oaks and various paperbarks as well as the swamp gum and Western Australian flooded gum. The understorey is composed of various grasses, sedges and rushes. See the following formations: Tall open forests with a herbal understorey (Chapter 5), Grassy woodlands (Chapter 6), Grassy low open woodlands (Chapter 7).

3. Riparian open forests and woodlands: these formations are found on the edges of streams, midstream bars and on the sandy beds of some rivers. Dominants include the river red gum and coolabah

along inland rivers. Other areas, especially the east coast, exhibit river she-oaks, water gums and bottlebrushes. In places young she-oaks will form quite a dense tree thicket. The understorey may be absent in some places although some grasses may be seen. In the tropical and temperate humid regions the increased light and moisture availability may be sufficient to support a narrow *closed forest* formation. Generally riparian forests and woodlands are only one to a few trees wide. See the following formations: *Casuarina* open forests and low open forests-2, *Melaleuca* open forests and low open forests (Chapter 5); Grassy woodlands (Chapter 6).

4. Paperbark swamp forests: see *Melaleuca* open forests and low open forests (Chapter 5).

5. Paperbark swamp woodlands: see *Melaleuca* woodlands and low woodlands-2 (Chapter 6).

6. Swamp scrubs: see Closed scrubs (Chapter 8).

7. Swamp heaths: located in peaty or sandy waterlogged soils in coastal and montane areas. In montane areas swamp heaths are often adjacent to tussock grasslands. See the following formations: Montane closed scrubs, Closed heaths (Chapter 8); Tropical and Subtropical wet and dry open heaths, Wet temperate wet and dry open heaths (Chapter 9).

8. Swamp shrublands: located along some inland waterways and dominated by lignum, generally in association with chenopods or grasses. Some places may exhibit a black box or river red gum overstorey. See the following formations: Riparian open forests and woodlands; Shrubby thickets (Chapter 8).

Riparian open forest: dominated by river red gums, this forest is only a few trees wide; the river is flooding, the water having risen about 50 cm overnight. (Darling River near Menindee, Upper Darling, NSW)

Swamp woodland: dominated by cadjeputs in alliance with Millstream fan palms; bulrushes occupy the shallow waters near the banks, water lilies the deeper water. (Millstream, Pilbara, WA)

9. *Swamp herblands:* these are typical of most wetlands in Australia. Most have already been described in the herbland and sedgeland formations (see the list at the end of this heading). Due to the diversity of these wetlands it is convenient to describe their physical forms. These include *floodplain meadows*, wetlands that are located on floodplains adjacent to streams. Most floodplain meadows are found within the eastern and southeastern coastal regions and along the northern monsoonal coastline. The plains are subjected to seasonal or irregular inundation. Dominants include a variety of grasses, sedges and rushes.

Meadow swamps are also located on floodplains subjected to occasional flooding. Normally they occupy depressions on the floodplain surface but are of insufficient depth to form open bodies of water for any length of time. Meadow swamps are normally located in the humid regions although it could also include irrigated pastures. The formation is composed of some grasses, and where the water level fluctuates, semi-aquatic plants. Species include water buttercups, pennyworts and some sedges. Generally meadow swamps are located near permanent streams and lakes.

Reed swamps and *shrub swamps* are usually located on the edge of standing water or occupy depressions such as dune swales, etc. Most are found in the humid and subhumid regions although there are many such 'oases' in the semi-arid and arid country especially around waterholes, bores, mound springs, etc. Most of these swamps support reeds, rushes and tall sedges and are often of such density that they produce thickets. A typical species is the common reed. In some places there may be a dense thicket of shrubs, commonly tea-tree; these then are shrub swamps.

Perched swamps are generally located on the edge of tablelands where the underlying rock is close to the surface; a similar formation, though not strictly a perched swamp, may be found when rock or impervious clay lies just beneath the surface. The net result of this shallow, impervious material is that groundwater often flows through the soil or collects there thus creating a wet habitat. Such swamps are generally restricted to humid regions. Typical plants include various heaths, grasses, sedges and rushes.

Formations beneath the drip line of cliffs are occasionally found in humid regions at the base of cliffs that are seasonally or permanently moist. The continual dripping from above, often from a perched swamp, keeps the ground beneath moist or permanently saturated thus supporting a diversity of plants such as ferns, sedges, grasses and other forbs.

These then are the major forms of swamp herblands. For further details see the following formations: Sedge-like heaths (Chapter 9); *Poa* and *Danthonia* closed tussock grasslands, *Eragrostis* and other closed grasslands, *Paspalum* closed grasslands, *Phragmites* closed grasslands, Alpine and subalpine bogs, Alpine and subalpine fens, *Oryza* and *Eleocharis* closed herblands, *Eleocharis* closed herblands, *Baumea* closed herblands, *Typha* closed herblands (Chapter 12); *Eriachne* and *Themeda* grasslands, Alpine and subalpine tussock grasslands, *Restio* herblands, *Gahnia* tussocky sedgelands, *Gymnoschoenus* tussocky sedgelands, *Carex* sedgelands, Other sedgelands (Chapter 13).

10. Open bodies of water: This includes lakes, billabongs, pools, quiet streams, etc. They are found in all regions, especially the humid ones. Open bodies of water may support aquatic plants, the type depending on the salinity of the water, its depth, degree of stillness and whether it is fresh or brackish. The plants are either floating leaved, emergent or submergent types. Some typical species include pondweeds, swamp lilies, water buttercups and ribbonweeds. In northern Australia water lilies of the *Nelumbo* and *Nymphaea* genera are found on tropical 'lagoons'. In stagnant waters waterblooms are common. Some open bodies of water exhibit island builders. These peculiar vegetation formations develop on floating mats of rhizomes. Plant debris collect around these mats and after a period of time grasses, sedges, shrubs and sometimes small trees develop. As the mats are floating they drift over the surface of the water. As time goes by the

Meadow swamp: exhibiting an emergent common rush on the left, and kikuyu grass; such swamps are temporary features; after six months the common rush had achieved dominance. (Bamarang, South Coast, NSW)

Reed swamp: dominated by the common reed in the foreground; behind are the remains of a floodplain woodland which has suffered the effects of an altered streamflow input due to irrigation farms drawing water otherwise destined for this wetland system. (Macquarie Marshes, North-West Plains, NSW)

Drip-line of cliff: the base of cliffs in humid areas is often wet, thus capable of supporting various ferns, sedges and mosses. (Red Rocks, South Coast, NSW)

mats become too heavy and sink into extinction. At any one time there may be many islands in various stages of formation.

11. Bogs: these are muddy places due to the waterlogged nature of the soil though some bogs are seasonally wet. Generally the ground is soft and spongy and composed of decaying vegetable matter. Bogs are found adjacent to watercourses and estuaries that experience regular flooding.

MARINE WETLAND FORMATIONS

Location: throughout coastal and estuarine Australia.

Habitat: Landforms: generally low-lying areas subjected to tidal influences including rare high tides and storm surges; also includes submerged situations. Other features: vary.

Marine wetlands form a number of formations depending on their location, situation, form and dominant type of vegetation. Marine wetlands also exhibit zonation of vegetative types in response to degree and duration of water coverage, the depth of water, degree of salinity, etc. For further information see the following formations: *Sporobolus* and other closed grasslands, Seagrass formations (Chapter 12); *Cyanophyta* based formations, *Rhodophyta* based formations, *Phaeophyta* based formations, *Chlorophyta* based formations (Chapter 15); Mangrove formations, Salt marsh formations (this chapter).

COASTAL DUNE FORMATIONS

Location: in various localities around the Australian coastline.

Habitat: Landforms: sand-dunes and intervening swales. Soils: calcareous sands, siliceous sands. Altitude: slightly above sea-level; may reach in excess of 150 m on some sand islands. Temperatures: vary; coastal temperatures are to some extent modified by their proximity to the sea. Precipitation: varies.

Coastal dune formations exhibit a diversity of formation types, generally over a small area. In southern Australia the following formations may be found on calcareous dune systems.

1. Open herblands: located inland from the bare sandy beach; dominated by a scattering of plants such as coastal saltbush, sea rocket occasionally with *Salsola kali* and the grass *Sporobolus virginicus.*

Open body of water: colonised by water buttercups near the pond edge and Azolla *ferns towards the middle (top left of plate); on the water's edge are common rushes while the bank is covered with curled dock. (Bamarang, South Coast, NSW)*

Coastal dune formation: fronting a tidal inlet; the dune is very low, virtually just an extension of the beach; the closed grassland is dominated by Poa *tussock grasses; at the foot of the main dune is a tea-tree closed scrub, the main dune being covered with a low open forest. (Corner Inlet, Gippsland, Vic.)*

141

2. *Grasslands:* these are located on the landward side of the open herblands and are represented by the rhizomatous native spinifex which binds the sand and allows other species such as the rush, *Scirpus nodosus,* the creeping succulent *Carpobrotus rossii, Lepidosperma gladiatum,* and *Scaevola* spp to establish themselves. The presence of each of these plants depends on the locality. Other small plants may grow in hollows in the dunes.

3. *Open heaths:* further inland are dwarf shrubs, protected to some degree from the wind, salt and sand. Species include the sea berry saltbush, ruby saltbush and sandhill daisy. Further inland the coastal acacia, Sydney golden wattle, beard heath, white correa and tea-tree are found forming a taller open heath. Again the presence of any particular plant depends on the locality.

4. *Closed scrubs:* in some places taller versions of the open heath species may be of such density that they constitute a closed scrub (see also Chapter 8, Closed scrubs).

5. *Low woodlands:* further inland on the older, more stable dunes there is usually a low woodland dominated by one or more of the following species; drooping she-oak, moonah, coast banksia, silver banksia as well as species of *Acacia* and *Eucalyptus.* In some places these dominant species may form low open forests. Generally the understorey of these low woodland and low open forests may have a scattering of small shrubs, grasses and forbs.

In northern Australia there is also a variety of formations over a short distance but they are not so readily defined. Foredunes exhibit spinifex grass with perhaps goats foot convolvulus. Shrublands of beach she-oak, buckbush, etc., lie further inland while the older, more stable dunes may exhibit herblands of *Gomphrena canescens* and *Bulbostylis barbata* or open herblands of spinifex (*Trioda* spp).

Transformations: most coastal dune formations remain intact except in areas of urban development and other beachside development. In these places the low woodland, closed scrub, open heath and perhaps the grassland and open herbland formations may be partially or totally removed. In extreme cases the dune itself may be replaced by boardwalks, roads, car parks or buildings.

COASTAL CLIFF FORMATIONS

Coastal cliff environments are subjected to erosion, salt spray and strong winds. Formations are many and varied though none are particularly extensive. The intertidal and littoral zones support algal and

Coastal cliff formation: dominated by sea box low open scrub on the lower cliff-face and sea box closed scrub along the cliff-top. (Cape Liptrap, Gippsland, Vic.)

Coastal cliff formation: exhibiting a Poa *grassland; this formation occupies a steep gully set into a very steep hillside. (Cape Liptrap, Gippsland, Vic.)*

lichen formations with perhaps some mosses. Further up the cliff-face may be found small communities occupying crevices and cracks in otherwise bare, rocky areas. These communities may be represented by grasses and low shrubs. Other areas may exhibit low shrublands, closed heaths and open heaths, each formation being represented by a range of plants depending on its location. (See also Chapter 8, Closed heaths; Chapter 10, Other low shrublands; Chapter 13, Other herblands.)

FORMATIONS ON 'BARE' SOIL AND ROCK SURFACES

Freshly excavated or scalded soil will, after a period of time, display a variety of herbs, generally considered as weeds. The type of herbs will depend on location, soil type, moisture availability and proximity to introduced plant species. This herbaceous cover will, under natural conditions, revert to the prevailing vegetation of the area after a certain period. In arid and semi-arid areas scalds will often remain bare until there is an improvement in the scald's moisture-retaining ability. Expanses of rock will often support vegetation. Mosses and lichens commonly inhabit rock surfaces if there is sufficient moisture (see various mosslands formations and fungi-algae symbiotic formations in Chapter 15) while some rocks may exhibit algal staining (see Chapter 15, *Chlorophyta* based formations). Grasses and herbs, even shrubs and trees, will exploit the soil and moisture which collects in minute joints and cracks of rocks. In some cases this exploitation of soil and moisture produces distinctive formations (see Chapter 7, *Callitris* low open woodlands). In these situations the dominant plants often exhibit a twisted and stunted form. In some arid ranges the fig, *Ficus platypoda*, forms over rock surfaces, its roots being firmly planted in the soil at the base of boulders. These plants may cover up to 100 square metres in area and produce their own distinctive formation.

ALPINE AND SUBALPINE FORMATIONS OR COMPLEXES

The alpine and subalpine formations are often small in area. They cover southern Australia's highest mountains with a mosaic of vegetative types that correspond to variations in altitude, aspect, slope, exposure, landform types, nearness to streams, period of snow cover, etc. A number of formations have been recognised and these are listed in the main body of formations as follows: Subalpine low open forests, *Athrotaxis* open forests and low open forests (Chapter 5); Subalpine low woodlands, Pine and/or beech low woodlands (Chapter 6); Shrubby open scrubs-3, Alpine and subalpine open heaths (Chapter 9); Dwarf heathlands and open heathlands (Chapter 10); Tall alpine herbfields, Short alpine herbfields, Alpine and subalpine bogs, Alpine and subalpine fens (Chapter 12); Alpine and subalpine tussock grasslands (Chapter 13); *Sphagnum* mosslands (Chapter 15).

DESERT FORMATIONS OR COMPLEXES

The term desert complex appears in some books. It is a term used to describe a variety of formations which exist in close proximity to one another. For instance in sand-dune country different dominants exist on the crests of dunes, at their bases and within the dune corridor; around saltlakes or shallow depressions there may exist a zonation of vegetative types. In this text each individual formation has been listed in the main body of the text. The main formations that comprise the 'desert complexes' are as follows (do not forget to consider the various low woodlands and shrublands as well): *Nitraria* low shrublands, Samphire low shrublands (Chapter 10); *Eragrostis* and other closed grasslands (Chapter 12); *Trioda* and *Plectrachne* open hummock grasslands, *Zygochloa* open hummock grasslands (Chapter 14); Other ephemeral formations (this chapter).

AREAS DEVOID OF VEGETATION

Some areas in Australia are completely devoid of any vegetation. This is due to many factors including lack of nutrients or moisture, high concentrations of salt, 'unstable' land surfaces or human interference. Typical areas lacking any vegetation cover include saltlakes, coastal salt pans, beaches, crests of active sand-dunes, extensive rock surfaces, very exposed rocky alpine ridges and summits and ground surfaces covered with concrete and/or bitumen.

Area devoid of vegetation: the salt lake surface supports no plant life; animal life includes kangaroos and motorised humans. (Lake Goongarrie, Eastern Goldfields, WA)

Formation of urban areas: in Central Business Districts plant life is sparse amongst buildings, concrete and bitumen; where allowance has been made for plants they generally occur as individual specimens. (Melbourne City, South Central Victoria, Vic.)

Man-Made Formations

FORMATIONS OF URBAN AREAS

The construction of settlements and urban areas implicitly involves the destruction of natural habitats and the construction, sometimes unintentionally, of new vegetative habitats. For instance the seemingly bare areas of bitumen and concrete can be likened to areas of bare ground or rock. Given a crack in the ground, a place where seeds can grow and moisture be retained, then a plant will surely establish itself. Common to cracks in footpaths, walls and steps are various grasses, thistles, docks and dandelions. Bare, shady and moist surfaces often accommodate mosses and lichens. One estimate has been made that there are 30 to 40 species of plants established on and around the inner suburban streets of Melbourne, Vic.

Established gardens and parks form habitats that are structurally similar to grassy woodlands and shrublands. Waterways and sewage farms can be likened to varieties of wetlands. On a larger scale there is a complexity of vegetation formations throughout suburban areas and rural towns and settlements raging from small closed herblands to woodlands and open forests. These man-made formations are commonly found in gardens, parklands, nature strips and roadway plantations. Of

Formation of urban areas: in the suburbs there is less artificial ground cover hence ground cover is more likely to thrive; this garden 'woodland' has a native eucalypt as a dominant with a variety of native and exotic plants in the understorey. (Tay Creggan, South Central Victoria, Vic.)

course many urban areas still retain pockets of the original natural formation though most have been altered to some extent by the accidental or deliberate introduction of exotic species or subjected to alterations by changing environmental conditions,e.g. changed fire frequency, increased runoff, partial clearing, pollution, etc.

FORMATIONS OF RURAL SETTLEMENTS, FARMS, ETC.

In rural settlements variations to natural formations have occurred by the accidental or intentional introduction of exotic species in order to create gardens, improve pastures, etc., as well as by land clearing. In and around most used and disused farmhouses, outbuildings, home paddocks and the like can be seen a variety of introduced plants including exotic trees, shrubs and herbs (generally referred to as weeds), many of which have spread and colonised natural areas of bush, e.g. lantana and blackberry thickets, variagated thistles, dandelions, jimson weed, castor oil plants, etc. Nonetheless where these plants have colonised they may be of such an extent so as to constitute a closed scrub, herbland and so on. Variations to natural formations caused by farming, etc., are mentioned in the transformations of each formation.

Formation of urban areas: a garden woodland dominated by oaks with an exotic grass understorey has been created in this urban park. (Edinborough Gardens, South Central Victoria, Vic.)

Agricultural formation: agriculture requires a guiding hand consequently a certain order is established as can be seen by the neat row of trees in this grove; the understorey grasses appear to be irrigated. (nr Clare, Lower North, SA)

AGRICULTURAL FORMATIONS

Since the arrival of European settlers from the late eighteenth century onwards the Australian landscape has undergone a significant change. The introduction of exotic plants and animals, the felling of timber, large-scale land clearing operations and the subsidary support trappings of modern civilisation have drastically altered the face of the Australian continent.

Notwithstanding the changes brought about by the Aborigines with their fire-stick farming practices, European man, through his actions, has influenced virtually every square kilometre of Australia. Even the vast desert and smaller forested wilderness areas have examples of introduced species of animal life. Much of this change was wrought in ignorance of the natural processes of the environment, processes that today are finally coming to light. As a result many early, and even some quite late agricultural practices have led to numerous problems; land rendered useless by increased salt in the soil, former woodlands being turned into grasslands because trees are unable to re-establish themselves, increased pollution of streams and estuaries by chemical pesticides and weedicides, soil erosion due to the removal of the protective covering of vegetation and the replacement of complex vegetation formations by monospecific plant crops. It is sobering to contemplate that over the millions of years that Australian vegetation evolved, over two-thirds of the continent is in some way affected by the agricultural practices of some 4 to 5 generations of European settlement.

Formation of rural settlements: this property has an exotic open forest surrounding the main buildings with a native open forest on the periphery; open areas support an exotic closed grassland. (nr the Gib, Southern Tablelands, NSW)

To attempt to describe all types of commercial agriculture would require another book. Nonetheless it is possible to group agricultural crops in terms of their plant types.

Agricultural crops dominated by trees or shrubs Represented by orchards and exotic tree plantations. Orchard crops include a wide range of genera including *Citrus* (oranges, lemons, limes, mandarins, grapefruits); *Prunus* (almonds, apricots, cherries, peaches, nectarines, plums); *Malus* (apples); *Persea* (avocado); *Ficus* (figs); *Oles* (olives); *Pyrus* (pears) and *Juglans* (walnuts) among others. Exotic tree plantations are represented by very few species even though such plantations may be locally widespread. Typical species include the softwoods *Pinus radiata* (Monterey pine) and the poplar.

Typical shrubby plants include the industrial crop cotton (*Gossypium* sp.) and the horticultural crops hops (*Humulus* sp.) and grape vines (*Vitus* sp.)

Agricultural crops dominated by herbs Most agricultural crops, both in terms of area and number of products, are represented by herbaceous species. In virtually all cases each crop is characteristic of a 'closed herbland' or 'herbland' formation. Of the POACEAE (grass) family the following genera represent the cereal crops: *Triticum* (wheat), the most widespread of all crops, equal in area to many of Australia's largest vegetation formations; *Avena* (oats); *Hordeum* (barley); *Secale* (rye); *Zea* (maize); *Oryza* (rice); *Sorghum* (sorghum) and various species of millet. The industrial crops include *Saccharum* (sugarcane); *Linum* (linseed); *Nicotiana* (tobacco) as well as the oil crops safflower, soybeans, sunflowers, peanuts, sesame and castor oil plants. Although the industrial crops are not as extensive as the cereal crops in area some 'formations' can be locally quite extensive.

Horticultural crops are many and varied though production is not as widespread or extensive as the grain or industrial crops. Typical plants include members of the LEGUMINOSEAE family (the pulse crops peas, beans, lentils, chick peas, etc.); the cruciferous crops (turnips, rape, cabbage, broccoli, brussels sprouts, radish, etc.; the *Solanum* species potato and the fruits passionfruit, pineapple and the various berries.

The fourth group of herbaceous agricultural crops are the sown pastures. These are found throughout the humid and subhumid regions of Australia, especially in coastal valleys, tableland grazing districts, the wheat-sheep country of the subhumid inland slopes and plains and in some of the northern extensive beef cattle grazing areas. Sown pastures are dominated by a variety of grasses and legumes. Along the humid subtropical coast paspalum is common; further inland and in the southern regions perennial rye grass is the major species. This in turn is replaced by phalaris in the drier country which experiences hot summers whilst Mediterranean legumes (subterranean clover, barrel medic) is common on the driest margins of the temperate subhumid environments. In southern Qld rhodes grass is common while along the tropical humid coast and in the north, Townsville stylo is a typical pasture-forming plant. In the driest regions, including some tropical semi-arid country buffel grass has been sown over a few small areas.

In addition to these intentionally planted crops other varieties of plant life will colonise land which has been cleared, harvested, overgrazed or otherwise left bare. These plants are a variety of herbs generally and collectively called weeds. Some weeds will occur in both crops and pastures. These include parthenium weed, Johnson grass, various burrs, spiny burr grass, cats head, Patersons curse, capeweed, black oats, rye grass, and saffron thistle among others. Other weeds appear in pastures; these include serrated tussock, African love grass, various thistles, fireweed, briar, galvanised burr and khaki weed. Some weeds which occur in crops include bindweeds, phalaris, wild radish, turnip weeds, barley grass, datura, Mexican poppy and so on. Many of these weeds appear after drought-breaking rains and are merely an attempt by nature to recolonise what is otherwise a bare and unvegetated surface. It is ironic that these weeds are virtually all introduced species.

Part Three

AUSTRALIAN PLANT LIFE

Introduction
Divisions and classes of plants
Orders, families, genera and species of plants
The names of plants
**Notes on the Dominant and Major Genera
(and Typical Species)
Notes on the Dominant and Major Families
(and Typical Genera and Species)
Notes on the Dominant and Major Divisions
(and Typical Genera and Species)**

Introduction

DIVISIONS AND CLASSES OF PLANTS

The plant life of Australia, and the rest of the world for that matter, presents a complex array of life forms strewn across landscapes, an array that appears bewildering to the uninitiated, a case of not seeing the forest for the trees. In order to simplify matters the world's plants have been arranged into groups, called phyla or divisions; each representing common aspects of the plants contained therein. There are a number of plant phyla, two of which, the viruses and bacteria, are of no concern within the context of this book. The others are. Of these it is convenient to divide them into two groups, the vascular plants and the non-vascular plants. The vascular plants possess a means of moving water and nutrients throughout the plant, this movement occurring along veins in leaves and through conducting tissue in the stems, etc. Non-vascular plants include all those plants which often do not look like plants. These include algae, fungi, seaweeds, mosses, liverworts, etc. Some of these non-vascular plants produce distinctive plant formations. For further information regarding non-vascular plants see the notes on the dominant and major divisions at the end of this chapter.

The vascular plants are divided into four classes; the ferns, cycads, conifers and flowering plants. Each of these classes, except the cycads (represented in Australia by the burrawang species among others) produces distinctive plant formations. The flowering plants account for most of Australia's formations simply because they account for most of Australia's plant species. The flowering plants or Angiosperms can be subdivided into two groups, the monocots (from monocotyledon which means a plant with only one cotyledon or seed leaf) and dicots (from dicotyledon which means the plant has two seed leaves — a cotyledon is the leaf-forming part of the embryo of seeds). Generally monocots and dicots can be readily distinguished by the following features. Monocots are generally non-woody (exceptions include palms and grass trees), are nearly always small, have numerous roots of equal length, parallel veins in the leaves, and flowers arranged in multiples of three. Dicots are usually woody, are often large (though some are small herbs, e.g. dandelions), have a main root or tap root, a network of veins in the leaves, and flowers arranged in multiples of four or five. One final distinction of the flowering plant is that its seeds are covered.

Of the remaining classes of vascular plants the conifers or Gymnosperms, have uncovered or

Currawang and ironbark. (nr Ashford, North-West Slopes NSW)

naked seeds, the ferns have no seeds but reproduce from spores, while the cycads are sort of a mixture of a flowering plant and a spore-bearing fern.

ORDERS, FAMILIES, GENERA AND SPECIES OF PLANTS

Because of the numerous variations between, and sheer numbers of, all types of vascular and non-vascular plants, they have been further subdivided into orders, families, genera and species. By this classification an order of plants, which constitutes a particular class, is composed of similar but different families (sometimes just one family); likewise similar but different genera (sometimes just one genus) constitute a particular family and similar species (sometimes just one) constitute a particular genus. This book, in order to assemble individual plants into a recognisable and distinctive formation, concentrates on the major or dominant genus (sometimes family) of plants present in any specific area.

As already mentioned a genus is composed of one or more similar species; a species on the other hand is the last basic unit of classification and includes all those plants which most resemble each other and are capable of reproducing themselves by breeding with each other but not with any other plant. Needless to say, like all classifications about nature and especially plant life there are exceptions to this rule; some species are capable of breeding with other species of the same genus.

The remainder of this chapter is given over to descriptions of the various genera whose species dominate the formations described in this book. In the case where formations are composed of a myriad of species and genera, e.g. heaths, etc., then the characteristic plant families have been described.

THE NAMES OF PLANTS

Virtually all plants that have been discovered and studied have at least one name, a scientific name, which is composed of two parts and is normally written in italics. The first part of the name, which begins with a capital letter denotes the plant's genus, e.g. *Eucalyptus, Acacia,* etc.

The second part denotes its species, e.g. *Eucalyptus maculata* so differentiating it from other species of the same genus. In addition many plants have at least one common or vernacular name though two or more is not unusual. This book concentrates on using a common name where possible in order to make the information more accessible to readers. Because of the diversity of common names for individual plants the reader should be prepared to consult the index when necessary as in nearly all cases only one common name is given.

In some instances plants may have more than one scientific name denoting their species. For instance the sea box (a dense shrub which is also known as a heath box, camel bush, etc.) has the scientific name *Alyxia buxifolia*. It has also been referred to as *Alyxia capitellata*. Both names are synonymous so the plant may be referred to as *Alyxia buxifolia* syn. *capitellata*.

When writing down a number of plants with the same genus name it is usual to abbreviate the genus name to the capital letter for the second and following names, e.g. the eucalypts river red gum, blackbutt and Sydney peppermint would be written *Eucalyptus camaldulensis, E. pilularis* and *E. piperita*.

Hairpin banksia. (nr Nowra, South Coast, NSW)

Young grey mangrove; note the breathing tubes. (Wagonga Inlet, South Coast, NSW)

Notes on the Dominant and Major Genera (and Typical Species)

As mentioned in Closed forests, Open forests, Woodlands, Open woodlands, Closed scrubs, Open scrubs, Shrublands, Open shrublands and fernlands.

ACACIA   MIMOSACEAE

The *Acacia* genus is represented by over 700 Australian species which are found in many formation types. They dominate much of the country's tall shrublands (mulga), form quite extensive open forests (brigalow) and occur in the understorey of most eucalypt open forests. In fact the sheer number and widespread extent of *Acacias* must make it the second major ubiquitous genera to dominate Australia's vegetated landscapes, the eucalypts being first.

Acacias, or wattles as they are commonly known, are generally short-lived plants, most completing their lives in 20 years or less. There are exceptions though; mulga, blackwood and cedar wattle are thought to live over 100 years while the waddywood, a rare plant found on the margins of the Simpson Desert, is assumed to be very old. This tree grows at a rate of 30 cm every 200 years. Many of these trees are over 10 m high.

Acacias are either of tree or shrub form although at times it is difficult to tell whether a particular specimum is a tree or shrub. Most species are relatively short, about 5 to 7 m although some species grow to over 20 m. The genus is characterised by its fine foliage when young. As a young plant it exhibits feathery or bipinnate leaves which, in most cases, are replaced on the growing plant by phyllodes. Some adult plants maintain their bipinnate foliage, e.g. Cootamundra wattle, black wattle. With a few exceptions the bipinnate *Acacias* (officially *Bipinnattae*) are found in the wetter regions of the country. Phyllodes come in many shapes and sizes including spikes, needles and flat leaf-like forms. The flat phyllodes may have sharp, partly rounded or rounded ends and may be narrow, curved, straight or have small hooks on their ends. In a few species the phyllodes are absent entirely.

The flowers of *Acacias* are very tiny. What is generally seen is a mass of flowers on relatively long stamens which may be grouped together as cylindrical rods or globular heads. Different *Acacias* flower at different times of the year, the colours of their blossoms varying with species and soil type. Generally wattle blossoms are clear yellow though different shades of red and off-white are found. All *Acacias* contain their seeds in seed pods. Normally the bark of wattles is dark and often rough with deep furrows.

The maintainance of *Acacia* stands is important for the nitrogen-fixing nodules on their roots supply nutrients to an (often) otherwise infertile soil. The nutrients supply not only the *Acacias* themselves but also other plants within that particular community. Unfortunately those most extensive stands of semi-arid and arid *Acacias*, the mulga, being palatable to stock, have, in some places, suffered to such an extent that they are unable to re-establish themselves. In their place the hopbushes and emu bushes, both unpalatable to stock, occupy the dominant position of these former *Acacia* formations.

Acacias are often difficult to differentiate. Mulga, the most widespread wattle may be a shrub or small open tree 3 to 7 m tall with erect narrow grey phyllodes, yellow spiky flowers and hard fissured bark. Umbrella mulga is similar but with spreading branches and curved tips on its phyllodes. Bramble wattle, often found as dense thickets on alluvial plains is a stiff grey-green shrub or tree up to 7 m tall with many crooked branches. The phyllodes are stiff and exhibit a vein down their centres. Weeping myall is an erect small tree 5 to 10 m tall with a rounded crown, silvery foliage and willow-like appearance. This plant is common on alluvial flats throughout the eastern subhumid/semi-arid inland. Brigalow, a tree common in Queensland, is generally slender with a dark trunk and a silvery open crown. In the wetter areas the blackwood commonly occurs in the understorey of tall open forests. This wattle is a tree some 6 to 30 m tall with a dense dark-green crown. The phyllodes are green, up to 14 cm long and exhibit 3 to 5 veins.

ACMENA   MYRTACEAE

A small genus with approximately 12 Australian species, all virtually limited to the subtropical and tropical rainforests. One species, the lilli-pilli is common throughout the eastern rainforests. It is a dense, dark green tree some 8 to 30 m high with smooth, grey bark on its trunk. The flowers are small and numerous. In the past the *Acmena* genus was included in, or considered to be a part of, the *Eugenia* genus.

ADANSONIA   BOMBACACEAE

The genus is represented by the nothern baobab, a tree that grows throughout the tropical woodlands of the Kimberleys and Ord-Victoria regions. It has an immense trunk and reaches a height of 23 m. (N.B. do not confuse with the Queensland bottle tree.)

ALSTONIA   APOCYNACEAE

A genus of 30 species, 2 of which appear to be endemic. They are found in the northern grassy forests and monsoonal rainforests. The species are the northern milkwood, an evergreen tree with rough bark and an open spreading crown which grows to 15 m, and the white cheesewood, a tall (reaches 33 m) tree with smooth, grey bark and a pagoda-like crown. In rainforests these trees seldom exceed 20 m.

ANGOPHORA   MYRTACEAE

A totally Australian genus of 9 species which includes the rough-barked apple and smooth-barked apple. Most *Angophoras* are trees though a few are shrubs. Tree heights vary from 6 to 25 m. Generally *Angophoras* are found in the east coast forests and may be mistaken for some types of gums.

ARAUCARIA   ARAUCARIACEAE

There are 3 species of this genus on Australian territory, the Bunya pine, the hoop pine and the Norfolk Island pine. The first 2 species are characteristic of some subtropical rainforests. *Araucarias* are tall pines with horizontal branches and spiky leaves. Heights vary from 20 to 45 m.

ARCHONTOPHOENIX   ARECAEAE

This Australian palm genus has 2 or 3 species, the most common being the Bangalow palm, a characteristic species of tropical and northern subtropical rainforests. Tree heights range from 3 to 15 m, the trunk is slender and erect and the leaves are up to 4 m long. The species prefers damp, even swampy environments, where in some places it forms distinctive rainforest formations.

ARTHROCNEMUM   CHENOPODIACEAE

See CHENOPODIACEAE family, next section.

ATALAYA   SAPINDACEAE

This genus is typified by the whitewood, a tall shrub or small tree some 6 to 12 m high. Generally the trunk divides into two near the ground and carries a moderately dense crown. It has an extensive range throughout inland Australia, reaching the coast in the north-west of W.A.

ATHEROSPERMA   MONIMIACEAE

This genus has one species and is restricted to the cool, humid areas of south-east Australia and Tasmania especially in cool temperate rainforests and on the margins of tall open forests. The species is the southern sassafras, a moderately short tree growing to 12 m high. It has a dense, spreading crown, narrow leaves (up to 10 cm long) and showy flowers. (N.B. do not confuse with the sassafras.)

ATRIPLEX   CHENOPODIACEAE

A large genus with about 40 Australian species. Typical species include the bladder saltbush, old-man saltbush and pop saltbush. All species are shrubs and range in height from 50 cm (bladder saltbush) to 3 m (old-man saltbush). Generally they have a blue-grey to silver-grey appearance with circular or oval leaves. *Atriplex* species are found throughout southern semi-arid and arid Australia either as a dominant shrub in low shrublands or within the understorey of some woodlands and open woodlands.

ATHROTAXIS   TAXODIACEAE

A small genus of 3 species including the King William pine and pencil pine, both plants being characteristic of the cool temperate rainforests of Tasmania. The King William pine may grow to 30 m, the other species being shorter. The bark of *Athrotaxis* plants is red-brown and soft and the leaves, arranged spirally on branchlets, are small and pointed.

AVICENNA   VERBENACEAE

This genus is represented by the grey or white mangrove, a tree or shrub found throughout Australian mangrove formations including those of the southern regions where it is the only species present. The grey mangrove varies from a small shrub to a medium-sized tree possessing a large trunk and glossy leaves. A characteristic feature of the grey mangrove is its breathing tubes and the fact that it is situated at the edge of mangrove formations when more than one species is present.

BANKSIA   PROTEACEAE

Banksias are entirely Australian plants (with one exception in New Guinea). There are about 80 species, most of which are found in Western Australia. Banksias are either of shrub or tree form with heights generally below 10 m. Banksias have showy flowering heads and as trees they exhibit a tough and often contorted trunk and branches. In some species the leaves are large and saw-toothed. Typically they are found on sandy soils in the southern parts of Australia. Typical species include the giant banksia, holly-leaved banksia, coast banksia and silver banksia.

BASSIA
CHENOPODIACEAE

See CHENOPODIACEAE family, next section.

BAUHINIA (LYSIPHYLLUM)
CAESALPINIACEAE

This genus has about 5 species in Australia. Most Bauhinias are of tree form between 5 and 10 m tall. They generally exhibit a slender trunk with smooth bark and a spreading crown. Typical species include the bean tree and Queensland ebony. Bauhinias are leafless during the late winter and early spring. They are found throughout the tropical northern and north-eastern temperate subhumid regions of Australia.

BOMBAX
BOMBACACEAE

A genus with a few Australian species commonly found in rainforests. One species, the silk cotton tree, found in semi-deciduous rainforests, grows to a height of 30 m and loses some of its leaves during dry seasons.

Bottletree trunk and branches (Blackall, the Mid-West, Qld)

BRACHYCHITON
STERCULIACEAE

This genus has about 16 species in Australia. Typical species include the Illawarra flame tree, various kurrajongs and the Queensland bottle tree. Species are of tree form and range in height from 4 to 20 m. Generally kurrajongs have a short bole and a large spreading canopy. The Queensland bottle tree has a large swollen bole and a large crown while the Illawarra flame tree, with its scarlet red flowers, is a tall tree of pyramidal form. (N.B. do not confuse the Queensland bottle tree with the northern baobab.)

CALLITRIS
CUPRESSACEAE

The genus *Callitris* has only a handful of species in Australia, nonetheless the genus is widespread throughout the subhumid and semi-arid regions and even extends to drier coastal areas. They have a tree form and range in height from 2 to over 30 m. In harsh rocky habitats they exhibit a twisted and stunted form. Typical species include the white cypress pine, the northern cypress pine, the black cypress pine and the Rottnest Island cypress pine. Overall they appear like pines from a distance and exhibit a tall pyramidal shape under ideal conditions.

Callitris trees have tiny scale-like leaves which whorl around small branchlets and its fruit is composed of 6 woody scales or valves, 3 large and 3 small. The bark is rough and deeply furrowed and extends to the smallest branches. It has a soft timber. (N.B. do not confuse with the *Casuarinas*.)

CANARIUM
BURSERACEAE

This genus is represented by the Melville Island white beech, a tall tree that reaches 20 m on rainforest or coastal fringes in the monsoonal north. The trunk is generally straight, the crown broad and spreading. In coastal rainforest areas it occurs just above the high-water mark. The tree is deciduous during the dry season.

CASSIA
CAESALPINIACEAE

Cassia is a large genus with over 400 species, 40 of which are found in Australia. Most are located in the semi-arid and arid interior. Most Australian *Cassias* are dense, bushy shrubs some 1 to 3 m tall. Their flowers are generally yellow. Typical species include the silver cassia and desert cassia.

CASUARINA & ALLOCASUARINA
CASUARINACEAE

The genera *Casuarina* and *Allocasuarina* have approximately 40 species and are found throughout the semi-arid and arid interior of the country as well as in the higher rainfall coastal areas. They usually take the form of trees which range in height from 2 to over 30 m. Major species include the river she-oak, forest she-oak, belah, buloke, desert oak, northern she-oak, rock she-oak and drooping she-oak. Some plants exhibit a pyramidal form somewhat similar to the traditional Christmas tree while others exhibit a globular, drooping form. Some, like the belah, are asymmetrical. *Casuarinas* and *Allocasuarinas* do not have leaves in the normal sense but long needle-like branchlets. Their real leaves are tiny scales which encircle the branchlets at regular intervals. On female trees

River she-oaks. (Shoalhaven River, South Coast, NSW)

Red bloodwood. (Yalwal Gap, South Coast, NSW)

small, woody cones are attached to the major branchlets. The bark is generally rough and hard and persists to the smaller branches. (N.B. do not confuse with the *Callitris* species of cypress pines.)

CERATOPETALUM   CUNONIACEAE
A small genus with 5 Australian species growing either as trees or tall shrubs. They have leathery leaves and small flowers. A typical species is the coachwood, a tree of subtropical rainforests which may occur in pure stands. The bark of the coachwood is rough and fragrant, the trunk is up to 1 m in diameter and erect while the crown is spreading with large leaves up to 15 cm long.

CHENOPODIUM   CHENOPODIACEAE
The species of this genera are erect perennial shrubs which grow to a height of 1 to 2 m. Typical species include the nitre goosefoot and golden goosefoot. Generally these plants are found along drainage lines and on riverflats in the southern semi-arid country.

Decorticating bark; mountain gum. (Coolamon Stn, Snowy Mountains, NSW)

CINNAMOMUM   LAURACEAE
Not a widespread genus although one species is found within the cloud rainforests of northern Queensland. This species, which may reach a height of 15 m, is a relative of the camphor laurel.

CUPANIOPSIS   SAPINDACEAE
A genus of 4 or 5 species in Australia, one of which is the tuckeroo, a short tree (up to 10 m) found on the monsoonal rainforest fringes as well as in other east coast forests. Tuckeroos are slender trees with spreading branches that may reach to the ground.

CYANTHEA   CYATHEACEAE
There are about 9 species of *Cyanthea* in Australia. All species are found in the eastern humid regions and are represented by terrestrial ferns with thick, massive trunks which produce spirally arranged fronds. The stalks of the fronds are scaly. A typical species is the rough tree fern, a plant which may grow to 14 m, have 4-m-long fronds and a trunk up to 1.5 m in diameter.

Spotted gum sapling. (Bamarang, South Coast, NSW)

153

DICKSONIA
DICKSONIACEAE

A small Australian genus of tree ferns similar in appearance to *Cyanthea* species but without the scales on the frond stalks. The trunk exhibits fine, soft rootlets. Plants are generally restricted to the cooler, humid eastern and southern regions. A typical species is the soft tree fern.

DODONAEA
SAPINDACEAE

Commonly known as hopbushes this genus has a wide distribution in the southern arid, semi-arid and subhumid regions. Generally they are small, compact shrubs with many stems at ground level. Heights range from 1.5 to 4 m.

DORYPHORA
MONIMIACEAE

A small genus best known by the widespread sassafras tree which is found throughout the east coast mainland rainforests. (N.B. do not confuse with the southern sassafras.) The sassafras tree grows from 10 to 25 m tall, exhibits grey bark and has dark green aromatic leaves with a distinct vein network on their paler undersides. Flowers are white and star-shaped.

EREMOPHILA
MYOPORACEAE

These are exclusively Australian plants with approximately 90 or more species. Most *Eremophilas*, commonly called emu bushes or native fuchsia, are densely branched shrubs some 1 to 4 m high. Occasionally they exhibit a tree habit with 2-m-long trunks and a maximum height over 6 m. They are an attractive bush with long, drooping green leaves and bell-shaped flowers. Typical species include the native fuchsia, berrigan and budda. *Eremophilas* are typically found in semi-arid and arid areas.

ERYTHROPHLEUM
CAESALPINIACEAE

This genus is typified by the ironwood species. (N.B. do not confuse with the *Acacia* species with the same common name), an evergreen or semi-deciduous species of the northern open forests. Generally it exhibits a spreading and dense crown of dark, green leaves. The bark is tessellated and has a dark grey colour.

EUCALYPTUS
MYRTACEAE

The *Eucalyptus* genus is *the* characteristic Australian genus. Located in all but the most extreme environments the eucalypts account for a least 445 species, subspecies and hybrids (previous estimates were over 600 species). They form considerable tracts of the country's open forests, woodlands and open scrubs.

As they are so widespread and the genus so extensive there is a great range of forms, heights and densities. Most species are trees ranging in height from below 3 m to over 100 m, quite a few are shrubs, some of which grow to 20 m or so while a few shrubs are little more than two or three slender stems carrying a minor leafy crown.

Classification of eucalypts

Such a large genus represents problems in classification. One attempt, by Pryor and Johnson (1971) was to divide the genus into four subgenera. These subgenera are *blakella, corymbia, monocalyptus* and *symphomyrtus*. Earlier Pryor had subdivided the eucalypts into the following groups; bloodwoods, red gums, blue gums, stringybarks, ashes, peppermints, boxes and ironbarks. Unfortunately not all trees fitted neatly into this grouping. Another person, Blakely (1965) divided these plants into bloodwoods, eastern blue gums, grey gums, red gums, southern blue gums, stringybarks, ashes, snow gums, peppermints, boxes and ironbarks. Again not all trees would fit into this scheme. Earlier attempts classified eucalypts by their bark and even though this is less than perfect it does allow lay people to at least attempt to group eucalypts into some sort of arrangement.

Bark groupings

There are 6 bark groupings into which a good many eucalypts can be slotted. These groupings roughly correspond to the earlier Pryor grouping although there are exceptions. The bark groupings are gums, bloodwoods, stringybarks (including mahoganies),

Bloodwood bark type −1; red bloodwood. (Yalwal Gap, South Coast, NSW)

ironbarks, boxes and peppermints. In addition some trees exhibit rough bark on their bases and over much of the trunk, above which the trunk and branches are smooth; these trees are commonly referred to as half-barks. Half-barks provide another 'bark' type.

Differentiating the bark of eucalypts is not too difficult.

Gums are distinguished by smooth bark on the trunks and branches with perhaps a few rough patches near the base. Usually the bark is shed annually and may hang in strips on the trees or fly off in the wind. Some people confuse the shredded, hanging bark for stringybarks. This is wrong.

Bloodwoods have rough, flaky or corky bark that extends to the smallest branches though it is often smooth on the twigs. It can be pulled off by hand.

Stringybarks (including some mahoganies) exhibit deep furrows surrounded by long, rough fibres that, if pulled, will run up the trunk. The bark covers all the branches. Often the furrows partially spiral around the trunk.

Ironbarks possess hard, deeply furrowed bark which is persistent to the smallest branches. It cannot be pulled off by hand unless it is old. Generally the furrows are quite straight.

Boxes have thin, subfibrous bark exhibiting shallow cracks. It comes off only in flakes or small sheets and covers the trunk and branches.

Peppermints have loose, fibrous bark without furrows. The bark generally only covers the trunks, the upper branches being smooth. Peppermints can also be distinguished by the strong peppermint odour of the crushed leaves.

Half-barks have already been described.

Box bark type. (Native Dog Bore, Upper Darling, NSW)

A fair number of eucalypts are distinguished by their common names as being a particular type of gum, ironbark or peppermint and so on. For example ghost gums, red ironbarks, narrow-leafed peppermints. These names are generally based on their bark type but a tree's common name is by no means indicative of the group to which it belongs in the later and more modern classifications. For instance the spotted gum belongs to the bloodwood group in some classifications while some ironbarks do not exhibit the typical ironbark bark.

Bloodwood bark type −2.

Gum bark type; scribbly gum.

Peppermint bark type.

155

Beefwood tree in silhouette. (Mootwingee, Far West, NSW)

Types of eucalypts

Gums are a widespread group though by far the best specimens are found in the tall open forests of eastern and southern Australia. Here they reach over 50 m high with clean, tall trunks topped by open crowns. Other gums, in drier areas or on poorer soils produce forests of shorter stature, their smooth trunks holding deeper crowns. Picturesque is the river red gum common throughout virtually all mainland Australian regions. Like most other red gums it has a short bole and thick, heavy widespread branches which give it a majestic appearance. Virtually limited to the higher and colder climates are the snow gum and related species, many of which exhibit a mallee form. In most cases they have irregular stems holding open crowns and particularly attractive markings on their trunks.

Bloodwoods are widespread throughout the northern and coastal eastern regions of the country. Generally they occupy drier or less favourable sites than the gums. The bloodwood is named after the red kino which issues from 'bleeding' trees. Generally they are of low stature, many are merely shrubs, though in some areas they grow to 30 m in height.

Stringybarks are mainly found in eastern and south-eastern coastal and subcoastal regions of Australia. In other areas of the country there are species which have stringy barks but are not strictly included in the stringybark group (depending on which classification is being used). Generally stringybarks grow on the less fertile soils, reach 20 to 40 m in height and form extensive stands in open forest and woodland formations. Virtually all stringybarks are readily identifiable by their bark.

Stringybark bark type. (Yalwal Gap, South Coast, NSW)

Ashes are important timber trees and include among their species the tallest flowering plants in the world. Nonetheless some ashes are small trees or mallees. Typically ashes are trees of the cooler tall open forests of south-eastern Australia. They often grow in pure stands where they form attractive forests (before logging). Ashes generally have tall and straight trunks supporting relatively small crowns. The bark of ash trees is variable; their heights may reach over 100 m.

Ironbarks are distinctive trees and are usually easily recognisable; there are a few ironbarks that have relatively soft bark. Ironbarks are found throughout the eastern and northern mainland regions and are most common in subhumid inland regions where they form open forests and woodlands, often in alliance with the white cypress pine. Rarely do ironbarks exceed 30 m in height.

Boxes are, to a large extent, trees of the inland where they form (or once did) extensive woodlands, especially in the eastern subhumid regions. Most trees are of a moderate height, below 25 m, while a few species are shrubs. Some species of boxes are found in the drier coastal and subcoastal regions.

Peppermints are attractive trees often with pendulous foliage. They prefer cool climates so are widespread along the tablelands and western slopes of the south-east mainland and in Tasmania. A few species inhabit the coastal regions, generally on less fertile soils. Due to their low stature, less than 25 m, and their affiliations with other cool-climate eucalypts, they occasionally form a tree layer in the understorey of ash and gum tall open forests. (N.B. do not confuse with the *Agonis* species Western Australian peppermint commonly found in the understorey of tall open forests and open forests in that State.)

Mallees are shrubby eucalypts virtually restricted to the subhumid/semi-arid country of southern Australia on sandy soils or to a few restricted habitats in eastern montane, coastal and subcoastal regions, usually on poor soils. As the mallee is as much a form as a distinctive grouping some otherwise tree-like plants assume the mallee form in extreme environments, e.g. snow gums. Such formations in this text are referred to as wet mallee formations. 'Genuine' mallees exhibit a short stature, usually less than 7 m, many stems emanating from a common root stock, and they often have smooth gum-like bark.

Other features

The classification and identification of eucalypts is not made any easier by the fact that size, shape, bark type and leaf size can vary within species from place to place due to variations in climate, soil and density of vegetation. It is also made difficult by the fact that some trees are hybrids, that is a cross between two different species. Hybrids occur within each subgeneric group (as described by Pryor and Johnson) and require the simultaneous flowering of both parents. One feature of hybrids is that they seem to result from human interference for most occur on the margins of cleared land, etc.

Eucalypts are well adapted to handle environmental stress although not all species possess these characteristics. Some plants are definite drought resisters and are capable of extracting moisture by having extensive root systems and tough wilt-resistent leaves that droop to avoid the intense radiation of the mid-summer sun. Other species are

Royal hakea. (East Mt Barren, South-Coastal Region, WA)

cold resisters, e.g. snow gums, cider gums, and are able to exist in subzero temperatures providing the soil does not freeze. Many eucalypts are able to survive destruction, especially by fire, by having lignotubers at the base of their stems. Lignotubers are woody swellings containing buds (and food reserves) from which new plants can grow. Mallee roots are large lignotubers. Other means of survival include epicormic shoots which grow from concealed buds protected by thick, persistent, insulating bark. These shoots produce leaves enabling photosynthesis to continue. This is important if the crown has been totally destroyed. Some eucalypts do not possess these properties but are capable of releasing seeds from fruit capsules which open when affected by the intense heat of a fire.

The maintenance of standing eucalypt forests is important in the control of soil erosion. In moist environments the crown provides protection for the shrubby understorey which in turn covers a ground layer of mosses and fallen leaves. This ground layer absorbs rainwater which in turn is gradually released thus regulating surface runoff and stream flow. In dry areas stands of trees maintain a ground surface mulch of humus as well as breaking the velocity of winds thereby minimising the effects of wind erosion. These erosion controls are also affected by the maintenance of other types of vegetative cover.

EUODIA
RUTACEAE

This genus has 12 species, mostly restricted to Australia. One species, the evodia occurs in the northern monsoonal rainforests. It grows to 15 m, has rough, creamy bark and pink, densely clustered flowers.

FICUS
MORACEAE

A relatively large genus with a number of Australian species which are found in the tropical northern and humid eastern regions of the mainland. Most species occur as large and majestic trees with smooth, light trunks, large leaves and a dense crown. Typical species include the Morton Bay fig, Port Jackson fig and the deciduous fig. Tree height varies from 6 to 45 m.

FLINDERSIA
RUTACEAE

A small genus of about 14 Australian species, mainly restricted to rainforests. Typical species include the crows ash, Queensland maple and the dry country species, leopardwood. The leopardwood is found in the subhumid/semi-arid regions of south-east Australia where it often grows in alliance with wilga (*Geijera* sp.). The leopardwood has distinctive 'leopard' spots on its trunk. This graceful, pendulous tree grows to a height of 10 m while the rainforest species reach 30 m or more.

GEIJERA
RUTACEAE

A small genus of 5 Australian species. The most common species of the genus is wilga, a low-growing, ornamental tree some 5 to 8 m tall. Wilga trees are found in the subhumid/semi-arid country of south-eastern Australia, or in alliance with leopardwood (*Flindersia* sp.). Another species, the scrub wilga, grows to nearly 30 m in the northern subtropical rainforests. Generally the bark of *Geijera* species is dark and rough while the leaves are long and thin.

GREVILLEA
PROTEACEAE

This is a large genus with over 250 species, virtually all being Australian plants. Most species are shrubs but a few are trees; these include the beefwood of the semi-arid and arid interior and the silky oak of the subtropical rainforests. Grevillea trees grow to a height of 3 to 8 m (beefwoods) or 15 to 30 m (silky oaks). A shrub form of this genus, *G. gordoniana,* is common along the temperate subhumid/semi-arid coast of Western Australia. Generally the bark of grevillea trees is furrowed and fissured and the leaves are long.

HAKEA
PROTEACEAE

This is a large Australian genus with about 140 species, at least half of which are confined to the south-west of Western Australia. Most *Hakeas* exhibit a shrub form although a few are trees, for example the needlewood and corkwood of the semi-arid and arid country. *Hakeas* are easily identified by their hard, woody capsule which divides into two to release 2 winged seeds. Generally its leaves are small with sharp points. Most shrubs are generally less than 2 m in height while the trees are generally less than 10 m. The bark of the trees is rough and corky, the trunk often twisted while the crown is dense with needle-like foliage.

HETERODENDRUM
SAPINDACEAE

A very small genus with about 5 Australian species. Most are shrubs although one, the inland rosewood, sometimes exhibits a tree-like form. The tree is short, less than 8 m, with large, irregular branches, a dense crown and thick, dark-brown, deeply fissured bark. The inland rosewood is found in the semi-arid and arid regions south of the tropics.

LEPTOSPERMUM
MYRTACEAE

This genus is mainly composed of shrubby species although tree forms do occur. Generally tea-trees, as they are commonly known (N.B. do not confuse with paperbarks, *Melaleuca* spp), have trunk and branches covered with loose, flaky bark, short leaves and numerous spring flowers. They are characteristically Australian plants and occur throughout the country, especially in southern and eastern coastal regions. A typical species is the coastal tea-tree.

LIVISTONIA
ARECACEAE

A genus of palms with about 6 Australian species which include the cabbage-tree palm, Millstream palm and red-leaved palm. These species are found in the tropical northern and humid eastern regions of the country with isolated stands in suitable arid and semi-arid regions. Trees range in height from 4 to 30 m, they have tall, erect and generally slender trunks, long leaves (over 1 m) and compact, dense crowns. Most species occur within or near rainforests or along watercourses.

MAIREANA
CHENOPODIACEAE

A large genus, formerly called *Kochia,* with about 40 Australian species. Typical species include the pearl bluebush, black bluebush, southern bluebush and cotton bluebush. All species have shrub forms and heights range from 1 to 2 m. The leaves are generally fleshy. The bluebushes are found in similar regions to the saltbush (*Atriplex* spp) species.

Swamp paperbark. (nr Spearwood, Coastal Plain, WA)

MELALEUCA   MYRTACEAE

This is a large Australian genus (bar one) of some 140 species. They are either of shrub or tree habit and have attractive leaves. Some species are readily indentifiable by their papery bark. (N.B. do not confuse with the tea-trees, *Leptospermum* spp which may also have a papery bark.) Most *Melaleucas* are of short stature with heights generally below 10 m. In the tropics some species may grow to 20 m or more. Generally their crowns are dense with spreading branches while their form, depending on the density of growth, is either tall and erect or short and bushy. *Melaleucas* are commonly found in wet environments, often soggy, sandy places, such as along coasts, estuaries, drainage lines, in swamps, etc. Typical species include the swamp paperbark, white paperbark, inland paperbark and moonah.

MYOPORUM   MYOPORACEAE

This genus has about 20 Australian species, the two most common being the sugarwood and boobialla. *Myoporum* species are either prostrate, ground-covering plants, shrubs or trees. The sugarwood and boobialla are small trees, sometimes shrubs, which grow to 10 m or so. They have a rough, flaky bark and fleshy leaves. The branchlets on the sugarwood are often drooping while its leaves are serrated.

MYRISTICA   MYRISTICACEAE

The genus is represented by the wild nutmeg, a tree found in the drier monsoonal and riverbank rainforests of the Northern Territory. The height varies from 6 to 13 m; it has brown and either finely fissured or scaly bark with thick, leathery dark green (above) leaves with off-white undersides.

NOTHOFAGUS   FAGACEAE

A small genus with 3 Australian species. As they belong to the beech family the *Nothofagus* plants are truly deciduous. Species are the Antarctic beech (myrtle beech), deciduous beech and tanglefoot. The tanglefoot is often a shrub, the others are trees reaching over 30 m in ideal conditions. The trees are characteristic of cool temperate rainforests and often occur in pure stands. They exhibit dense foliage, rounded leaves and have thick, rough bark on a large trunk.

OWENIA   MELIACEAE

A small Australian genus of 6 species exhibiting either a shrub or tree form. Generally the bark is corky, the leaves large and thick. Typical species include the emu apple and desert walnut.

PACHYCORNIA   CHENOPODIACEAE

See CHENOPODIACEAE family, next section.

PANDANUS   PANDANACEAE

A genus with 12 Australian species. A typical species is the screw palm. The screw palm is common throughout monsoonal northern Australia. Generally *Pandanus* species grow to 7 m in height, have long, thin leaves and may exhibit prop roots at their base. The screw palm does not exhibit these roots. *Pandanus* species, some of which are found along the tropical and eastern subtropical coasts, inhabit stream banks, coastlines and fringe waterlily lagoons.

PHYLLOLLADUS   PODOCARPACEAE

A small genus with one Australian species, the celery-top pine, a characteristic plant of Tasmanian cool temperate rainforests. The celery-top pine is 15 to 30 m tall, has hard, thick and scaly bark, flattened, wedge-shaped leaves and a slender form with a light, rather attractive, crown.

PINUS   PINACEAE

The *Pinus* is not an Australian genus but since European settlement this genus has become common within most of the country's softwood plantations. The most common species is the Monterey pine. Other species are also used in plantations and for ornamental planting, etc.

PODOCARPUS   PODOCARPACEAE

A small genus commonly referred to as the plum pines. Plants are either dense shrubs or trees and they are found in rainforests and some open forests. The male plants exhibit small 'pine' cones. Plum pines emit a resinous pine-like smell.

PONGAMIA   FABACEAE

A genus of one species found in northern Australia (and South-East Asia) along seashores and in monsoonal rainforests. The species is the Indian beech, a tree that grows to 14 m. It has a short trunk, dense crown and widely spreading branches with sweet smelling flowers that grow to a length of 12.5 cm.

SALICORNIA   CHENOPODIACEAE
See CHENOPODIACEAE family, next section.

SALSOLA   CHENOPODIACEAE
See CHENOPODIACEAE family, next section.

SCHEFFLERA   ARALIACEAE
In the wet monsoonal rainforests of northern Australia grows the *Schefflera* representative, the umbrella tree, a plant that grows to 20 m and has a large spreading crown. Leaves are glossy and dark green, flowers are a dull pink, its fleshy seeds a dark red.

STERCULIA   STERCULIACEAE
Some species of this genus are found throughout South-East Asia, e.g. the kelumpang; this species is deciduous, grows to 10 m in the northern monsoonal rainforests and has large palmate leaves. Another species, the endemic red-fruited kurrajong occurs in coastal rainforests of the tropics. It has smooth grey bark and a dense canopy of leaves which fall in areas experiencing a dry season.

SYNCARPIA   MYRTACEAE
A small genus with 4 Australian species. Most common is the turpentine, an erect, densely crowned, rough-barked species that is found in east coast tall open forests and on the margins of nearby rainforests.

TERMINALIA   COMBRETACEAE
This genus is widespread throughout the tropics and there are 29 Australian species. The trees are deciduous or partly deciduous. Typical species include the nutwood, okari and kotamba. The plants are either trees or shrubs, usually with large leaves. Flowers are small. In the tree form the plant is erect with a compact, rounded crown. The nutwood looks a little like a weeping willow and has dark, tessellated bark. Generally tree height varies between 5 and 15 m with some species reaching 30 m.

TRISTANIA   MYRTACEAE
With 13 Australian species the *Tristania* genus is better known by the brush box and watergum species. These two species occur in the rainforests and on the margins of tall open forests in eastern Australia. Some other species occur as tall shrubs.

(N.B. the following genera have not been discussed: *Argyrodendron, Balanops, Hylandia, Pisonia, Schizomeria, Sloanea.*)

Notes on the Dominant and Major Families (and Typical Genera and Species)

As mentioned in Closed heaths, Open heaths, Closed herblands, Herblands, Open herblands and Vegetation of extreme and varied habitats within the upperstorey (where applicable).

ASTERACEAE   daisy family
This is a very large family of at least 800 Australian species. Known as the daisy family, representatives are found in virtually all formations. Daisies are most obvious in those landscapes dominated by herbs, e.g. tall alpine herblands and ephemeral herblands. Typical species include billy buttons, everlastings, poached-egg daisies, groundsels, snow daisies, white mountain daisies and the *Olearia* genus of daisy bushes.

CASUARINACEAE   she-oak family
The she-oak family has representatives in heath formations.

CHENOPODIACEAE   chenopod family
Members of this family have already been mentioned in the previous notes. Nonetheless the CHENOPODIACEAE or goosefoot family deserves a mention as they are characteristic of many of the southern semi-arid and arid landscapes as well as salty estuarine environments. Goosefoots or chenopods are salt-tolerant plants with thick skins. All are shrubs. The main genera are *Atriplex, Maireana* and *Chenopodium* as well as *Bassia,* a genus that produces spiny seeds or burrs, and *Salsola,* species of which become detached from the earth after death and roll around in the wind. These are commonly known as roly-polies. Also included in this family are the samphires. Samphires are a grouping of those genera which represent the really salt-tolerant plants. Genera include *Arthrocnemum, Pachycornia* and *Salicornia*. Species of these genera are commonly found around salt lakes and on coastal salt marshes. The plants themselves are short shrubs with hard stems topped by succulent green growth.

CYPERACEAE   sedge family
The sedge family is characterised by having no petals to their flowers and by generally possessing a solid, sometimes cylindrical stem surrounded by a sheath of leaves. Sometimes the leaves are particu-

Tall spike-rushes. (Calymea Creek, South Coast, NSW)

larly sharp. Sedges grow in water or in wet soil. Typical species include button grass and club rushes.

EPACRIDACEAE southern heath family

This is the southern heath family and should not be confused with the true heath family (ERICACEAE) of which Australia has very few species. Southern heaths are generally small shrubs with pointed leaves and tubular white, pink or red flowers. The shrubs are generally quite dense. One genus, the *Epacris* has about 40 species which are common to the south-eastern mainland and Tasmanian heaths. Other types are virtually restricted to Tasmania. These include the *Richea* (giant grass tree or pandanus) and the *Cyathodes* (mountain berries) genera.

FABACEAE pea family

A common family found throughout Australia. The Fabaceae or pea family has numerous species in virtually all vegetation formations. The flowers of the pea family are very showy *en masse*, especially during springtime in the south-west of Western Australia. Other species such as Sturts desert pea flower after rain in the country's semi-arid and arid regions.

MANGROVES

For further information see RHIZOPHORACEAE family, this section and *Avicenna* genus, previous section.

MIMOSACEAE wattle family

The wattle family has representatives in heath formations.

MYRTACEAE myrtle family

The myrtle family, as well as including the *Eucalyptus, Leptospermum, Melaleuca, Angophora, Syncarpia, Tristania* and *Acmena* genera, includes some genera that occur in open heaths, particularly in the south-west of Western Australia. Species include members of the *Beaufortia* genus, commonly and locally known as bottlebrushes (they have brilliant, red flowers); members of the *Calothamnus* genus (the claw flowers) and members of the *Chamelaucium* genus (the wax flowers). Other members of this family are the *Kunzeas,* species of which appear similar to tea-trees; the heath-myrtles, the fringe-myrtles, the bells (genus *Darwinia*) and the feather flowers, commonly found on sandy country.

Sturt's desert pea. (Hearson Cove, Pilbara, WA)

ORCHIDACEAE   orchid family

The orchid family is found in virtually all Australian formations and, in very limited habitats, may be said to be the major plant. The family is very large with some 5600 genera worldwide and some 600 Australian species. Orchids live in a variety of situations; most are terrestrial (grow out of the ground), some are epiphytic (attach themselves to rocks or other plants but not as parasites) while a few are subterranean, living, flowering and growing completely underground. A typical species is the rock orchid, a member of the *Dendrobium* genus.

POACEAE   grass family

A family of over 700 Australian species, all commonly referred to as grass. The grass family is widespread in Australia and occurs in virtually all vegetation formations except for some wetlands. Most grasses are small plants and each species exhibits one of two types of growth forms. Some have creeping stems with shoots occurring at places

Close-up of cane grass. (nr Lake Bindegolly, Bulloo, Qld)

Unidentified tussock grass on railway embankment. (nr Bourke, Upper Darling, NSW)

called nodes. Typical of creeping grasses are those found in sandy environments, meadows and lawns. Other grasses grow from tussocks where the growing point is near the ground and bunches of 'branches' emanate from this point. Tussock grasses include all the annual varieties and many perennials. One particular type of grass, porcupine grass, better known as spinifex, forms hummocks. As the grass grows outwards the original tussocks die off leaving a dead centre surrounded by new growth.

Some forms of grass grow to 15 m or more. They are the bamboos which occur in the tropical humid and monsoonal north of Australia. Most Australian native grasses are tussock types and include such species as wallaby grass, kangaroo grass, Mitchell grass, bluegrass, kerosene grass, spear grass, snow grass, etc. In the north of the country some of these grasses, called collectively tall grasses, grow to a height of 2 m or more. The southern grasses, collectively the short grasses, grow to less than 2 m

Spinifex grass; coastal type. (Woodmans Point, Coastal Plain, WA)

Spinifex hummock grass ring. (Amphi Sandhills, Upper Darling, NSW)

family exhibit a variety of leaf, flower and branch shapes and many have a gnarled, woody 'feel' to them.

RANUNCULACEAE   buttercup family

This family, the buttercup family, has representatives in many formations but is most obvious in the alpine herblands, especially in the summer when the various species are in flower.

RHIZOPHORACEAE

A fair-sized family of tropical plants composed of some 20 genera and 120 species worldwide. In Australia there are three genera: *Bruguiera, Ceriops* and *Rhizophora*. The *Rhizophora* genus represents the classic mangrove group, those which stand on prop roots. Mangroves in Australia are composed of

Spinifex hummock grass; widespread throughout the inland. (Mt Tom Price, Pilbara, WA)

in height. Other grasses include the common reed (*Phragmites* genus) which grows in swamps, and beach spinifex, common on sand-dunes. In many cases the identification of individual species of grasses is particularly difficult and can only be established with the aid of a microscope.

POSIDONIACEAE

See Seagrasses, this section.

PROTEACEAE   proteus family

The proteus family includes the following genera: *Banksia, Grevillea, Hakea, Telopea* (the waratahs) and *Persoonia* (the geebungs). Though some of these genera include tree species most species of this family exhibit a shrub or heath form. Members of the PROTEACEAE family are common in the Western Australian heaths and, to a lesser extent, the heaths of New South Wales. Members of the proteus

15 families (including RHIZOPHORACEAE), 17 genera (including the three above) and some 29 species. Most are restricted to the northern tropical coastline.

SEAGRASSES

Seagrasses are not a family of plants but a collection of families. The families are named POSIDONIACEAE, ZANICHELLIACEAE and ZOSTERACEAE and Australia has about 12 species. All grow in estuarine waters or off the coast, generally in sheltered areas such as bays, gulfs, etc. Typical species include the dugong grass and strapweed.

TYPHACEAE   bulrush family

This family grows in swamps and fresh waters and is characterised by bulrushes or reed mace. Bulrushes are creeping or rhizomatous plants growing from underground shoots. They flower in the spring or summer.

Grass trees. (Bungonia Caves, Southern Tablelands, NSW)

XANTHORRHOEACEAE   grasstree family

A family of plants that may also be included in the lily family. Typical species include the yaccas, blackboys or grasstrees, all members of the genus *Xanthorrhoea*. Grasstrees are common in many heath formations, along some exposed rocky ridges and in the understorey of some open forests. (N.B. the plant iron grass belongs to the lily family.)

ZANICHELLIACEAE

See Seagrasses, this section.

ZOSTERACEAE

See Seagrasses, this section.

Moss and small ferns. (Yalwal, South Coast, NSW)

Notes on the Dominant and Major Divisions (and Typical Genera and Species)

As mentioned in Mosslands and Other non-vascular plant formations.

BRYOPHYTA

The Bryophyta division of plants includes those that have no true root structures or moisture and nutrient conducting systems. It includes those plants commonly known as true mosses, sphagnum mosses, liverworts and hornworts, of which the true mosses and sphagnum mosses form small but distinctive formations. Mosses and liverworts are very similar and can be distinguished by their arrangement of 'leaves'. Mosses have their 'leaves' arranged regularly around the stalk, the 'leaves' of liverworts are irregularly arranged. There are approximately 600 species of mosses and 1000 species of liverworts in Australia. Due to their structure mosses need to be on the edge of, or near, water or else in a humid environment. Consequently they are found adjacent to streams, lakes, in bogs or on sheltered, moist cliff-faces. Occasionally they are found in the understorey of forests, especially cool temperate rainforests. Though most individual moss plants are very small some, such as the sphagnum moss, grow to over 1 m in length.

TALLOPHYTA

This division includes all the algae as well as fungi and the symbiotic 'plant' lichen. Algae is a single-celled plant capable of an independent existence. Algae has been divided into 11 groups, some of which can be thought of as forming distinctive plant formations. Algae are basically water plants of which seaweeds and waterblooms are the most commonly known representatives. They can exist in virtually all 'wet' habitats from snowfields to brackish and marine waters to hot springs. Some species also exist on otherwise bare rock surfaces or within the soil. Details about the different types of algae are mentioned in Other non-vascular plant formations.

The fungi are not considered to form distinctive plant formations. Some fungi, in association with some algae, symbiotically exist as lichen, a 'plant' that does form a distinctive formation. Lichens exist in the most forbidding areas. They adapt themselves to live on the surface of desert soils, encrust themselves on rocks or dangle from trees and other plants within the understorey of some forests. The algal part of lichen is generally the blue-green or green algae, the fungal part normally belongs to the Ascomycetes group. Lichens are either crustose, where they cling closely to rocks or soil, or foliose, where they grow on trees, fallen logs, etc., and possess growths shaped like leaves. Another type of

Crustose lichen on sandstone. (Bamarang, South Coast, NSW)

Sea lettuce? (Halls Head, Coastal Plain, WA)

lichen, the fruticose type, is capable of absorbing water vapour through its stalks. The crustose lichen forms minor but distinctive formations in some areas of Australia, especially in very rocky environments.

Crustose lichen and pigface. (Mimosa Rocks, South Coast, NSW)

APPENDIX 1 CO-DOMINANT OR ALLIED GENERA OF TREE AND SHRUB FORMATIONS

as described in Open forests, Woodlands, Open woodlands, Open scrubs, Shrublands and open shrublands (excluding Very open low shrublands)

CO-DOMINANT GENERA	see the following FORMATIONS	CO-DOMINANT GENERA	see the following FORMATIONS
ACACIA with			
Banksia	*Banksia* open scrubs	*Hakea*	Other open woodlands and low
Brachychiton	Softwood scrubs		open woodlands
	Acacia woodlands and low		*Banksia* open scrubs
	woodlands		*Acacia* shrubby tall open
Callitris	North-eastern *Acacia* forests		shrublands- 1
	and low open forests- 1		*Acacia* hummock grass tall open
	Callitris woodlands and low		shrublands
	woodlands	*Heterodendrum*	Southern *Acacia* shrubby
	Acacia shrubby tall open		low woodlands
	shrublands- 2		*Acacia* tall shrubby tall shrublands
Cassia-Dodonaea-		*Heterodendrum-Hakea*	
Eremophila	Mixed tall shrublands- 1	*Atalaya*	Mixed tall shrublands- 2
Casuarina	North-eastern *Acacia*	*Lysiphyllum*	North-eastern *Acacia* Open
	forests and low open		forests and low open forests- 1
	forests- 1	*Melaleuca*	*Acacia* shrubby tall open
	Southern *Acacia* shrubby low		shrublands- 2
	woodlands	*Myoporum*	Southern *Acacia* shrubby and
	Acacia shrubby low open		grassy low woodlands
	woodlands	*Terminalia*	North-eastern *Acacia* open
	Acacia shrubby and heathy		forests and low open forests- 1
	open scrubs	*AGONIS* with	
	Acacia shrubby tall open	*Banksia*	*Agonis* open forests
	shrublands-2	*ANGOPHORA* with	
	Casuarina shrubby low open	*Callitris*	*Callitris* woodlands and low
	woodlands		woodlands
Eremophila	Mixed tall shrublands- 1	*Eucalyptus*	Shrubby open forests
	Acacia shrubby tall open		Shrubby woodlands
	shrublands- 2	*ATALAYA* with	
Eucalyptus	Shrubby open forests	*Acacia-Heterodendrum-*	
	Shrubby woodlands	*Hakea*	Mixed tall shrublands- 2
	North-eastern *Acacia*	*Grevillea*	Other woodlands and low
	forests and low open		woodlands
	forests- 1	*Lysiphyllum*	Other woodlands and low
	Southern *Acacia* shrubby		woodlands
	and grassy low woodlands	*ATHROTAXIS* with	
	Eucalyptus and *Acacia*	*Eucalyptus*	*Athrotaxis* open forests and
	mixed tall shrublands		low open forests
	Acacia shrubby tall open	*Nothofagus*	Pine and/or beech low
	shrublands-2		woodlands
	Eucalyptus and *Acacia* mixed	*ATRIPLEX* with	
	tall open shrublands	*Ixiolaena*	*Atriplex, Chenopodium* and
Flindersia	Other woodlands and low		*Maireana* low shrublands
	woodlands	*Maireana*	*Atriplex, Chenopodium* and
Grevillea	*Acacia* shrubby tall open		*Maireana* low shrublands
	shrublands- 1	*Nitraria*	*Nitraria* low shrublands
	Acacia shrubby tall open	See also *Atriplex,* Appendix 5	
	shrublands- 2	*BANKSIA* with	
	Acacia hummock grass tall	*Acacia*	*Banksia* open scrubs
	open shrublands	*Agonis*	*Agonis* open forests

CO-DOMINANT GENERA	see the following FORMATIONS
Casuarina	*Casuarina* open forests and low open forests-2
	Banksia open forests and low open forests
	Banksia woodlands and low woodlands
Eucalyptus	Shrubby low woodlands
	Banksia woodlands and low woodlands
	Shrubby low open woodlands
Hakea	*Banksia* open scrubs
BRACHYCHITON with	
Acacia	Softwood scrubs
	North-eastern *Acacia* open forests and low open forests-1
CALLITRIS with	
Acacia	North-eastern *Acacia* forests and low open forests-1
	Callitris woodlands and low woodlands
	Acacia shrubby tall open shrublands-2
Angophora	*Callitris* woodlands and low woodlands
Casuarina	*Callitris* woodlands and low woodlands
	Casuarina woodlands and low woodlands
Casuarina-Geijera	*Callitris* woodlands and low woodlands
	Casuarina woodlands and low woodlands
Eucalyptus	*Callitris* open forests and low open forests
	Callitris low open woodlands
	Grassy open forests
	Layered open forests
	Grassy woodlands
	Shrubby low woodlands
	Shrubby open scrubs-1
Geijera	*Callitris* woodlands and low woodlands
Heterodendrum	*Callitris* woodlands and low woodlands
Myoporum	*Callitris* woodlands and low woodlands
CASSIA with	
Acacia-Dodonaea-Eremophila	Mixed tall shrublands-1
Eremophila	Mixed tall shrublands-1

CO-DOMINANT GENERA	see the following FORMATIONS
CASUARINA with	
Acacia	*Casuarina* shrubby low open woodlands
	North-eastern *Acacia* open forests and low open forests-1
	Southern *Acacia* shrubby low woodlands
	Acacia shrubby low open woodlands
	Acacia shrubby and heathy open scrubs
	Acacia shrubby tall open shrublands-2
Banksia	*Casuarina* open forests and low open forests-2
	Banksia open forests and low open forests
	Banksia woodlands and low woodlands
Callitris	*Casuarina* woodlands and low woodlands
	Callitris woodlands and low woodlands
Callitris-Geijera	*Casuarina* woodlands and low woodlands
	Callitris woodlands and low woodlands
Eucalyptus	*Casuarina* open forests and low open forests-1
	Shrubby open forests
	Shrubby woodlands
	Shrubby low woodlands
	Shrubby open scrubs-1
Flindersia	*Casuarina* woodlands and low woodlands
Geijera	*Casuarina* woodlands and low woodlands
Hakea	Other open woodlands and low open woodlands
Heterodendrum	*Casuarina* woodlands and low woodlands
Melaleuca	*Casuarina* woodlands and low woodlands
	Other woodlands and low woodlands
Myoporum	*Casuarina* woodlands and low woodlands
CHENOPODIUM with	
Nitraria	*Nitraria* low shrublands
DODONAEA with	
Acacia-Cassia-Eremophila	Mixed tall shrublands-1
EREMOPHILA with	
Acacia	Mixed tall shrublands-1
	Acacia shrubby tall open shrublands

CO-DOMINANT GENERA	see the following FORMATIONS	CO-DOMINANT GENERA	see the following FORMATIONS
Acacia-Cassia-Dodonaea	Mixed tall shrublands-1	*Myoporum*	Shrubby open scrubs-1
Cassia	Mixed tall shrublands-1		Shrubby tall shrublands
Eucalyptus	Shrubby low woodlands	*Santalam*	Shrubby tall shrublands
ERYTHROPHLEUM with		*Terminalia*	Other woodlands and low woodlands
Eucalyptus	Layered low woodlands		
Terminalia	Other woodlands and low woodlands	*Tristania*	Shrubby tall open forests
		Ventilago	Grassy very low woodlands
EUCALYPTUS with			Shrubby low open woodlands
Acacia	Shrubby open forests	*FLINDERSIA* with	
	Shrubby woodlands	*Casuarina*	*Casuarina* woodlands and low woodlands
	North-eastern *Acacia* open forests and low open forests	*Geijera*	Other woodlands and low woodlands
	Southern *Acacia* shrubby and grassy low woodlands	*GEIJERA* with	
	Eucalyptus and *Acacia* mixed tall shrublands	*Casuarina-Callitris*	*Casuarina* woodlands and low woodlands
	Acacia shrubby tall open shrublands- 2		*Callitris* woodlands and low woodlands
	Eucalyptus and *Acacia* mixed tall open shrublands	*Callitris*	*Callitris* woodlands and low woodlands
Angophora	Shrubby open forests	*Flindersia*	Other woodlands and low woodlands
	Shrubby woodlands	*Geijera*	Shrubby low woodlands
Athrotaxis	Subalpine low open forests	*Grevillea*	Other woodlands and low woodlands
	Athrotaxis open forests and low open forests	*GREVILLEA* with	
Banksia	Shrubby woodlands	*Acacia*	*Acacia* shrubby tall open shrublands- 1
	Banksia woodlands and low woodlands		*Acacia* shrubby tall open shrublands- 2
Brachychiton	Other woodlands and low woodlands		*Acacia* hummock grass tall open shrublands
	Shrubby low open woodlands	*Atalaya*	Other woodlands and low woodlands
Callitris	Grassy open forests	*Geijera*	Other woodlands and low woodlands
	Layered open forests		
	Grassy woodlands	*Hakea*	Other woodlands and low woodlands
	Shrubby low woodlands	*Lysiphyllum*	Other woodlands and low woodlands
	Callitris open forests and low open forests		
	Callitris low open woodlands	*HAKEA* with	
Casuarina	Shrubby open forests	*Acacia*	Other open woodlands and low open woodlands
	Shrubby woodlands		*Banksia* open scrubs
	Shrubby low woodlands		*Acacia* shrubby tall open shrublands- 1
	Casuarina open forests and low open forests- 1		*Acacia* hummock grass tall open shrublands
Eremophila	Shrubby low woodlands	*Acacia-Atalaya-Heterodendrum*	Mixed tall shrublands- 2
Erythrophleum	Layered low woodlands		
Geijera	Shrubby low woodlands	*Banksia*	*Banksia* open scrubs
Hakea	Other open woodlands and low open woodlands	*Casuarina*	Other open woodlands and low open woodlands
Heterodendrum	Southern *Acacia* shrubby low woodlands	*Eucalyptus*	Other open woodlands and low open woodlands
	Shrubby open scrubs- 1		
	Shrubby tall shrublands	*Grevillea*	Other low woodlands
Lysiphyllum	Other woodlands and low woodlands	*Heterodendrum*	Other woodlands and low woodlands
Melaleuca	Grassy woodlands		
	Melaleuca woodlands and low woodlands- 1		

CO-DOMINANT GENERA	see the following FORMATIONS
HETERODENDRUM with	
Acacia	Southern *Acacia* shrubby and grassy low woodlands *Acacia* tall shrubby tall shrublands
Acacia-Atalaya-Hakea	Mixed tall shrublands- 2
Callitris	*Callitris* woodlands and low woodlands
Casuarina	*Casuarina* woodlands and low woodlands
Eucalyptus	Shrubby tall shrublands
Hakea	Other woodlands and low woodlands
IXIOLAENA with	
Atriplex	*Atriplex, Chenopodium* and *Maireana* low shrublands
LYSIPHYLLUM with	
Acacia	North-eastern *Acacia* open forests and low open forests- 1
Atalaya	Other woodlands and low woodlands
Eucalyptus	Other woodlands and low woodlands
Grevillea	Other woodlands and low woodlands
Melaleuca	*Melaleuca* low woodlands *Melaleuca* low open woodlands
Pandanus	Other woodlands and low woodlands
MAIREANA with	
Atriplex	*Atriplex, Chenopodium* and *Maireana* low shrublands
Nitraria	*Nitraria* low shrublands
MELALEUCA with	
Acacia	*Acacia* shrubby tall open shrublands- 2
Casuarina	*Casuarina* woodlands and low woodlands Other woodlands and low woodlands
Eucalyptus	Grassy woodlands *Melaleuca* woodlands and low woodlands- 1

CO-DOMINANT GENERA	see the following FORMATIONS
Lysiphyllum	*Melaleuca* woodlands and low woodlands- 1 Other woodlands and low woodlands
Terminalia	*Melaleuca* woodlands and low woodlands- 1
MYOPORUM with	
Acacia	Southern *Acacia* shrubby low woodlands
Callitris	*Callitris* woodlands and low woodlands
Casuarina	*Casuarina* woodlands and low woodlands
Eucalyptus	Other woodlands and low woodlands Shrubby open scrubs- 1 Shrubby tall shrublands
NITRARIA with	
Atriplex	*Nitraria* low shrublands
Chenopodium	*Nitraria* low shrublands
Maireana	*Nitraria* low shrublands
NOTHOFAGUS with	
Athrotaxis	Pine and/or beech low woodlands
PANDANUS with	
Lysiphyllum	Other woodlands and low woodlands
SANTALUM with	
Eucalyptus	Shrubby tall shrublands
TERMINALIA with	
Acacia	Northern *Acacia* open forests and low open forests- 1
Erythrophleum	Other woodlands and low woodlands
Eucalyptus	Other woodlands and low woodlands
Melaleuca	*Melaleuca* woodlands and low woodlands- 1
TRISTANIA with	
Eucalyptus	Shrubby tall open forests
VENTILAGO with	
Eucalyptus	Grassy very low woodlands Shrubby low open woodlands
Terminalia	Other woodlands and low woodlands

APPENDIX 2　CO-DOMINANT OR ALLIED GENERA OF HERBLAND FORMATIONS

as described in Closed herblands, Herblands, Open herblands, Very open herblands (including Very open low shrublands) and fernlands

CO-DOMINANT GENERA	see the following FORMATIONS
ANARTHRIA with	
Evandra-Lyginia	Other sedgelands
ARISTIDA with	
Astrebla	*Astrebla* tussock grasslands
Calandrinia	*Trioda* and *Plectrachne* open hummock grasslands
Eragrostis	*Trioda* and *Plectrachne* open hummock grasslands
Plectrachne	*Trioda* and *Plectrachne* open hummock grasslands
Trioda	*Trioda* and *Plectrachne* open hummock grasslands
ASTREBLA with	
Aristida	*Astrebla* tussock grasslands
Atriplex	*Atriplex* and *Bassia* very open low shrublands
Bassia	*Atriplex* and *Bassia* very open low shrublands
	Astrebla open tussock grasslands
Dichanthium	*Astrebla* tussock grasslands
	Dichanthium closed tussock grasslands
Eragrostis	*Astrebla* tussock grasslands
	Astrebla open tussock grasslands
Panicum	*Astrebla* tussock grasslands
ATRIPLEX with	
Astrebla	*Atriplex* and *Bassia* very open low shrublands
Bassia	*Atriplex* and *Bassia* very open low shrublands
	Astrebla open tussock grasslands
Eragrostis	*Atriplex* and *Bassia* very open low shrublands
	Eragrostis and other closed grasslands
Ixiolaena	*Atriplex* and *Bassia* very open low shrublands
Marsilea	*Eragrostis* and other closed grasslands
Panicum	*Atriplex* and *Bassia* very open low shrublands
See also *Atriplex*, Appendix 4	
BASSIA with	
Astrebla	*Astrebla* open tussock grasslands
Atriplex	*Atriplex* and *Bassia* very open low shrublands

CO-DOMINANT GENERA	see the following FORMATIONS
Samphires	*Atriplex* and *Bassia* very open low shrublands
Tripogon	Other grasslands
BAUMEA with	
Gahnia	*Baumea* closed herblands
Lepidosperma	*Baumea* closed herblands
Restio	*Baumea* closed herblands
Scirpus	*Baumea* closed herblands
BOTHRIOCHLOA with	
Dichanthium	*Dichanthium* closed tussock grasslands
CALANDRINIA with	
Aristida	*Trioda* and *Plectrachne* open hummock grasslands
Eragrostis	*Trioda* and *Plectrachne* open hummock grasslands
Plectrachne	*Trioda* and *Plectrachne* open hummock grasslands
Trioda	*Trioda* and *Plectrachne* open hummock grasslands
CALOROPHUS with	
Danthonia	Alpine and subalpine tussock grasslands
Leptocarpus	Other sedgelands
Poa	Alpine and subalpine tussock grasslands
Themeda	Alpine and subalpine tussock grasslands
CAREX with	
Eleocharis	*Carex* sedgelands
Poa	*Poa* and *Danthonia* closed tussock grasslands
Sphagnum	*Carex* sedgelands
Themeda	*Poa* and *Danthonia* closed tussock grasslands
CHENOPODIUM with	
Eragrostis	*Eragrostis* and other closed grasslands
CRESSA with	
Eragrostis	*Eragrostis* and other closed grasslands
CYANTHEA with	
Dicksonia	*Cyanthea* and *Dicksonia* fernlands
CYPERUS with	
Sporobolus	*Sporobolus* closed grasslands
DANTHONIA with	
Calorophus	Alpine and subalpine tussock grasslands

CO-DOMINANT GENERA	see the following FORMATIONS
Lomandra	*Lomandra* tussock grasslands
Poa	*Poa* and *Danthonia* closed tussock grasslands
	Alpine and subalpine tussock grasslands
Stipa	*Stipa* grasslands
Themeda	*Themeda* and *Danthonia* tussock grasslands
DICHANTHIUM with	
Astrebla	*Dichanthium* closed tussock grasslands
	Astrebla tussock grasslands
Bothriochloa	*Dichanthium* closed tussock grasslands
Eulalia	*Dichanthium* closed tussock grasslands
Panicum	*Dichanthium* closed tussock grasslands
DICKSONIA with	
Cyanthea	*Cyanthea* and *Dicksonia* fernlands
DISTICHLIS with	
Gahnia	*Gahnia* tussock sedgelands
Sporobolus	*Sporobolus* closed grasslands
ELEOCHARIS with	
Carex	*Carex* sedgelands
Oryza	*Oryza* and *Eleocharis* closed herblands
Phragmites	Reed swamps and shrub swamps
ERAGROSTIS with	
Aristida	*Trioda* and *Plectrachne* open hummock grasslands
Astrebla	*Astrebla* tussock grasslands
	Astrebla open tussock grasslands
Atriplex	*Atriplex* and *Bassia* very open low shrublands
	Eragrostis and other closed grasslands
Calandrinia	*Trioda* and *Plectrachne* open hummock grasslands
Chenopodium	*Eragrostis* and other closed grasslands
Cressa	*Eragrostis* and other closed grasslands
Leptochloa	*Eragrostis* and other closed grasslands
Marsilea	*Eragrostis* and other closed grasslands
Plectrachne	*Trioda* and *Plectrachne* open hummock grasslands
Trioda	*Trioda* and *Plectrachne* open hummock grasslands
ERIACHNE with	
Themeda	*Eriachne* and *Themeda* grasslands
EULALIA with	
Dichanthium	*Dichanthium* closed tussock grasslands

CO-DOMINANT GENERA	see the following FORMATIONS
EVANDRA with	
Anarthria-Lyginia	Other sedgelands
GAHNIA with	
Baumea	*Baumea* closed herblands
Distichlis	*Gahnia* tussocky sedgelands
Poa	*Gahnia* tussocky sedgelands
GYMNOSCHOENUS with	
Heath species	*Gymnoschoenus* tussocky sedgelands
Restio	*Gymnoschoenus* tussocky sedgelands
IXIOLAENA with	
Atriplex	*Atriplex* and *Bassia* very open low shrublands
JUNCUS with	
Sporobolus	*Sporobolus* closed grasslands
LEPIDOSPERMA with	
Baumea	*Baumea* closed herblands
LEPTOCARPUS with	
Calorophus	Other sedgelands
LEPTOCHLOA with	
Eragrostis	*Eragrostis* and other closed grasslands
LOMANDRA with	
Danthonia	*Lomandra* tussock grasslands
LYGINIA with	
Anarthria-Evandra	Other sedgelands
MARSILEA with	
Atriplex	*Eragrostis* and other closed grasslands
Eragrostis	*Eragrostis* and other closed grasslands
ORYZA with	
Eleocharis	*Oryza* and *Eleocharis* closed herblands
PANICUM with	
Astrebla	*Astrebla* tussock grasslands
Atriplex	*Atriplex* and *Bassia* very open low shrublands
Dichanthium	*Dichanthium* closed tussock grasslands
PHRAGMITES with	
Eleocharis	Reed swamps and shrub swamps
PLECTRACHNE with	
Aristida	*Trioda* and *Plectrachne* open hummock grasslands
Calandrinia	*Trioda* and *Plectrachne* open hummock grasslands
Eragrostis	*Trioda* and *Plectrachne* open hummock grasslands
Trioda	*Trioda* and *Plectrachne* open hummock grasslands
POA with	
Calorophus	Alpine and subalpine tussock grasslands
Carex	*Poa* and *Danthonia* closed tussock grasslands
Danthonia	*Poa* and *Danthonia* closed tussock grasslands

CO-DOMINANT GENERA	see the following FORMATIONS	CO-DOMINANT GENERA	see the following FORMATIONS
Gahnia	*Gahnia* tussocky sedgelands	*Danthonia*	*Poa* and *Danthonia* closed tussock grasslands
Stipa	*Stipa* grasslands		*Themeda* and *Danthonia* tussock grasslands
Themeda	*Poa* and *Danthonia* closed tussock grasslands	*Eriachne*	*Eriachne* and *Themeda* grasslands
	Alpine and subalpine tussock grasslands	*Poa*	*Poa* and/or *Danthonia* closed tussock grasslands
RESTIO with			Alpine and subalpine tussock grasslands
Baumea	*Baumea* closed herblands	*Stipa*	*Stipa* grasslands
Gymnoschoenus	*Gymnoschoenus* tussocky sedgelands	*TRIODA* with	
		Aristida	*Trioda* and *Plectrachne* open hummock grasslands
SCIRPUS with			
Baumea	*Baumea* closed herblands	*Calandrinia*	*Trioda* and *Plectrachne* open hummock grasslands
SPHAGNUM with			
Carex	*Carex* sedgelands	*Eragrostis*	*Trioda* and *Plectrachne* open hummock grasslands
SPOROBOLUS with			
Cyperus	*Sporobolus* closed grasslands	*Plectrachne*	*Trioda* and *Plectrachne* open hummock grasslands
Distichlis	*Sporobolus* closed grasslands		
Juncus	*Sporobolus* closed grasslands	*Zygochloa*	*Zygochloa* open hummock grasslands
STIPA with			
Danthonia	*Stipa* grasslands		
Poa	*Stipa* grasslands	*TRIPOGON* with	
Themeda	*Stipa* grasslands	*Bassia*	Other grasslands
THEMEDA with		*ZYGOCHLOA* with	
Calorophus	Alpine and subalpine tussock grasslands	*Trioda*	*Zygochloa* open hummock grasslands
Carex	*Poa* and *Danthonia* closed tussock grasslands		

APPENDIX 3 FORMATIONS ARRANGED BY SPECIFIC HABITATS AND

CLIMATIC ZONES

The formations listed hereunder are classified firstly according to specific habitat types then climatic zones. In order to identify a particular formation check to see if it might be found within the habitat types described below and whether the formation is dominated by trees, shrubs or herbs (see Chapter 3). If so then refer to the likely references. If not found under habitat type then ascertain the climatic zone (see Chapter 2), whether the zone is temperate or tropical (arid and monsoonal regions are not so divided) and whether the formation is dominated by trees, shrubs or herbs. Refer to the appropriate headings. In both cases the location and habitat descriptions for each formation should pinpoint the correct formation once the dominant genus type, understorey type and spacing of dominants has been determined; again refer to Chapter 3.

HABITAT TYPES

LITTORAL FORMATIONS: located adjacent to the coastline and some estuaries; formations are found on, in or near beaches, coastal dunes, headlands, rock platforms, salt marshes, sea cliffs, estuaries, sublittoral situations, etc.
Trees: *Casuarina* open forests and low open forests-2; *Banksia* open forests and low open forests; *Agonis* open forests; *Casuarina* woodlands and low woodlands; *Banksia* woodlands and low woodlands.
Shrubs: Closed scrubs; Closed heaths; *Nitraria* low shrublands; Samphire low shrublands.
Herbs: *Sporobolus* closed grasslands; *Chionachne* closed grasslands; Seagrass formations; *Baumea* closed herblands; *Typha* closed herblands; *Pseudorphis* closed herblands.
Algae: *Cyanophyta* based formations; *Rhodophyta* based formations; *Phaeophyta* based formations; *Chlorophyta* based formations.
Varied: Mangrove formations; Salt marsh formations; Marine wetland formations; Coastal dune formations; Coastal cliff formations.
FRESH OR BRACKISH WATER FORMATIONS: located mainly on coastal lowlands; formations are found on, in or near lakes, swamps, streams, adjacent floodplains, coastal plains and other seasonally or periodically flooded areas.
Trees: Palm-vine closed forests; Other *Acacia* low open forests; *Casuarina* open forests and low open forests-2; *Melaleuca* open forests and low open forests; *Melaleuca* woodlands and low woodlands-2.
Shrubs: Closed scrubs.
Herbs: *Paspalum* closed grasslands; *Phragmites* closed grasslands; *Oryza* and *Eleocharis* closed herblands; *Eleocharis* closed herblands; *Baumea* closed herblands; *Typha* closed herblands; *Pseudorphis* closed herblands; *Chionachne* closed herblands; *Eriachne* and *Themeda* grasslands; *Carex* sedgelands; *Gahnia* tussocky sedgelands; *Gymnoschoenus* tussocky sedgelands; *Restio* herblands; *Cyanthea* and *Dicksonia* fernlands.
Algae: *Rhodophyta* based formations; *Chlorophyta* based formations.
Varied: Freshwater wetland formations.

INLAND WATERWAY FORMATIONS: generally located away from the coast except in semi-arid and arid areas; formations are found on, in or near streams, lakes, salt lakes, 'swamps', floodplains, frontage country, floodouts, discharge areas, etc.
Trees: Tall open forests with a herbal understorey; Grassy low open forests; Grassy low woodlands; Grassy low open woodlands.
Shrubs: Mixed tall shrublands-1; *Atriplex, Chenopodium* and *Maireana* low shrublands; *Nitraria* low shrublands; Samphire low shrublands.
Herbs: *Eragrostis* and other closed grasslands.
Varied: *Echinochloa* and other closed grasslands; *Trigonella* and other closed herblands; Other ephemeral formations; Freshwater wetland formations.
ALPINE AND SUBALPINE FORMATIONS: located in upland areas in south-east Australia and Tasmania, being generally over 1400 m on the mainland and 800 m in Tasmania.
Trees: Subalpine low open forests; Subalpine low woodlands; Pine and/or beech low woodlands.
Shrubs: Shrubby open scrubs-3; Alpine and subalpine open heaths; Dwarf heathlands and open heathlands.
Herbs: Tall alpine herbfields; Short alpine herbfields; Alpine and subalpine bogs; Alpine fens; Alpine and subalpine tussock grasslands; *Carex* sedgelands; *Sphagnum* mosslands.

CLIMATIC ZONE TYPES

HUMID REGIONS: temperate areas.
Trees: Vine-fern closed forests-1; Vine-fern closed forests-2; Fern and/or moss closed forests; Vine-fern low closed forests-1; Fern and/or moss low closed forests; Hoop pine scrubs; Softwood scrubs; Shrubby tall open forests; Grassy tall open forests; Tall open forests on the margins of some rainforests; Tall open forests and open forests on poor soils in wet areas; Tall open forests and open forests with a closed understorey; Shrubby and heathy open forests; Grassy open forests; Shrubby and heathy low open forests; Grassy low open forests; Other *Acacia* low open forests; *Casuarina* open forests and low open

forests-2; *Banksia* open forests and low open forests; *Athrotaxis* open forests and low open forests; *Agonis* open forests and low open forests; Tall woodlands; *Melaleuca* woodlands and low woodlands-2; *Banksia* woodlands and low woodlands; Shrubby or heathy low open woodlands.

Shrubs: Closed scrubs; Montane closed scrubs; Closed heaths; Shrubby open scrubs-3; Tropical and subtropical open heaths; Wet temperate open heaths; Dry temperate open heaths; Sedge-like heaths; Montane open heaths.

Herbs: *Poa* and *Danthonia* closed tussock grasslands; *Cyanthea* and *Dicksonia* fernlands; *Pteridium* fernlands; Other mosslands.

HUMID REGIONS: tropical areas (excluding monsoonal regions).

Trees: Vine tall closed forests; Vine and semi-deciduous vine closed forests; Montane vine-fern low closed forests; *Pisonia* low closed forests; Softwood scrubs; Cyclone scrubs; Shrubby tall open forests; Tall open forests on the margin of some rainforests; Grassy open forests; Grassy low open forests.

Shrubs: Closed scrubs; Closed heaths; Tropical and subtropical open heaths.

SUBHUMID REGIONS: temperate areas.

Trees: Tall open forests with a herbal understorey; Grassy open forests; Grassy low open forests; North-eastern *Acacia* open forests and low open forests-1; North-eastern *Acacia* open forests and low open forests-2; *Casuarina* open forests and low open forests-1; *Casuarina* open forests and low open forests-2; *Callitris* open forests and low open forests; Shrubby woodlands; Grassy woodlands; Shrubby low woodlands; North-eastern *Acacia* woodlands and low woodlands; Southern *Acacia* shrubby and grassy low woodlands; *Casuarina* woodlands and low woodlands; *Callitris* woodlands and low woodlands; *Melaleuca* woodlands and low woodlands-2; Other woodlands and low woodlands; Shrubby or heathy low open woodlands; *Casuarina* shrubby and grassy low open woodlands.

Shrubs: Closed scrubs; Shrubby open scrubs-1; Shrubby open scrubs-2; Grassy open scrubs; *Acacia* and *Casuarina* open scrubs; *Melaleuca* (closed and) open scrubs; *Banksia* open scrubs; Dry temperate open heaths; Mixed tall shrublands-3; Shrubby or heathy tall open shrublands.

Herbs: *Poa* and *Danthonia* closed tussock grasslands; *Lomandra* tussock grasslands; *Themeda* and *Danthonia* tussock grasslands; *Stipa* grasslands.

SUBHUMID REGIONS: tropical areas (excluding monsoonal regions).

Trees: Softwood scrubs; North-eastern *Acacia* open forests and low open forests-1; North-eastern *Acacia* open forests and low open forests-2; *Casuarina* open forests and low open forests-1; *Casuarina* open forests and low open forests-2; *Callitris* open forests and low open forests; Grassy woodlands; North-eastern

Acacia woodlands and low woodlands; Other woodlands and low woodlands.

SEMI-ARID REGIONS: temperate areas.

Trees: Grassy woodlands; Mixed low woodlands and tall shrublands; Southern *Acacia* shrubby and grassy low woodlands; *Casuarina* woodlands and low woodlands; *Callitris* woodlands and low woodlands; Other woodlands and low woodlands; Grassy low open woodlands; Hummock grass low open woodlands; Southern *Acacia* low open woodlands; *Casuarina* shrubby low open woodlands; *Callitris* low open woodlands.

Shrubs: Shrubby open scrubs-1; Shrubby open scrubs-2; Hummock grass open scrubs; *Acacia* and *Casuarina* open scrubs; *Banksia* open scrubs; Spinifex heaths; Shrubby tall shrublands; *Acacia* tall shrubby tall shrublands; *Acacia* low shrubby tall shrublands; *Acacia* heathy tall shrublands; Southern and central *Acacia* grassy tall shrublands; Mixed tall shrublands-1; Mixed tall shrublands-2; Mixed tall shrublands-3; *Atriplex, Chenopodium* and *Maireana* low shrublands; *Nitraria* low shrublands; Samphire low shrublands; *Acacia* hummock grass tall open shrublands; *Acacia* shrubby low open shrublands; *Atriplex* and *Bassia* very open low shrublands.

SEMI-ARID REGIONS: tropical areas.

Trees: Grassy woodlands; Layered woodlands; Grassy low woodlands; Layered low woodlands; Hummock grass low woodlands; Grassy very low woodlands; Hummock grass very low woodlands; North-eastern *Acacia* woodlands and low woodlands; *Melaleuca* woodlands and low woodlands-1; Other woodlands and low woodlands; Shrubby low open woodlands; Grassy low open woodlands; Hummock grass low open woodlands; *Acacia* grassy low open woodlands.

Shrubs: Hummock grass open scrubs; *Acacia* hummock grass open scrubs; Hummock grass tall shrublands; *Northern Acacia* grassy tall shrublands; *Acacia* hummock grass tall shrublands; Acacia low shrublands; Mixed tall shrublands-2; Samphire low shrublands; *Eucalyptus* and *Acacia* mixed tall open shrublands; *Acacia* hummock grass tall open shrublands; *Acacia* hummock grass low open shrublands.

Herbs: *Dichanthium* closed tussock grasslands; *Astrebla* tussock grasslands; *Trioda* and *Plectrachne* open hummock grasslands.

ARID REGIONS:

Trees: Grassy low woodlands; Shrubby low open woodlands; Grassy low open woodlands; Hummock grass low open woodlands; Southern *Acacia* low open woodlands; *Acacia* grassy low open woodlands; *Acacia* hummock grass low open woodlands; *Casuarina* hummock grass low open woodlands; *Callitris* low open woodlands.

Shrubs: *Acacia* and *Casuarina* open scrubs; Hummock grass tall shrublands; *Eucalyptus* and *Acacia*

mixed tall shrublands; *Acacia* tall shrubby tall shrublands; *Acacia* low shrubby tall shrublands; Northern *Acacia* grassy tall shrublands; Southern and central *Acacia* grassy tall shrublands; *Eremophila* tall shrublands; Mixed tall shrublands-1; Mixed tall shrublands-2; *Atriplex, Chenopodium* and *Maireana* low shrublands; *Nitraria* low shrublands; Samphire low shrublands; Hummock grass tall open shrublands; *Eucalyptus* and *Acacia* mixed tall open shrublands; *Acacia* shrubby tall open shrublands-1; *Acacia* shrubby tall open shrublands-2; *Acacia* grassy tall open shrublands; *Acacia* hummock grass tall open shrublands; *Acacia* shrubby low open shrublands; *Atriplex* and *Bassia* very open low shrublands. **Herbs:** *Trioda* and *Plectrachne* open hummock grasslands; *Zygochloa* open hummock grasslands; *Astrebla* open tussock grasslands.

Varied: *Echinochloa* and other closed grasslands; *Trigonella* and other closed grasslands; Other ephemeral formations.
MONSOONAL REGIONS:
Trees: Semi-deciduous and deciduous low closed forests; Layered tall open forests; Layered open forests; Layered low open forests; *Casuarina* open forests and low open forests-2; *Callitris* open forests and low open forests; *Melaleuca* open forests and low open forests; Layered woodlands; Layered low woodlands; *Melaleuca* woodlands and low woodlands-1; Other woodlands and low woodlands; Low open woodlands with a mixed substrata.
Shrubs: Closed scrubs; Closed heaths; *Acacia* low shrublands.
Herbs: *Dichanthium* closed tussock grasslands.

BIBLIOGRAPHY

Atlas of Australian Resources 3rd series Vol 6 *Vegetation* Auslig Canberra 1990

Australian National Parks and Wildlife Service *Plant Invasions — The Incidence of Environmental Weeds in Australia* ANPWS Canberra 1991

Beadle N. *The Vegetation of Australia* CUP Cambridge 1981

Beard J.S. *Vegetation Survey of Western Australia* 'Explanatory Notes Nos 1 to 7' UWAP Nedlands 1974–81

Bodkin F. *Encyclopaedia Botanica* A&R Sydney 1986

Buchanan R.A. *Bush Regeneration: Recovering Australian Landscapes* TAFE Student Learning Publications Sydney 1989

Bureau of Flora and Fauna *Flora of Australia Vol 1 Introduction* AGPS Canberra 1981

Carolin R. & Clarke P. *Beach Plants of South-Eastern Australia* Sainty & Associates Sydney 1991

Clarke I. & Lee H. *Name that Flower* MUP Melbourne 1987

Costermans L. *Native Trees and Shrubs of South-Eastern Australia* Rigby 1981

Cronin L. *The Concise Australian Flora* Reed Books Sydney 1989

Fuhrer B. *Seaweeds of Australia* A.H. & A.W. Reed Sydney 1981

Gillison A.N. & Anderson D.J. *Vegetation Classification in Australia* ANU Press Canberra 1981

Groves R.L. ed *The Vegetation of Australia* CUP Cambridge 1981

Harden G. ed *Flora of New South Wales* Vols 1–4 UNSW Press Sydney 1991–4

Harris T.Y. *Alpine Plants of Australia* A&R Sydney 1970

Heatwole H. & Lowman M. *Dieback: Death of an Australian Landscape* Reed Books Sydney 1986

Holliday I. & Watton G. *A Field Guide to Australian Native Shrubs* Hamlyn Melbourne 1989

Jeans D.N. ed *Australia —A Geography* SUP Sydney 1977

Jessop J. ed *Flora of Central Australia* A.H. & A.W. Reed Sydney 1981

Jones D. & Clemesha S. *Australian Ferns and Fern Allies* A.H. & A.W. Reed Sydney 1976

Lamp C.A., Forbes S.J. & Cade J.W. *Grasses of Temperate Australia* Inkata Press Melbourne 1990

Leeper G.W. ed *The Australian Environment* CSIRO 1970

Moore R.M. ed *Australian Grasslands* ANU Press Canberra 1970

Mosley G. ed *Australia's Wilderness* ACF Hawthorn 1978

Pearson S. & A. *Rainforest Plants of Eastern Australia* Kangaroo Press Kenthurst 1992

Rotherham E.R. et alia *Flowers and Plants of New South Wales and Southern Queensland* A.H. & A.W. Reed Sydney 1975

Sainty G. & Jacobs S. *Water Plants of New South Wales* Water Resources Commission of NSW 1981

Specht R.L. *The Vegetation of South Australia* Committee for Handbooks of Flora and Fauna of South Australia 1972

Urban A. *Wildflowers and Plants of Central Australia* Portside Editions Melbourne 1990

Wheeler D., Jacobs S. & Norton B. *Grasses of New South Wales* Monograph 3 UNE Armidale 1982

Wrigley J.W. & Fagg M. *Bottlebrushes, Paperbarks and Tea Trees* A&R Sydney 1993

—— *Banksias, Waratahs and Grevilleas* Collins Sydney 1989

GLOSSARY

Alliance - the grouping of various plants which have the same structural characteristics and belong to similar or related species as upperstorey dominants.

Annual - a plant with a life cycle of about one year.

Association - the grouping of various plants which have the same structural characteristics and belong to the same species as upperstorey dominants.

Bole - stem or trunk of a tree.

Bush, the - a common term referring to virtually all types of vegetation formations.

Cay - a small coral or sandy island.

Coastal lowlands - flat or undulating country near the coast; see also **Lowlands**.

Coastal plains - flat country near the coast.

Co-dominant - indicates more than one dominant species.

Crown - that part of a tree or shrub above the lowest branching.

Deciduous - the falling of leaves of non-evergreen trees, due to cold or drought conditions.

Depauperate - implies forest heights are of reduced size in areas where the environment is less favourable.

Dominants - the most common and characteristic species in the uppermost stratum (excluding emergents) of a plant community.

Downs - relative flat country with reasonably close rises or undulations.

Edaphic - relating to soil or topographic conditions rather than climate.

Emergents - individual plants that rise up above upperstorey dominants; generally widely spaced.

Ephemeral - a plant which has a life cycle of about one season.

Epicormic (buds and shoots) - new growth emanating from beneath (damaged) bark.

Epiphyte - a non-parasitic plant which grows upon another plant.

Evergreen - a tree or shrub always exhibiting green foliage.

Exotic - a plant introduced either accidentally or deliberately from another country.

Floodplains - plains subjected to flooding.

Floristic - pertaining to the plants of a particular region.

Formation - a grouping of vegetation with similar structural characteristics but possibly different floristics: in this text it applies to mature and fully developed plant communities which may or may not be disturbed.

Frontage country - floodplains (and sometimes adjacent plains).

Genera (sing. genus) - a grouping of similar species.

Gullies - small sheltered valleys.

Habitat - the natural environment where plants and animals naturally occur.

Hilly country - moderately rugged country of hills and valleys.

Jump-ups - flat-top hills with steep sides, found in the outback.

Lignotuber - a woody swelling at the base of a stem.

Lowlands - moderately flat country with undulations, low hills, rises or ridges.

Monospecific - dominated by one species.

Mountainous country - rugged to very rugged country of mountains and deep valleys.

Outcrops - rocky hills, ranges, etc., rising above the surrounding country.

Overstorey - that part of a formation which includes the dominant's crown plus any emergents.

Perennial - a plant which has a life cycle of many years' duration.

Periodicity - refers to events that occur at fairly regular intervals.

Plains - flat or nearly flat country.

Pure stand - a grouping of one species of dominant plants.

Ranges - linear hills or mountains; escarpments of tablelands.

Rhizome - a prostrate stem normally growing underground.

Ridge - linear hills or low ranges, usually with a narrow crest.

Riverflats - small floodplains.

Sandplains - plains covered with sand.

Sclerophyll - a plant which has hard or stiff leaves.

Seismic lines - long linear clearings made to assist seismic surveys.

Species - a basic classification of plant (and animal) life. Similar species are potentially capable of interbreeding.

Strata (sing. stratum) - levels or layers within the vertical cross-section of a plant formation.

Swales - small valleys between sand-dunes.

Tablelands - elevated country bounded by (steep) slopes.

Tarns - glacially formed lakes.

Thicket - a small wood of trees or shrubs with a dense understorey, overstorey or with dense branches growing near ground level.

Tops - rounded peaks or summits in upland areas.

Understorey - that part of a formation beneath the dominant, emergent or upper levels.

Undulating country - country exhibiting low hills, ridges, etc., and shallow valleys.

Undulating plains - relatively flat country with widely spaced rises or undulations.

Uplands - high country rising above the general level of tablelands, etc.

Watercourses - stream channels with or without water.

INDEX

Genus names appear in italics begin with a capital letter

Numbers in italics refer to an illustration